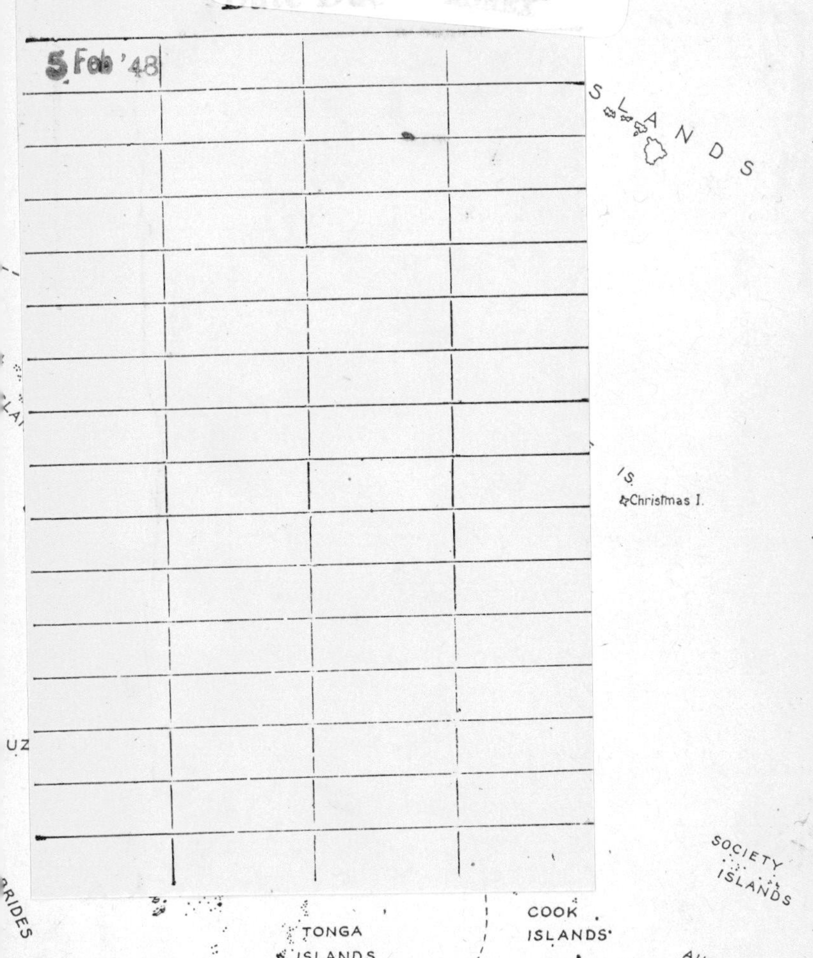
5 Feb '48
ISLANDS
IS.
Christmas I.
SOCIETY
ISLANDS
COOK
ISLANDS
TONGA
ISLANDS
AUSTRAL IS.
180
160

BIRDS OF THE SOUTHWEST PACIFIC

A Field Guide to the Birds of the Area between Samoa, New Caledonia, and Micronesia

BY

ERNST MAYR

CURATOR, WHITNEY-ROTHSCHILD COLLECTION
AMERICAN MUSEUM OF NATURAL HISTORY

With Color Plates By

FRANCIS LEE JAQUES

And Line Drawings By

ALEXANDER SEIDEL

THE MACMILLAN COMPANY · NEW YORK

1945

First Printing

A WARTIME BOOK

THIS COMPLETE EDITION IS PRODUCED IN FULL COMPLIANCE WITH THE GOVERNMENT'S REGULATIONS FOR CONSERVING PAPER AND OTHER ESSENTIAL MATERIALS

PRINTED IN THE UNITED STATES OF AMERICA
BY THE VAIL-BALLOU PRESS, INC., BINGHAMTON, N. Y.

TO

MY WIFE

Table of Contents

Table of Contents

List of Illustrations

Plates

Map

Figures

Preface

UNTIL war focused the limelight on the Southwest Pacific, few parts of the world were less familiar to the average American. What proportion of our people, for example, could claim more than the vaguest ideas about islands such as Espiritu Santo, Ponapé, Bougainville—or Guadalcanal, which our armed forces have now turned into an immortal name?

And if the islands themselves lay in an indistinct haze of memory, how much greater the blank concerning their native human inhabitants and their plant and animal life!

Shortly after the first of our sailors and troops had reached New Caledonia, the New Hebrides, the Solomon Islands, and other Pacific outposts, the American Museum began to be flooded with letters asking information about the natural history of the islands and archipelagos. And high among these requests were calls for a popular book on the birdlife of the region.

Unfortunately, little could be suggested except for technical reports on collections of island birds, scattered through many scientific journals over a long period of time and printed in several languages. There was not a single comprehensive monograph or handbook suitable for a field student, whether amateur or professional zoologist.

By good fortune, however, the conditions had been set for the preparation of the needed volume. Throughout almost two decades the Whitney South Sea Expedition of the American Museum of Natural History, supported by a generous gift of the late Harry Payne Whitney, had worked among the Pacific islands, obtaining representative collections of birds and voluminous field notes. By equal good luck, a member of our scientific staff who had taken part in the Whitney Expedition, and who had devoted his subsequent researches almost exclusively to the ornithology of the area, was at hand to undertake the book.

Dr. Mayr spent two and a half years studying birds in New Guinea, the Bismarck Archipelago, and the Solomon Islands. For 17 years he has worked constantly on the ornithology of these and neighboring parts of the Pacific. He is acknowledged by his scientific colleagues everywhere as the first authority on the whole area. His book, containing a great deal of previously unpublished information. not only supplies a useful tool for a practical purpose, but also puts into the hands of those who possess it the latest and soundest scientific conclusions on the relationships and distribution of a rich and remarkable, and hitherto little-known, bird fauna.

ROBERT CUSHMAN MURPHY, *Chairman*
Department of Birds
American Museum of Natural History
New York 24, N.Y.

Introduction

NOT a single book in the English language is available on the birds of the wide area between Fiji, New Caledonia, and Micronesia. This is not surprising if one realizes how little was known of the birds of the area until about 25 years ago. Then the Whitney South Sea Expedition toured the Pacific from 1921 to 1939, visiting many previously unexplored islands. The splendid work of this expedition has filled the worst gaps in our knowledge and has made possible the preparation of this volume, which may serve as guide to the visitor of the region.

The present handbook is intended primarily for the field student. It will help him to identify and name the birds that he encounters, and to ascertain what kinds of birds can be expected on a given island. The emphasis has therefore been placed on identification marks, the "field characters." In addition, a condensed summary is given of the present knowledge of distribution, geographical variation (subspecies), and habits. This information is not readily available in any other volume and will be useful not only to the naturalist who visits the islands, but also to museum curators and ornithologists in general.

The region covered by this volume includes the following groups of islands: Samoa, Fiji, New Caledonia, Loyalty Islands, New Hebrides, Banks Islands, Santa Cruz Islands, Solomon Islands, Marshall Islands, Carolines, Marianas, and

Palau. This area forms a rough triangle with the corners at Samoa, New Caledonia and Palau. Every species of bird known to occur within this area is described—a total of 388 species. The additional listing of 415 subspecies brings to 803 the number of forms covered in this volume. It would have been gratifying to include New Guinea and the Bismarck Archipelago, but the limits of space make this impossible. No less than 650 species with more than 1400 subspecies are known from New Guinea and the adjacent islands, more than a single volume can adequately cover. However, many of the more common species of these islands are widespread and are also found in the Solomon Islands or Melanesia. It is therefore believed that this handbook will also be useful to visitors to New Guinea. Reference to the birds of the Bismarck Archipelago has been made throughout the systematic section.

A book treating the widely diverging bird fauna of more than ten different archipelagos must be organized quite differently from a book on the birds of Great Britain or the United States. Most of the seabirds and shorebirds, and some of the land birds, are found throughout the entire area. About two-thirds of the land birds, however, occur only on a single island group, and most of the remaining ones are restricted to two or three archipelagos. It would be extremely confusing to the visitor of a certain island, if he had to hunt up in a book of 400 species, the 20 or 30 species that occur there. On the other hand, much repetition would be unavoidable if the complete faunas of Samoa, Fiji, and so forth, were listed without reference to neighboring archipelagos.

It was therefore decided to attempt a compromise between a general systematic and a purely regional treatment. The seabirds and the shorebirds of all the island groups are treated in two separate sections of Part I and are not again referred to in the regional section. All the general information referring to the land and fresh-water birds has been combined in a systematic section containing a descriptive definition of all the families of land and fresh-water birds, except for the monotypic Kagu family (*see* New Caledonia) and the introduced bulbul family (*see* Fiji). This method of treatment should be particularly useful to American and European bird students who are not familiar with the Australian and Oriental bird families. Also included in this systematic section are the descriptions of a number of widespread species. Although there are cross references from the geographical sections to the systematic section, the visitor to any of the island groups should first turn to this systematic section because it gives much information not repeated in the regional sections of Part II.

BIRD NAMES

Popular Names.—Most birds of the Southwest Pacific have no generally accepted English name. In fact, I was forced to invent new ones for well over half the species. The choice of the suggested names was guided by the following principles. Names that refer to a characteristic habit or call note are preferable to ones that describe the coloration, but, unfortunately, not enough is known about the habits of most species to serve as the exclusive basis for a successful nomenclature. Geographical names (Malaita White-eye) are more descriptive than dedication names (Stresemann's White-eye) and have usually been chosen when no other conspicuous attribute was known. Such misleading and meaningless combinations as "cuckoo-shrike" have been avoided whenever some other name was available. Following the best current usage, it was considered unnecessary and even unwise to supply vernacular names for subspecies.

Scientific Names.—A liberal use of scientific names is a necessity, in view of the dearth of generally accepted popular names. The emphasis has been placed on the species name, since the subspecies is primarily of interest to the specialist only. Where a scientific name (in Latin) is listed without its author, it indicates the name of a polytypic species, i.e. of a species composed of several geographical races or subspecies.

The year in which a scientific name was first proposed is given for all species and subspecies described after 1910. This will facilitate the finding of the original description with the help of reference works (e.g. *Zoological Record*). The technical literature on the birds of the Southwest Pacific is so compact and easily accessible to the museum worker that it was considered unnecessary to list all the bibliographic details of the original descriptions. Most of the more recent ones can be found in the series, "Birds Collected during the Whitney South Sea Expedition," published from 1923 to date in the *American Museum Novitates* (American Museum of Natural History, New York City). In June 1944, there were 53 numbers in this series, with more planned for publication.

Subspecies.—Most species of Pacific land birds are somewhat different on every island. Each geographically segregated distinct population of a species is called a subspecies. Every subspecies known from the Southwest Pacific is listed in this volume, together with an exact indication of its distribution. On the whole, the distinguishing characters of only those subspecies are mentioned that can be recognized through field glasses.

HOW TO IDENTIFY BIRDS

Description.—Those color characteristics have been emphasized which are likely to be most noticeable in the field. By necessity these descriptions had to be based on museum specimens, and a study of the birds in the field will undoubtedly reveal certain shortcomings. I would appreciate it if users of this book would communicate to me any additional fieldmarks which they may discover in the course of their observations.

Keys.—Whenever feasible, keys have been supplied to facilitate identification. All these keys are strictly dichotomous, unless it is indicated by the use of the letters *a, b, c,* that three alternatives are given. Attempting an identification with the help of a key involves the making of a number of decisions, some of which may be difficult. The key may have the alternatives "top of head green" or "top of head red," but the bird is visible only from underneath. In such a case both branches of the key should be followed up, and one of them will invariably produce a more likely identification.

Size.—The total length (in inches) is given for each species, to provide a rough indication of general size. These are absolute measurements, while the attributes "large" or "small" are relative. A "small" hawk is, of course, larger than a "large" honey-eater. To provide a comparative yardstick, I list here the sizes of some well-known European and American birds (in inches): Kinglet (3½–4), House Sparrow (5–6), Starling (7½–8½), European Blackbird or American Robin (9–10), American Blue Jay (11–12), European Jay (13–14), Crow (19), American Red-tailed Hawk or European Buzzard (19–24), Golden Eagle (30–40). One inch = 2.5 cm.

Illustrations.—At least one representative of all of the more prominent bird families of the Southwest Pacific is figured on the three plates. A series of line drawings illustrates quite a number of additional species. These pictures will be particularly valuable to American or European bird students who have never before seen a wood-swallow, a flower-pecker, a white-eye, or a triller. Many additional colored figures of Southwest Pacific birds can be found in Cayley's *What Bird Is That?* (Sydney, Australia, Angus & Robertson, Ltd.), an almost complete set of colored pictures of Australian birds.

HINTS TO OBSERVERS

The study of the birds of the Southwest Pacific has just begun. To be sure, not many new species remain to be discovered, except perhaps in the mountains of Guadalcanal and New Ireland. More than 90 per cent of the subspecies have probably been described and the main outline of the distribution of most species is well established. On the other hand, next to nothing is known about the life histories of most of the species. To fill this gap, every amateur can make observations that are of the greatest value and interest to science. Below I have tried to give a bare outline of some of the subjects that need particular attention.

ECOLOGY

(1) In what kind of habitat does a species occur (rain forest, forest edge, native gardens, grasslands, swamps)?

(2) At what height is it usually found (treetops, lower branches, undergrowth of forest, small trees outside of forest, ground)?

(3) Are the singing perches at the same height as the feeding places?

(4) What is the annual cycle? (Is there any evidence of a definite breeding season? Count the number of nests and eggs of every species in every month. Record at different seasons the number of songs in the first morning hour.)

(5) What is the daily cycle? (Are there any feeding or roosting flights? What birds sing during the night? What birds sing most commonly in the heat of the day?)

(6) How many birds are found in a given area? (Make an accurate census of a ten-acre area. Make a rough census of the total population of a single species on a small island.)

(7) Study the activities in flowering and in fruit trees. (How many species visit them? How long does an individual stay? How many birds are in a tree at the same time? How many come and go every ten-minute period?)

HABITS

(1) Describe the call notes, the song.

(2) Describe the feeding habits. (Are insects caught by flying out from branches in the manner of flycatchers? Are they picked off leaves, off branches, or off the bark? Does any feeding take place on the ground? Are fruits swallowed whole?)

(3) Describe situation and structure of nests.

(4) Describe each species as to whether it is usually found singly, in pairs, or in flocks.

(5) Describe size and composition of bird flocks. (Follow a flock for 10 minutes or 60 minutes and record its activities. How far has it moved? Is the flock a closed unit? Does it have a leader?)

(6) Which species defend the area around the nest (territory) against other individuals of the same species? (Do males of these species occupy definite singing perches? Does singing and feeding alternate?)

(7) What share does the male take in nest building, incubation, feeding of the young? (Record actual figures of minutes spent on the nest or number of feedings per hour. Does the male incubate during the day or during the night?)

(8) How many singing males are not mated? Do more than two birds take part in the feeding of the young?

Whenever possible these questions should be answered by carefully watching a definite individual for several hours (same day or several days) and counting and recording carefully all of its activities. Additional questions can be found in Hickey's *A Guide to Bird Watching* (New York: Oxford Univ. Press, 1943). Much of his advice is well applicable to tropical birds; *see* particularly chapters 3 and 4 and Appendix C.

ACKNOWLEDGMENTS

This volume owes its existence to the unfailing help given me by many friends. H. Hamlin contributed field notes on the birds of the New Hebrides, W. Beecher on the Solomon Islands, L. Macmillan on New Hebrides and New Caledonia, and W. Coultas on Micronesia and the Solomon Islands. D. L. Serventy, George M. Sutton, R. A. Falla, and Robert Cushman Murphy read parts of the manuscript and made numerous suggestions for improvement. Francis Lee Jaques contributed the plates and Alexander Seidel provided the line drawings. R. T. Peterson kindly permitted the use of figure 2. Margaret B. Hickey read and edited the entire manuscript. I am deeply grateful to all of these persons for their share in the preparation of this volume.

By showing the gaps in our knowledge, I hope that this volume will stimulate naturalists to try to fill them.

E. MAYR

American Museum of Natural History,
New York 24, N.Y.

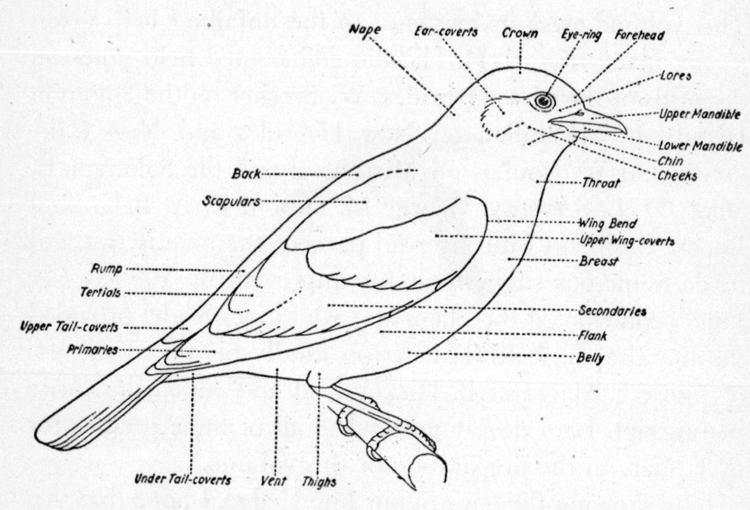

FIG. 1. Body regions and plumage features.

Part One

GENERAL SECTION

I

The Seabirds of the Southwest Pacific

TERNS are the dominant seabirds of this region. Aside from them the oceanic bird life is remarkably poor in variety of resident species. Penguins, skimmers, pelicans, and marine cormorants are entirely absent. The order of Tubinares, which includes albatrosses, shearwaters, petrels, and Mother Carey's chickens, is represented by a few resident species and some additional regular visitors, while many others barely reach the southern edge near New Caledonia or the northern edge near the Marianas during their far-flung wanderings between breeding seasons. It is impossible to enumerate and describe all such accidental visitors in this short guide. Bird students who are especially interested in seabirds should consult W. B. Alexander's *Birds of the Ocean* (Putnam, 1928). The subsequent discussion of seabirds leans heavily on this volume.

Our knowledge of the seabirds of the Pacific (their relationships, distribution, and life histories) is still very incomplete. Field students can make significant contributions by recording the situation of breeding colonies, the breeding seasons of each species at a given locality, and the wanderings of nonbreeding birds between seasons.

TUBE-NOSED SWIMMERS
ORDER TUBINARES OR PROCELLARIIFORMES

In spite of a slight superficial resemblance, these oceanic birds are not related to the gulls. The Tubinares are a very distinct and rather homogeneous group. They are excellent fliers and spend most of their time on the open ocean. Most of them nest colonially, and many of them in self-excavated burrows. All species lay only a single egg. The incubation and fledging periods are extraordinarily long. The size difference between the smallest petrels (Mother Carey's chickens) and the largest albatrosses is unique among orders of birds. The waters of the southern hemisphere are the headquarters of this order, but a number of species occur north of the equator, particularly in the Pacific. There are only a few tropical species.

ALBATROSSES (FAMILY DIOMEDEIDAE)

Albatrosses are typically birds of cold waters, but they reach the S.W.P. from the north and occasionally from the south. Three species are known from the North Pacific and all 3 occur probably in Micronesia. Most albatrosses breed in colonies, their nests with single eggs being on the ground.

Key to North Pacific Albatrosses

(1) Head and body white 2
Head and body brown or sooty 3

(2) Whole body including middle of back white; top of head buffy; wing tips and tail tips brown; bill pinkish; feet bluish white .... *albatrus* (adult)

Head, body, and rump white; back, wings, and end of tail sooty brown; bill gray; feet fleshy pink .... *immutabilis*

(3) Chocolate brown; bill pinkish; feet flesh color .... *albatrus* (young)

Sooty brown; area around bill whitish; bill dark reddish brown; feet black .... *nigripes*

Short-tailed Albatross (*Diomedea albatrus* Pallas): Ranged formerly through the entire North Pacific. Bred on Wake Isl. and on the Bonin Isls. Now nearly extinct. Eggs have been found from August to December.

Laysan Albatross (*Diomedea immutabilis* Rothschild): In the central North Pacific. Breeds on the islands west of Hawaii (Midway, Laysan, etc.). Young similar to adults. Wingspread 6′ 8″.

Black-footed Albatross (*Diomedea nigripes* Audubon): This species also called the Gooney, is the most common albatross of the North Pacific. Breeds on the islands northwest of Hawaii, Midway Isl., Marshall Isls., Volcano Isl., and Bonin Isls. Young similar to adults, but have more white on the head and rump.

Two species of South Pacific albatrosses occasionally reach the waters along the southern edge of the S.W.P. Adults and immatures are very different in one of these species (*exulans*), while there are no pronounced sexual or age differences in the other one (*epomophora*).

Key to Southwest Pacific Albatrosses

(1) Underparts and middle of back more or less brown; face and underside of wing white .... *D. exulans* (juv.)

Underparts more or less white 2

(2) Tail all white; body always entirely white; wing usually rather solid blackish brown .... *D. epomophora*

Tail dark or tipped with black; body often mottled with black wavy lines. Inner wing frequently with much white .... *D. exulans*

Wandering Albatross (*Diomedea exulans* L.): Females usually have a dark brown cap. Nests on the islands south of New Zealand. Wanders north to about 20° S.

Royal Albatross (*Diomedea epomophora sanfordi* Murphy): Nests on the Chatham Isls. and in other parts of the New Zealand region. Wanders north to about 20° S.

PETRELS AND SHEARWATERS (FAMILY PROCELLARIIDAE, SUBFAMILY PROCELLARIINAE)

There is probably no other family of birds that causes more difficulties to the field observer. Even experienced students enter in their notebooks as unidentified most of the individuals of this family that they encounter in the waters of the South Pacific. The beginner should not feel too much discouraged if he experiences similar difficulties. The situation is aggravated by the fact that several species have both a white-bellied and a dark-bellied color phase.

Members of this family are somewhat gull-like in appearance, but their flight is very different and quite diagnostic. They skim over the water—on windy days gliding rapidly without flapping their wings. The body is usually tilted, with one wing almost touching the water ("shearwater"), while the other points skyward. In tropical waters entire days sometimes pass without a shearwater coming into sight, but when a squall darkens the sky and roughens the water, a flock of them may suddenly appear from nowhere, zigzagging across the water, and disappear just as mysteriously. The native shearwaters of the S.W.P. are still very poorly understood. Many of them are known only from 2 or 3 specimens. In addition the area they inhabit is visited, between breeding seasons, by many of the species that breed in south Australian or New Zealand waters.

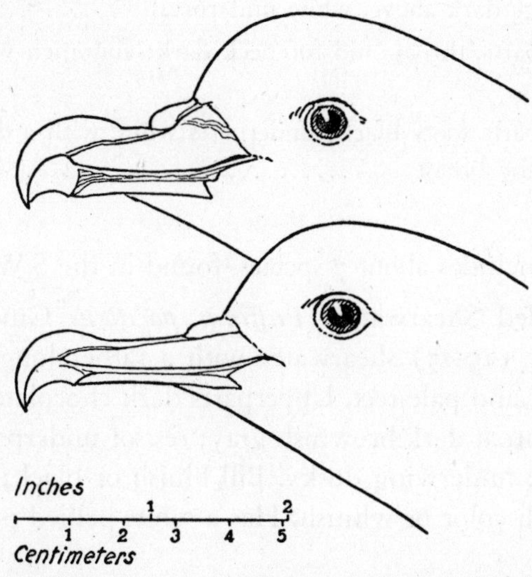

FIG. 2. Bill of *Pterodroma r. rostrata* (top) and of *Puffinus p. pacificus* (bottom). The bill of a typical petrel (*Pterodroma*) is short and thick, that of a shearwater (*Puffinus*) longer and more slender.

Shearwaters nest in colonies, usually in holes in the ground. Females and immatures do not differ from the males in coloration. Shearwaters, as compared to petrels, are on the whole characterized by their flattened "legs" (tarsi), their more slender bills, greater ability to dive, and greater tendency to congregate in flocks, both when resting on the water and in flight. This distinction between the 2 groups is, however, by no means diagnostic.

Key to the Shearwaters and Petrels

(1) Plumage dark or black .... Section A
(2) Plumage dark above, white underneath .... Section B
(3) Upperparts, throat, and foreneck dark; abdomen white .... Section C
(4) Upperparts sooty black; underparts white with a dark band across the breast .... Section D

Section A

This includes about 7 species, found in the S.W.P.[1]

Wedge-tailed Shearwater (*Puffinus pacificus* Gmelin): A dark, large (15–17) shearwater with a rather long, wedge-shaped tail and pale feet. Upperparts dark chocolate brown; face and throat dark brownish gray; rest of underparts grayish brown; underwing dusky. Bill bluish or black; feet yellowish flesh color or whitish. Has a white-bellied phase (*see* below).

A number of races in the warmer part of the Indian and Pacific oceans eastward to the Hawaiian Isls. Nests on New Caledonia and the southern New Hebrides, Fiji, Tonga, Samoa, and Micronesia. Casual in the Solomon Isls. This is probably the most common and widespread shearwater of the S.W.P.

[1] *See also* dark phase of *Pterodroma heraldica* and *Pt. philipii,* Section B.

Indistinguishable in the field is the slightly larger Pale-footed Shearwater (*Puffinus carneipes* Gould) with a fleshy white bill. The latter nests only in the southern Pacific and for the most part occurs to the south of the preceding species.

Christmas Shearwater (*Puffinus nativitatis* Streets): Very similar to *pacificus,* but smaller (15) and with bill and feet black. Underparts about as dark as upperparts. Tropical Pacific. Breeds at Laysan, Wake, and Christmas Isls. and in the Phoenix, Marquesas, Tuamotu, and Austral archipelagos.

Short-tailed Shearwater (*Puffinus tenuirostris* Temminck): Large (16). Sooty brown, much paler and more grayish underneath, throat occasionally white. Tail short and rounded. Bill dark, lead gray; feet vinaceous gray on inner, brown on outer side. This species, known in Australian waters under the name Mutton Bird, nests mainly on the islands of Bass Straits (between Australia and Tasmania) but reaches the tropical Pacific on its extensive migrations.

A similarly colored shearwater with whitish under wing-coverts is the Sooty Shearwater (*Puffinus griseus* Gmelin), the Mutton Bird of the New Zealand seas, which strays only rarely into the central Pacific. Larger and heavier than *tenuirostris.*

Heinroth's Shearwater (*Puffinus heinrothi* Reichenow): Small (11). Sooty brown (darker above), except for a whitish area in the middle of the belly and an admixture of white on chin and throat. White under the wing. Bill slender and very long; legs light brown. Known only from the seas near Rabaul, New Britain. Breeding place unknown.

Bulwer's Petrel (*Bulweria bulwerii* Jardine and Selby): A small (10) sooty petrel with a long, wedge-shaped tail. Bill black, feet dusky flesh color. It is smaller than any other dusky petrel and slightly larger than any of the storm-petrels (Hydrobatidae). Ranges through the entire northern Pacific from the islands near the coast of China to the Hawaiian Isls. and Marquesas.

A closely related species (*Bulweria macgillivrayi* Gray) is known from a single specimen from Ngau Isl., Fiji. It is slightly larger with a much larger bill.

Section B

This group includes about 8 species in the S.W.P.

Dusky Shearwater (*Puffinus l'herminieri*): Small (11). Upperparts sooty, underparts white. Under tail-coverts black; sides of breast gray. Bill blackish or bluish black; feet flesh color; outer toes black.

Several subspecies, *polynesiae* Murphy 1927 (Samoa and eastern Polynesia), *gunax* Mathews 1930 (New Caledonia and New Hebrides), *dichrous* Finsch and Hartlaub (Phoenix, Carolines, Palau), do not differ by field characters.

Little or Allied Shearwater (*Puffinus assimilis*): Small (10). Upperparts dark bluish gray; underparts entirely white including under wing-coverts. Bill bluish black; feet bluish. Differs little in field characters from the Dusky Shearwater. Individuals of the populations nesting on Lord Howe, Norfolk, Kermadecs, and New Zealand might be expected to wander northward occasionally.

Fluttering Shearwater (*Puffinus gavia* Forster): A small shearwater (12½), brownish black above, white below. Sides of head and neck mottled gray; lores and region below eye dark; under wing-coverts and under tail-coverts white; axillaries dusky with white tips. Bill dark horn color; feet fleshy white, dark on outer side. As in all small shearwaters the birds fly mostly with rapid wing beats except in very strong winds.

Breeds on New Zealand, possibly along the coast of Australia (New South Wales), on New Caledonia, and on the New Hebrides.

Gadfly Petrels

Under this name are grouped a number of closely related and very similar species, at least 2 of which can be expected in the S.W.P. Small (12½). Upperparts slaty black; face and underparts white. Bill black.

Stout-billed Gadfly Petrel (*Pterodroma hypoleuca*): Back neutral gray; crown, nape, and sides of breast much darker (sooty black). Underparts white, forehead more or less white. Legs and basal half of feet flesh color; tips of toes and webs black.

The race (*hypoleuca* Salvin) breeds on Laysan, Midway and the Bonin Isls. and probably visits most of Micronesia. Additional races (*axillaris* Salvin, *nigripennis* Rothschild) on the Chatham Isls., Kermadec and Austral Isls.

Gould's Gadfly Petrel (*Pterodroma leucoptera*): Small (12). Like *hypoleuca,* but more bluish above. Feet bluish; bill more slender. The nominate race (*leucoptera* Gould) nests along the eastern coast of Australia, the subspecies *brevipes* Peale breeds on New Caledonia, New Hebrides, and Fiji.

Herald Petrel (*Pterodroma heraldica* Salvin): A fairly large petrel (15) with dark brown upperparts (each feather on back indistinctly edged with gray). Forehead often white.

Underparts very variable (sometimes entirely dark brown except for some whitish feathers on the throat, but more usually white with gray lines on the sides of the neck, breast, and flanks, and occasionally with a dark band across the chest). Wings and tail blackish with concealed white patches at base of feathers showing in flight on the underside of the wing as a fairly large patch of white. Under wing-coverts chiefly blackish, partly white in middle line. Bill black; legs flesh color; tips of feet and webs black. Breeds on Chesterfield, Tonga, Marquesas, Tuamotu and Easter Isls.

Kermadec Petrel (*Pterodroma philipii* Gray) (often listed as *neglecta* Schlegel): Very similar to the Herald Petrel and equally variable, but larger (16) and with a more distinct white area toward the tip of the underwing surface and with white shafts to the primaries. Bill black; feet black or yellow with tips of webs black. Ranges from the Kermadec Isls. in the west to the islands off the coast of Mexico in the east.

White-faced Shearwater (*Puffinus leucomelas* Temminck): A large (17–18) variegated shearwater, with the white face streaked with black. "Upper surface brown, feathers of back and wings with pale edges, front and sides of head, neck and underparts, including under surface of wings, white. Feathers of face and neck, and edge of wing with dark streaks. Primaries black, tail brown, bill horn color, feet flesh color."—*Alexander*.

Breeds on the Bonin Isls. and on other islands of the Japan and China seas. Ranges south to the Indo-Australian archipelago. Not uncommon in the seas north of New Guinea and the Bismarck Archipelago.

PLATE I—For the common and scientific names of the birds shown here see page vii

Section C

Tahiti Petrel (*Pterodroma rostrata*): Large (15–16). Abdomen and under tail-coverts white, remainder of plumage, including undersurface of wings, deep blackish brown; throat, upper breast, and flanks paler brown. Bill black; legs yellowish flesh color; feet black.

Breeds on New Caledonia (*trouessarti* Brasil 1917) and the Society Isls. (*rostrata* Peale). Ranges through southwestern and central Pacific. A much smaller (11½) race (*becki* Murphy 1928) is known from only 2 specimens from the waters south of the Solomon Isls. and east of the Bismarck Archipelago.

Section D

Phoenix Petrel (*Pterodroma alba* Gmelin): Medium (14). Undersurface of wings dark, under tail-coverts white; flanks mottled with brown. Tail wedge-shaped. Bill black; legs and feet whitish; tips of toes and webs black. Ranges throughout the tropical Pacific. Breeds on Christmas Isl., the Phoenix, Marquesas, Tonga, and Tuamotu Isls.

The Herald, Kermadec, and Gould's (*brevipes*) Petrels sometimes have a similar black band across the breast.

STORM-PETRELS (SUBFAMILY HYDROBATINAE)

The storm-petrels are those small seabirds which, like swallows, flutter along the surface of the ocean, often in the wake of steamers. To sailors they are known as Mother Carey's chickens. Except for their manner of flight and slender bills, they are rather similar to their larger relatives, the shearwaters. The legs and feet of some of the species are quite long. In the southern Pacific about 6 species are most likely to be encountered.

Key to the Storm-Petrels

(1) All sooty black .... *Nesofregetta moestissima*

(2) Black; upper tail-coverts white .... *Oceanites oceanicus*

(3) Upperparts mostly sooty black; underparts largely white .... Genus *Fregetta* and *Nesofregetta albigularis*

(4) Upperparts mostly gray, underparts white .... *Pelagodroma marina*

(1) **Samoan Storm-Petrel** (*Nesofregetta moestissima* Salvin): Uniformly sooty black, with wings and tail rather blacker. Known only from a single individual from Samoa. Larger (9½) and more long-winged than other small (7½–9) blackish storm-petrels (*Oceanodroma markhami, O. melania,* and *O. monorhis*) which might wander into the northern part of the S.W.P. I doubt that anybody, even an expert, could distinguish between these species on the open ocean.

(2) **Wilson's Storm-Petrel** (*Oceanites oceanicus* Kuhl): Small (7). Dark portions of plumage sooty black, inner half of wing paler. A white band across base of the square tail. Nests in the Antarctic, but scatters over all oceans between breeding seasons. Very rare in the S.W.P.

(3) The 3 storm-petrels of this group, mainly black above, largely white below, are probably difficult to distinguish in life. They can possibly be separated as follows:

(a) Tail deeply forked .... *albigularis*
Tail almost square; throat sooty black .... b

(b) Underparts, except throat, entirely white .... *grallaria*
A dark band along the center of the underparts, from the middle of the throat to the base of the tail .... *tropica*

White-throated Storm-Petrel (*Nesofregetta albigularis* Finsch): Above sooty black with a narrow white band across the rump. Underparts white, with a broad sooty band across the chest. Flanks and belly sometimes streaked with black; tail long, deeply forked. Breeds on Christmas Isl., the Phoenix, Marquesas, Fiji Isls., and New Hebrides.

White-bellied Storm-Petrel (*Fregetta grallaria* Vieillot): Upperparts sooty black, tail and wing tips darkest; back and mantle lighter (feathers are grayish black and margined with white). Rump white; throat sooty black; remainder of underparts white; underside of wings, except wing-tips, white. Southern Pacific, ranging north to the tropics. Breeds on Lord Howe Isl., Austral Isls. (Rapa), and Juan Fernandez group (3 subspecies).

Black-bellied Storm-Petrel (*Fregetta tropica* Gould): Very much like the preceding species except for the black band along the middle of the belly and the black under tail-coverts. Rump white. Upper throat sometimes white or whitish. Nests farther south in subantarctic waters and rarely reaches the tropics. Recorded from the Solomon Isls.

(4) **White-faced Storm-Petrel** (*Pelagodroma marina*): Small (8). Forehead, face, eyebrow stripe, and entire underparts (including under wing-coverts) white. Top of head, nape, and broad stripe back of eye dark slate gray. Lower rump and patch on either side of throat pale gray. Mantle brown; wings and tail black. Tail very slightly forked. Bill and legs black, webs between toes yellow. Breeds in the New

Zealand area and Kermadec Isls. Wanders into the tropical and eastern Pacific. Not yet recorded from S.W.P.

TROPIC-BIRDS (FAMILY PHAETHONTIDAE)

The beginner might confuse these beautiful, white, long-tailed seabirds with terns, but their robust figures and different, more pigeon-like flight are clearly diagnostic. The wings are flapped constantly and steadily. Tropic-birds fly rather high over the water and are often seen far away from the nearest land.

The head is white except for a black line through the eye. The white plumage of the body is frequently tinged with pink or salmon color and is narrowly barred in immatures. The 2 central tail feathers of adults are very much elongated.

Adults of the 2 species of the S.W.P. can be distinguished as follows:

Bill yellowish; back and tail white .... *lepturus*

Bill and very long central tail feathers red .... *rubricauda*

Young birds lack the elongated tail feathers, are coarsely barred with black across the back, and the white of the plumage is not washed with pink. They are very much alike, but may be distinguished as follows:

Large (18–20). Bill black; outer wing feathers white with black shafts .... *rubricauda*

Small (14). Bill flesh color (with a black tip); outer edge of wing black, caused by the black outer web of the 3 or 4 outermost wing feathers .... *lepturus*

White-tailed Tropic-bird (*Phaethon lepturus*): All white, except for some marks which are black: a stripe through the eye, the front edge of the wing, a broad bar across the base of the wing, and a patch on the flanks. Bill yellowish, base grayish; legs flesh color; feet black.

Widespread in all tropical seas. Breeding on many islands of the S.W.P., from Palau to New Caledonia and the Tuamotus, but apparently not in the Bismarck Archipelago. Nests usually on cliffs.

Red-tailed Tropic-bird (*Phaethon rubricauda*): *See* Plate 1: 1. Large (18), with a long (16) tail. All pinkish white, except for the following black markings: a spot before the eye, the shafts of the wing feathers, a small patch on the inner wing and on the flanks.

Found in the Indian Ocean and in the Pacific Ocean north and south of the equator. Breeds on islands off Queensland, Kermadec Isls., Tonga, Samoa, Phoenix, Society, Line Isls., Hawaii, and Bonin Isls. Nests on flat ground. Is said to flap its wings rather slowly and to indulge in occasional sailing.

GANNETS AND BOOBIES (FAMILY SULIDAE)

The tropical species of this family are generally called boobies. They are robust seabirds, related to the cormorants, pelicans, and tropic-birds. They nest in large colonies and are usually found in loose flocks near their colonies. In areas where they do not nest, as in the Solomons, they are often encountered singly. Like the related brown pelicans and tropic-birds, they dive for fish by plunging down from heights up to 60 feet. Their flight is direct and steady, and they usually stay fairly close to the surface of the water. The wing beat is deliberate, like that of gulls.

Only 3 species of boobies are found in the S.W.P., but their identification is made somewhat difficult by the fact that the immatures are colored quite differently from the adults.

Key to the Southwest Pacific Boobies

(1) Tail white or grayish white; feet red .... *sula* (ad.)
Tail black 2
(2) Entire upperparts uniform brown ....
.... *leucogaster* (and *sula* juv.)
Entire upperparts (except outer wing and tail) white .....
.... *dactylatra* (ad.)
Only part of back white .... *dactylatra* (imm.)

Brown Booby (*Sula leucogaster*): *See* Plate 1: 2. The belly is white, the rest of the plumage is dark chocolate brown in adult birds. In immatures the belly is more or less washed with brown, but a sharp line usually separates the dark breast from the lighter abdomen. Face and gular pouch yellowish; bill light bluish; feet light green in adults, light yellowish in immatures.

This is the most common booby of the S.W.P. (*plotus* Forster). Nests on ledges and on the ground; lays 2–3 eggs, but usually raises one young only.

Red-footed Booby (*Sula sula*): Adults are either all white (partly buffy) with black wing-tips, or back, mantle, and underparts are more or less washed with gray. Tail pure white, or more or less gray in a gray phase. These plumages are not yet understood. Bill light blue with brown tip and red base. Naked skin of face blue or green, of throat black (gray in females). Legs and feet bright red. Young birds are sometimes all brown (including tail) with blue-black bill and chrome-yellow legs. They are probably indistinguishable from immature *leucogaster*.

The subspecies *rubripes* Gould is widespread in the Indian Ocean and in the tropical Pacific. The nests (with one egg) are usually placed in shrubs or trees.

Masked or Blue-faced Booby (*Sula dactylatra*): All white, but wing- and tail-feathers brown. Iris yellow; bill with horn-colored tip, base orange yellow in males, pink or light red in females; face blue black; feet olive drab in males, lead gray in females. Immatures are white, except for head, throat, mantle, wings, and tail, which are dark brown. Upper back and underwing white.

The subspecies *personata* Gould is found in the Indian Ocean and in the tropical Pacific. Nests on the ground.

FRIGATE-BIRDS OR MAN-O'-WAR BIRDS (FAMILY FREGATIDAE)

Once identified, frigate-birds can never be mistaken for any other bird. They glide effortlessly through the air, sometimes for hours without a wing beat, the deeply forked tail opening and closing like a pair of scissors. Usually they fly in smaller or larger groups at about twice-masthead's height. They never settle on water but pick their food with the bill from the surface or, even more often, rob other seabirds. They are seldom found far away from land. Males during the breeding season are characterized by the blown-up, balloon-like, red gular pouches.

Only 2 species are found in the S.W.P.

Key to the Southwest Pacific Man-o'-War Birds

(1) More or less black underneath 2
Breast and abdomen more or less white 3

(2) Brownish bar on upper side of wing; breast lighter than belly
.... *minor* ♂
No bar on upper side of wing; breast black, white patch on lower flank .... *ariel* ♂

(3) a. Entire head and most of underparts whitish ... immatures
b. Top of head black; throat whitish .... *minor* ♀
c. Top of head black; throat black; breast only white . . *ariel* ♀

Pacific Man-o'-War (*Fregata minor* Gmelin): Wingspread 82–88. In the S.W.P. apparently less common than the Least Man-o'-War. Immatures are distinguished by the liberal rusty wash on the white parts of the plumage. In the south Atlantic and throughout the Indian and Pacific oceans.

Least Man-o'-War (*Fregata ariel* Gray): The white patch on either side of the lower flanks and, if seen with the Pacific Man-o'-War for comparison, the relatively small size (wingspread 70–76) are diagnostic. Common on the coast of tropical Australia and ranges northward into the S.W.P. Recorded from the Solomon Isls., New Caledonia, New Hebrides, Fiji Isls., and other groups.

GULLS (FAMILY LARIDAE, SUBFAMILY LARINAE)

Gulls are so well known that their characteristic morphological features (short neck, robust body, short tail, fairly heavy bill) need not be described in detail. Gulls can soar quite easily but do so generally at a greater height above the ocean than shearwaters. They often settle on the water to feed or to rest. Gulls are preëminently coastal birds following steamers when they leave port, but usually disappearing from within the ships' sight by the next morning. There is only one gull in the S.W.P.

Australian Silver Gull (*Larus novaehollandiae*): A small white gull (15) with a gray mantle, some black on a few of the wing-feathers. Bill and feet red. Young similar, but tail with a narrow subterminal brown band; mantle mottled with brown; bill brownish; feet grayish. Queensland, New Caledonia, and Loyalty Isls. (*forsteri* Mathews 1912).

TERNS (FAMILY LARIDAE, SUBFAMILY STERNINAE)

Terns are the most conspicuous seabirds in tropical waters. Wherever there is a sand bar safe above the high-tide line, there will be some terns nesting. Wherever a school of fish churns the water, a flock of terns will quickly gather, diving for little fish, and whenever a piece of driftwood or merely a floating coconut is encountered there is a good chance that it will be occupied by a resting tern. For, although most terns are competent swimmers and divers, they like to rest on floating objects.

Terns are easily recognized by their slender, graceful shapes, by their long tapering wings and long tails (usually forked), and by their jerky nonsoaring flight. The sexes are alike in all species. The 13 species of terns encountered in the S.W.P. can be identified with the help of the following key:

Key to the Southwest Pacific Terns

(1) Crown black; back grayish; underparts white or pale gray 2
Not so 7

(2) Bill red, orange, yellow, or greenish 3
Bill black or blackish 5

(3) Very large (16–18). Crested; powerful bill greenish yellow; legs black; back and tail rather dark gray; forehead white .... *Thalasseus bergii*
Smaller (10–14). Bill yellow, orange, or red; tail white 4

(4) Forehead and crown black .... *Sterna dougallii*
Forehead white; crown black .... *St. albifrons* and *St. nereis*

(5) Back a smooth uniform gray 6
Back mottled or barred with black or dark brown .... *St. dougallii* (imm.)

(6) This bracket applies to 3 species:

a. Medium (13–14). Anterior half of crown white or black speckled with white; underparts white or pale gray; mantle and wings fairly dark gray; tail and rump white; streamers edged with gray ... *St. h. longipennis* (eclipse)

b. Like (a), but fairly dark; anterior part of crown always white; tail grayish; a dark patch on the shoulders .... *St. h. longipennis* (imm.)

c. Small (9–10). Bill blackish red; most of crown white but entire nape black; underparts white; upperparts very light gray; tail white; feet brown .... *St. albifrons* and *St. nereis* (imm.)

(7) Entirely white; bill black .... *Gygis*
Some gray or black in plumage 8

(8) Entire underparts white 9
Underparts partly or entirely gray, sooty or black 11

(9) Entire upperparts sooty or dark gray except for white forehead 10
A black band across the nape; mantle pale gray ....
.... *Sterna sumatrana*
(*see also* young of *St. albifrons* and *St. nereis*)

(10) This includes 3 species of *Sterna* that probably cannot be identified with certainty in the field:
a. Large. A broad white band across the forehead, ending above the eye; upperparts blackish; belly grayish white .... *fuscata*
b. Smaller. White band across forehead narrower and extending as a superciliary behind the eye; back brownish; belly grayish white .... *anaetheta*
c. Very much like *anaetheta,* but lighter and grayer above and pure white below; white on outermost tail-feather more pronounced .... *lunata*

(11) Entire plumage pearl gray .... *Procelsterna*
Entire plumage sooty brown or blackish, forehead or crown pale gray or whitish .... 12 (*Anous*)

(12) Larger. Dark brown; crown pale gray; forehead whitish
.... *A. stolidus*
Smaller. Blackish; crown whitish .... *A. tenuirostris*

Little Tern (*Sterna albifrons*): A very small (10–11) tern, with a white forehead and orange-yellow bill and feet. Crown, nape, and stripe from bill to eye black. Upperparts pearl gray; underparts white; tail deeply forked.

The race *sinensis* Gmelin ranges from the coast of Asia to the New Guinea region and rarely to the Bismarck Archipelago.

Nereis Tern (*Sterna nereis*): Very similar to the Little Tern, but lighter above (mantle pale pearl gray), less black before the eye (black spot in front of eye not connecting with bill, a narrow black ring around the eye), and with a bright yellow bill. Immatures similar, but crown and nape grayish, mottled with brownish black, mantle spotted with dull white.

In the S.W.P. found only in New Caledonian waters (*exsul* Mathews 1912), otherwise in Australia, Tasmania, and New Zealand.

Black-naped Tern (*Sterna sumatrana*): *See* Plate 1: 3. A small (12–13) tern with black bill and feet. Appears all white except for a black band across the nape and a small black spot in front of the eye. Mantle and back are actually very pale gray. The white of the underparts often has a pink hue. Tail long and deeply forked. *Young.* The white of the head buffy, the back darker gray, entire upperparts with a mottling of blackish gray and buff.

Tropical India and Pacific Ocean from Madagascar to central Polynesia. Found throughout the S.W.P. from Micronesia to New Caledonia, Samoa, Union, and Phoenix Isls. (*sumatrana* Raffles).

Roseate Tern (*Sterna dougallii*): Medium (14). Similar to the British and American Common Tern. Top of head black; mantle pale pearl gray; rump and tail white; underparts white, often with a rosy tinge. Bill orange red; feet red to orange. Tail deeply forked with very long streamers. The forehead is spotted with white after the breeding season. Young similar, but upperparts streaked and mottled; bill blackish.

In all the oceans. In the S.W.P. known from Bismarck Archipelago, the Solomon Isls., Loyalty Isls., and New Caledonia (*bangsi* Mathews 1912).

Black-billed Common Tern (*Sterna hirundo longipennis* Nordmann): Medium (13–14). Nearly all the birds of this species encountered in the S.W.P. are in immature or eclipse plumage. Birds with an all-black cap (adults in nuptial plumage) differ from *dougallii* by the black bill and the gray wash of the underparts. Immatures might be confused with *striata,* a species which does not seem to occur in the S.W.P.

Nests in eastern Asia, only passing through Micronesia (Palau). Fairly common winter visitor to the New Guinea region, the Bismarck Archipelago, and the Solomon Isls., occasionally to Cape York and to Lord Howe Isl.

Very similar is the Arctic Tern (*Sterna paradisaea*), which has been found repeatedly in New Zealand waters and might pass through the S.W.P. in September–October and again in March–April. Immature *paradisaea* differ from immature *longipennis* by having a snow-white rump. Adults in the eclipse plumage are probably indistinguishable in the field.

Sooty Tern (*Sterna fuscata*): *See* Plate 1: 4. Large (16). Tail deeply forked, black; outer edge of largest tail-feather white. Bill and feet black. Young brown, darker above, paler below. Feathers of the mantle with white tips, tip of outermost tail-feather white.

All tropical and subtropical seas. Samoa, Tonga, Fiji, and New Caledonia (*serrata* Wagler); Phoenix, Micronesian Isls. (*oahuensis* Bloxham). Breeds in immense colonies in which there is noise and activity by day and night ("Wideawake" Tern). The accurate recording of the breeding dates and seasonal movements of this species is very important.

Brown-winged Tern (*Sterna anaetheta*): Rather large (15).

Dark brown above with a black cap; whitish or grayish below. In the young, feathers of the upperparts have pale tips, underparts are white.

All tropical and subtropical seas, often seen far from land. Smaller and lighter than *fuscata,* the young differing in their whitish underparts. Reported from Tonga, Fiji, Solomon Isls., Bismarck Archipelago, and Palau (*anaetheta* Scopoli).

Bridled Tern (*Sterna lunata* Peale): Medium (14). Similar to *anaetheta,* but above grayish, not brown, and whiter below in all plumages. *Young.* Head mottled with black and white; mantle brownish gray, feathers tipped with white; underparts white.

Restricted to the tropical Pacific Ocean. Common at Samoa, Tonga, Fiji, Phoenix, rarer in the Solomons, Bismarck Archipelago, and in Micronesia. Breeding range not well known. A great wanderer on the open ocean.

Crested Tern (*Thalasseus bergii*): The largest tern (17–18) of the tropical Pacific. Large size, white forehead (even in fully adult plumage), and greenish yellow bill are diagnostic. Crown and crest black. Underparts snow-white. Immatures and individuals in eclipse plumage with top of head black mottled with white.

Indian and Pacific oceans. From the coast of Asia, through Micronesia and Sunda Isls. to Australia, New Caledonia, Tonga, Society, and Phoenix Isls. (*cristatus* Stephens). Very common and widespread in S.W.P. Nests in small colonies.

Blue-gray Fairy Ternlet (*Procelsterna cerulea*): Small (10–11). Gray, paler below; inner wing-feathers in fresh plumage with white tips. Bill black; feet black with lemon-yellow webs. Tail forked in center, but no streamers. Phoenix, Ellice, Samoa, Tonga, Fiji (subsp?), and Micronesia (*saxatilis* Fisher).

Fairy Tern (*Gygis alba*): Medium (13). This snow-white bird with black eye, black bill and feet, and deeply forked tail cannot be mistaken for any other tern. Throughout the S.W.P. (*candida* Gmelin), but apparently not nesting in the Bismarck Archipelago, Solomon Isls., Santa Cruz Isls., and New Hebrides. More regular in subtropical than tropical waters. The single egg is placed, without nest material, on a rock or on the horizontal branch of a tree.

Common Noddy (*Anous stolidus*): *See* Plate 1:5. An entirely brown, large (16) tern with gray crown and whitish forehead. Tail slightly forked. *Young.* Lighter and browner; top of head grayish brown; a narrow white line above the eye!

Tropical waters of the Atlantic and Pacific. Throughout the S.W.P. (*pileatus* Scopoli). Nests in large colonies. Builds substantial nests, sometimes on the ground, but more often in bushes or trees. Record every breeding colony you encounter! On the open ocean often found far from the nearest breeding ground.

White-capped Noddy (*Anous tenuirostris*): Similar to the Common Noddy and hardly distinguishable at a distance. Smaller (15), crown more whitish, body plumage more blackish. Habits like *stolidus*. Nests on cliffs or in tall shrubs or trees. From the Bismarck Archipelago to Fiji, Samoa, and New Caledonia (*minutus* Boie), and Micronesia (*marcusi* Bryan).

II

The Shorebirds of the Southwest Pacific Snipe, Sandpipers, Curlew, Plovers and Other Waders

SHOREBIRDS are a conspicuous component of the bird fauna of the Southwest Pacific, even though only 2 species breed in the area. It is the favorite winter quarters of many species; for others it is a stepping stone on the annual migration from the breeding grounds in northern Asia or Alaska to the winter home in Australia and New Zealand.

Wading birds are notoriously difficult to identify. To begin with, they are usually encountered in the Southwest Pacific in their drab winter plumage, in which most of the smaller species are confusingly similar to one another. In addition, many of them are wary and their diagnostic characters cannot be studied without the aid of a good pair of field glasses, at least 6-power.

All of the migratory species, with the exception of the Australian stilt, are visitors from the north, i.e. northern Asia or Alaska. They begin to arrive in the Southwest Pacific late in August and depart again in April and May. A few individuals of all species, however, linger throughout the summer. These nonbreeding birds (not yet adult or with impaired health) are often particularly difficult to identify, because they may be in only a partial nuptial plumage.

FIG. 3. Typical plumage patterns of shorebirds. (a) Curlew Sandpiper (*Calidris testacea*), (b) Sharp-tailed Sandpiper [middle of rump black, sides white], (c) Greenshank, (d) Tattler, (e) Black-bellied Plover, (f) Common Sandpiper. After R. T. Peterson from Serventy 1939.

To offset the difficulties in identifying the shorebirds of this area a twofold approach to their identification is herewith presented. In the first section the principal diagnostic features of each species are emphasized in an artificial key. This key will be particularly helpful to the beginner who may not even know the difference between a curlew, a godwit, a sandpiper, and a plover. The second section is a systematic synopsis of all the species, with an indication of their known geographical ranges and with emphasis on those characters that separate each species from its nearest relatives. As soon as a species has been identified with the help of the key, it should be looked up in this synopsis for additional information and for a confirmation of the identification. The reader of the synopsis should also check back to the key for more detailed descriptive features.

The key is based partly on specimens, partly on the notes of the experienced observers Peterson and Serventy.[1] It will have to be considered experimental until tested in the field. The author would be grateful for suggestions toward improvements. Shorebird characters fall into 2 classes, those that can be determined from observation of the resting or feeding bird (size, general coloration, size and shape of the bill, color of bill and legs), and those that can be recognized only in the flying bird (color of rump and tail, presence of a white wing bar, color of the axillaries). It is therefore advisable to flush each bird after its characters in the resting position have been exhaustively studied.

[1] Peterson, R. T. 1941. *A Field Guide to Western Birds*. Boston: Houghton Mifflin. 240pp. Serventy, D. L. 1938. "A Guide to the Field Identification of Waders." *The Emu*, 38:65–76.

Preliminary Key to the Shorebirds of the Southwest Pacific

(1) a. Conspicuous black in plumage 2
b. Plumage composed of gray, brown, rufous, and/or white 6

(2) a. Rump white or partly white 3
b. Rump colored like back; bill short 4

(3) Includes 3 species:
a. Large (13–16) and long legged; all white except mantle, wings, and back of neck, which are glossy black. Bill thin, long, straight, black; legs pink, very long ... *Himantopus*
b. Fairly large (11). Bill short; legs short. Underparts white with many or few black feathers; axillaries black in all plumages; upperparts mottled gray, black, and white .. .. *Squatarola*
c. Medium (9). Bill short, black, tapering; legs short, orange. A broad white wing-stripe; a black bar across the white rump. Breeding plumage black, rufous, and white. Winter plumage blackish brown above. Underparts white except for a black or brownish collar across lower throat .... *Arenaria*

(4) a. Rather small (6–9). Back, mantle, and tail plain gray; axillaries white 5
b. Medium (9½). Back, mantle, and rump mottled with blackish brown, white, and golden yellow; axillaries gray. Underparts more or less mixed with black feathers; bill black; legs olive green .. *Pluvialis* (breeding plumage)

(5) Underparts white except for a collar separating throat and breast; forehead white, bordered by a black bar across the head from eye to eye. Another black line from the bill below the eye along the side of the head—a characterization applying to 3 small plovers in their breeding plumage.

a. Medium (7½–9). Breast collar rufous or tawny ocher; no black on hind-neck. Legs gray. White wing bar .... *Charadrius leschenaultii* and *Ch. mongolus*

b. Very small (6). Collar black, continued across upper back; entire forepart of crown black. Bill black; eyelid and base of bill yellow; feet flesh color . *Charadrius dubius*

(6) a. Rump white or partly white 7

b. Centers of tail and of rump dark like back; sides white 11

c. Entire rump dark like back 12

(7) a. Fairly large (less than 12) or small. Bill not much longer than head 10

b. Large (13 or more). Bill thin, more than twice as long as head 8

c. Very large (20). Bill big and heavy (3), slightly longer than head. Upperparts brown; underparts white except for an indistinct brownish gray breast band. A remarkable pattern of white and black on sides of face. A white bar across gray tail and a complicated pattern of white, gray, and brown on wing. Bill black, base dull yellow; legs dull yellow; feet lead blue .... *Esacus magnirostris*

(8) a. Bill straight, slightly upturned; lower back and tail blackish; tail crossed by a broad white bar. *Winter plumage:* a uniform dark gray, with whitish on throat and abdomen. *Breeding plumage:* underparts rufous barred with blackish brown; head and mantle spotted with blackish .... *Limosa limosa*

b. Bill downcurved; upperparts dark brown, mottled with white or buff. Eyebrows and center line of head pale (whitish buff); rest of head dark brown, giving it a striped appearance 9

(9) a. With a noticeable rufous or cinnamon wash in plumage. Breast, belly, and under tail-coverts uniformly buffy white;

throat only spotted with brown. Pattern of upperparts bolder. Tail and upper tail-coverts light, contrasting with dark back. Axillaries black with buff bars .... *Numenius tahitiensis*

b. Throat, breast, flanks, and under tail-coverts with narrow dark streaks or bars; abdomen white. Lower back and rump whitish, contrasting with dark tail and upper tail-coverts. Spotting of upperparts fine. Axillaries white with brown bars .... *Numenius phaeopus*

(10) a. Fairly large (11). Bill short, thick; underparts whitish, more grayish on breast, with black axillaries (very conspicuous in flight). Upperparts mottled yellowish gray and dark brown; tail white with inconspicuous dark bars; a short wing-stripe .... *Squatarola* (winter)

b. Small to medium (8½). Bill thin, straight; eyebrow white; breast gray; rest of underparts white; axillaries white with inconspicuous gray bars; rump pure white; black bars across tail-feathers. Upperparts dark gray brown with an olive tinge and liberal light spotting .... *Tringa glareola*

(11) a. Small (8). White below and on face. Upperparts in winter plumage very pale whitish gray, rusty in spring. A prominent white wing-stripe; bill slender, short, black; legs short, black. On sandy beaches feeding along the water line .... *Crocethia alba*

b. Medium (9). Breast grayish or buff; eyebrow white. Upperparts mottled brown, rufous, and black; crown more rufous; inconspicuous wing-stripe. Bill slender, black; legs dull green .... *Calidris acuminata*

c. Very small (6). Underparts white (throat rufous in breeding plumage); face rather white. Upperparts, including head, gray in winter, rusty in breeding plumage; wing-stripe inconspicuous .... *Calidris minuta ruficollis*

(12) a. Bill very long, more than twice as long as head 13
b. Bill slender and long, 1–2 times as long as head 15
c. Bill thick, shorter than head (i.e. plovers) 16

(13) a. Bill straight or upturned 14
b. Bill long (6), downcurved. Very large (25). Upperparts, including rump, mottled black and pale brown. Underparts light (i.e. buff) with dark narrow streaks; middle of throat and of belly unstreaked. No eyebrow nor stripe along center of crown ...... *Numenius madagascariensis*

(14) a. Large (15–17). Bill very long, slightly upturned; basal half pale, distal half dark. Rump and tail barred black and white, lighter than back; no distinct wing-stripe. Upperparts dark brown mottled with buff or pale gray; indistinct eye-stripe. Breast pale gray brown, belly white; feet black .... *Limosa lapponica*
b. Medium (10–11). Bill long, straight. A striped brown bird. A broad eye-stripe and a broad buffy stripe along middle of crown. Short tawny-orange tail ... *Gallinago megala*
c. Medium (9–10). Bill long and very slender, slightly upturned. Upperparts uniformly plain dark gray; breast grayish or white; belly white. A distinct white wing-stripe. Legs yellow, short .... *Xenus cinereus*

(15) a. Fairly large (11). Upperparts uniform dark gray; no wing-stripe; rump and tail like back; short white eyebrow; breast gray, legs yellow .... *Heteroscelus*
b. Small (8). Upperparts pale gray with much white on head and nape; a conspicuous white wing-stripe. Underparts white; bill and legs black; bill long, very slender .. .. *Phalaropus lobatus*
c. Small (7½). Upperparts dark gray with greenish wash

and darker spots; white wing-stripe; white eyebrow. Underparts white except for more or less gray breast. Lateral tail-feathers white barred with black. Legs olive green .. .. *Actitis hypoleucos*

(16) a. Medium (9½). Back dark with small golden spots. Throat and breast buffy gray with a yellowish tone; belly whitish; no wing-stripe; axillaries gray .... *Pluvialis*

b. Small to medium (8–9). Back uniform gray, sometimes with a slight rufous tinge. Underparts pure white, except for a narrow gray (sometimes interrupted) collar across the breast. Forehead and eyebrow white; axillaries white; bill long for a plover and thick, black; legs rather short, gray green; indistinct wing-stripe. .... *Charadrius leschenaultii* (winter)

c. Small (7½). Like *leschenaultii* but bill very short and relatively thick, averaging darker above .... *Charadrius mongolus* (winter)

This key contains only the species that occur regularly in the S.W.P. Additional species, like *Tringa nebularia, Calidris minutilla subminuta, Calidris melanota, Gallinago gallinago, Charadrius asiaticus veredus* and *Charadrius alexandrinus dealbatus,* have been recorded as rare stragglers from Micronesia or the New Guinea region and are described in the following pages. More intensive field work is likely to reveal the presence of additional species in the S.W.P. If a user of the above key observes a bird that does not seem to belong to one of the species mentioned in the key, he should make careful notes of the diagnostic features and compare them in some museum with skins of the following species: *Lobibyx miles, Numenius minutus, Tringa stagnatilis, Calidris tenuirostris,*

Calidris testacea (*see* Figure 3), and *Limicola falcinellus.* All of these species can be expected to occur occasionally in the western section of the S.W.P., since they have been found in the New Guinea area, Australia, or New Zealand.

Suggestions to Observers

The seasonal movements and habits of the shorebirds of the S.W.P. are still poorly understood. Any amateur observer can make valuable contributions by keeping an exact record of the following data:

(1) Date of observation and number of individuals of each species.

(2) Arrival and departure at a given locality of individually recognizable birds or of small flocks.

(3) Association of species. Which species unite into feeding groups or migrating flocks?

(4) Type of beach on which feeding takes place (muddy, sandy, rocky, etc.).

(5) Behavior characteristics (voice, wariness, activity, etc.).

Systematic List of the Shorebirds of the Southwest Pacific

PLOVERS (FAMILY CHARADRIIDAE, SUBFAMILY CHARADRIINAE)

Black-bellied or Gray Plover (*Squatarola squatarola* Linnaeus): *See* Figure 3. Fairly large (11). Light colored. Black underparts more or less replaced by white in the winter plumage. Larger size, black axillaries, and white rump and tail distinguish this species from the Golden Plover. Voice a plaintive whistle: *whee-er-eee. See* key 3b, 10a.

Breeding range circumpolar in the Arctic tundras; winters in the tropics and subtropics. Rather rare in the S.W.P. Recorded from Micronesia (Truk).

Pacific Golden Plover (*Pluvialis dominica fulva* Gmelin): Medium (9½). Underparts black in breeding plumage. Differs from the Gray Plover, the only similar species, by the lack of white on rump and wing, and by the uniform gray underwing and axillaries. Found more often in pastures and other inland localities than other shorebirds. Voice a harsh whistled *queedle*. *See* key 4b, 16a.

Nests in northern Siberia and Alaska; winters throughout Oceania south to Australia. One of the most common shorebirds in the S.W.P.

Papuan Ring-necked Plover (*Charadrius dubius papuanus* Mayr 1938): The only very small (6) plover of the S.W.P. with white underparts and a well-defined black collar around the throat. Brown above except for black and white pattern on head and neck; forehead white. Found on gravel beds of rivers rather than at seashore. Call: a soft *pee-o*. Resident in New Guinea and New Ireland. *See* key 5b.

The Eurasian race (*curonicus* Gmelin), with identical field characters, occasionally passes through Micronesia as a migrant.

Kentish Plover (*Charadrius alexandrinus dealbatus* Swinhoe): Very small (6½). Found once on the Palau Isls. A whitish collar across the hind-neck. Broadly interrupted breast band, black in breeding plumage, brown in winter. Differs from *mongolus* (in winter plumage) by smaller size, white nuchal collar, and broad interruption of breast band. Wing-stripe present.

Mongolian Dotterel (*Charadrius mongolus* and subspecies): Small (7½). White below, sandy above. Rufous tawny of the breast in breeding plumage is replaced by a narrow gray ring across lower throat in the winter. *See* key 5a, 16c.

Breeds in eastern Asia; winters from India to Australia. In the S.W.P. found throughout Micronesia, also in the Bismarck Archipelago, Solomon Isls., and Santa Cruz Isls., eastward as far as Tucopia.

Large Sand Dotterel (*Charadrius leschenaultii* Lesson): Exactly like the preceding species, both in winter and breeding plumage, but larger (8–9) and with longer bill. Accurate field characters unknown. Gray breast band perhaps less conspicuous, sometimes missing; rump more whitish; legs lighter, paler gray green. *See* key 5a, 16b.

Nests in Asia; winters from Africa to the Australian region. In the S.W.P. recorded from Micronesia, Bismarck Archipelago, and Solomon Isls.

Oriental Dotterel (*Charadrius asiaticus veredus* Gould): Like the Sand Dotterel, but underparts with a grayish or buffish wash, not pure white. Buff collar broad, including most of breast. Rump not appreciably lighter than back. Dark brown crown sharply defined against buffy eye-stripe and pale nape, like a cap. Axillaries gray. Bill slender; legs dirty yellow.

Nests from Mongolia to northern China; winters from the Malay Archipelago to Australia. Occasional migrant visitor to Micronesia; not yet recorded from other parts of the S.W.P.

CURLEWS, GODWITS, SANDPIPERS, AND TATTLERS (FAMILY SCOLOPACIDAE, SUBFAMILY TRINGINAE)

This subfamily includes a number of superficially rather dissimilar types. The curlews are easily recognized by their very long, downcurved bills (least pronounced in the Little Whimbrel [*Numenius minutus*]). The godwits also have extremely long bills, but they are straight or even slightly upcurved. Sandpipers of the *Tringa* group, which includes such familiar species as the Redshank in England and the Yellow-legs in the Americas, are represented in the S.W.P. by a few medium-sized, long-legged, thin-billed species; they are usually solitary or found in small groups and tend to be rather wary. The tattlers are similar and are conspicuous by their very plain, uniform dark gray upperparts.

Whimbrel (*Numenius phaeopus variegatus* Scopoli): A medium-sized curlew (16). Call "a rippling whistle, *tĕt-tĕt-tĕt,* repeated about 5–7 times." On the beach, on mud flats, and on the banks of rivers. *See* key 9b.

Breeds in eastern Siberia; migrates and winters throughout the Indo-Australian Archipelago. In the S.W.P. found commonly in Micronesia, Bismarck Archipelago, and Solomon Isls., more rarely in the New Hebrides, New Caledonia, Santa Cruz Isls., and Fiji.

Bristle-thighed Curlew (*Numenius tahitiensis* Gmelin): Similar to the Whimbrel, but larger (17½), lighter underneath, and with a rufous tinge in the plumage. Upper tail-coverts uniformly buffy white; tail pale rufous tawny with black bars. Call a whistled "long drawn out *Aweu-wit.*" See key 9a.

Breeds in western Alaska; winters in eastern and central Polynesia. In the S.W.P. recorded from Samoa, Tonga, Fiji, Santa Cruz Isls. (Tucopia), Marshall Isls., and as a straggler from the Carolines and Marianas.

Long-billed Curlew (*Numenius madagascariensis* Linnaeus): Very large (25). Rump and tail colored like the back. No conspicuous striped pattern on head, but cap darker than sides of head. Voice a ringing *ker-lee*. *See* key 13b.

Breeds in eastern Siberia; winters from the Malay Archipelago to Australia and New Guinea. In the S.W.P. recorded from Micronesia, the Bismarck Archipelago, and the Solomon Isls.

Black-tailed Godwit (*Limosa limosa melanuroides* Gould): A large shorebird (13) with a very long, thin, almost straight bill (3). Breeding and winter plumage strikingly different. *Breeding plumage*. Much rust color on head, back, and breast; breast and belly partly barred with blackish. *Winter*. Breast pale gray or buffy gray; remainder of underparts white. Upperparts brownish gray, paler on head and neck. Axillaries pure white. In flight shows broad white wing-stripe and legs trail beyond tail. Usually solitary. Call: *gritto-gritto*. *See* key 8a.

Breeds in eastern Asia; winters from the Malay Archipelago to Australia and as a straggler to New Guinea and the Bismarck Archipelago.

The American race, called the Hudsonian Godwit (*L. l. haemastica* Linnaeus), has been observed 7 times in New Zealand, which it must have reached by way of the S.W.P. It differs from the Asiatic race by having shorter bill and legs. In flight the legs do not trail conspicuously behind the tail. There is *no* conspicuous white wing-stripe; underwing and axillaries are blackish. In the breeding plumage there is very little rufous on the upperparts.

Bar-tailed Godwit (*Limosa lapponica baueri* Naumann): Much like the Black-tailed Godwit, but larger (15–17) and bill slightly upturned. Underwing and axillaries barred gray and white. Breast, flanks, and under tail-coverts often mottled or barred. In flight legs do not extend distinctly beyond tail. Call: *tĕrrĕk-tĕrrĕk*. This is the common godwit of the S.W.P. *See* key 14a.

Breeds in northeastern Siberia and Alaska; winters from the Malay Archipelago to Australia and New Zealand. Throughout S.W.P. as far east as Tonga and Samoa.

Greenshank (*Tringa nebularia* Gunnerus): *See* Figure 3. Large (13). Rump pure white, the white extending up the back to the level of the wings. Tail with inconspicuous black bars; rest of upperparts greenish gray; no wing-stripe; face white. Underparts whitish with dark streaking along sides of neck. Bobs head. Rather wary. Call, on rising, a ringing 2-or-3-syllabled *tju-tju-tju,* or *tchew-tchew-tchew*.

Breeds in northern Europe and Asia; winters in the Old World tropics, eastward to Australia, New Guinea, and New Zealand. In the S.W.P. recorded only from the Carolines (Yap, Truk).

Wood Sandpiper (*Tringa glareola* Linnaeus): Small to medium (8½). Bill straight, slender, and somewhat longer than head, as in all *Tringa*. Legs long, olive brown. Call a sharp *giff-giff-giff*. *See* key 10b.

Breeds in northern Europe and Asia; winters in the Old World tropics eastward to Australia and New Guinea. In the

S.W.P. recorded only from western Micronesia (Palau, Guam).

Terek Sandpiper (*Xenus cinereus* Güldenstaedt): Medium (9–10). Bill long, thin, slightly upcurved, black. Face, indistinct eyebrow, and upper throat white. Bobs tail; runs actively. Call note a melodious trill, *tiririr*. *See* key 14c.

Breeds from northern Europe to Siberia; winters from Africa and India to Australia and New Guinea. Recorded from New Britain.

Common Sandpiper (*Actitis hypoleucos* Linnaeus): *See* Figure 3. Small (7½). Bill thin, straight. "Teeters" (i.e. bobs head and tail) almost continuously; solitary or in pairs, usually near rocks or on gravel. Often found on inland streams and creeks, up to 5000 feet altitude. Rarely on outer beaches. Call: *tee-ti-ti*. Flies with a peculiar, stiff wing beat, interspersed with frequent glides in which the wings are held below the horizontal. Very common. *See* key 15c.

Breeds from Europe to eastern Asia; winters from Africa to Australia and New Guinea. In the S.W.P. recorded from Micronesia, the Bismarck Archipelago, Solomon Isls., Santa Cruz and Banks Isls.

Wandering Tattler (*Heteroscelus incanus*): A fairly large (11) sandpiper. Long, straight, black bill. Belly white. Gray portions of underparts barred in the spring or breeding plumage, but plain gray in the eclipse or winter plumage. Frequents rocky places along the ocean shore. There are 2 very similar races. (*See* key 15a.)

American Wandering Tattler (*H. i. incanus* Gmelin): Larger. In the breeding plumage the barring of the underparts is heavier and more extensive; only a small area in the middle of the abdomen remains unbarred. Under tail-coverts always distinctly barred. In the winter plumage probably indistinguishable from *brevipes*. Upperparts darker gray, very uniform.

Breeds in Alaska; winters from the coast of Peru to the western Pacific. In the S.W.P. found commonly on Samoa, Tonga, Fiji, and the Carolines. More rarely in the New Hebrides, Santa Cruz Isls., Solomon Isls., Bismarck Archipelago, Palau, and Marianas.

Asiatic or **Gray-tailed Tattler** (*H. i. brevipes* Vieillot): *See* Figure 3. Smaller. *Breeding plumage*. Barring restricted to throat, upper breast, and flanks. Lower breast, entire belly, and under tail-coverts white. *Winter*. Upperparts lighter gray. There is some fine white barring on the rump that might be visible at close range. Gray breast band narrower.

Breeds in eastern Siberia; winters in the Malay Archipelago, Australia, and New Guinea. In the S.W.P. recorded from Micronesia, Bismarck Archipelago, and Solomon Isls.

TURNSTONES (SUBFAMILY ARENARIINAE)

Turnstone (*Arenaria interpres* Linnaeus): Medium (9). Heavy bodied. *Winter*. Blackish brown above with a blackish brown collar across breast; upper throat and belly white. *Breeding plumage*. Breast collar deep black; upperparts a mixture of black and rust brown. Characteristic pattern of back and rump identical in all plumages: lower back white, followed by a V-shaped black and a similar white band; tail black, tipped with white. *See* key 3c.

Breeding range circumpolar; winter range circumtropical. In the S.W.P. recorded from every island group, although nowhere common. Prefers rocky or pebbly beaches.

SNIPE (SUBFAMILY SCOLOPACINAE)

Marsh Snipe (*Gallinago megala* Swinhoe): Medium (10–11). The squat body, long bill, and the brownish coloration are diagnostic. Eyes set far back in head. Head has a peculiar striped pattern. Back mottled and barred with a rich pattern of black, rufous, and buff, which gives a striped impression. Middle of belly white. When flushed, it may fly off in a zigzag manner, uttering a sharp rasping note, although no good description is available. Frequents grassy marshes or muddy edges of streams, never beaches. *See* key 14b.

Breeds in east-central Asia; winters from the Malay Archipelago to Australia and New Guinea. In the S.W.P. recorded from the Bismarck Archipelago and Micronesia (Guam, Palau).

There is a record of the Common Snipe (*Gallinago gallinago*) from Micronesia (Saipan). It is doubtful whether the 2 species can be distinguished with certainty in the field.

STINT SANDPIPERS (SUBFAMILY CALIDRIINAE)

Sanderling (*Crocethia alba* Pallas): A small (8), plump, very pale sandpiper with a broad white wing-stripe, straight bill, and black feet. Little groups run actively back and forth along the high-water line of sandy beaches. *See* key 11a.

Circumpolar breeding range; during the migratory sea-

Plate II—For the common and scientific names of the birds shown here see page vii

son almost worldwide in distribution. Reaches only the northern fringe of the S.W.P. (Marianas, Marshall Isls., Union and Phoenix groups).

Little Stint (*Calidris minuta ruficollis* Pallas): Very small (6). Thin, straight bill; black legs. No gray breast band; middle of rump black, sides white. Usually in small or large flocks; prefers mud flats. *See* key 11c.

Breeds in northeastern Siberia and northwestern North America; winters from the Malay Archipelago to Australia and New Guinea. In the S.W.P. recorded from Micronesia, Bismarck Archipelago, and the Solomon Isls.

Long-toed Stint or **Least Sandpiper** (*Calidris minutilla subminuta* Middendorff): Very similar to the Little Stint, but has greenish yellow legs and is a little more brownish above. A spotted, grayish band across the lower throat. Recorded from Palau.

Sharp-tailed Sandpiper (*Calidris acuminata* Horsfield): *See* Figure 3. Medium (9). Rufous-gray breast, often with streaking or barring, not sharply set off against white abdomen. Differs from the Little Stint by larger size, the rufous-brown tinge of the upperparts in all plumages, the green legs, and the grayish breast. *See* key 11b.

Breeds in northeastern Siberia; winters from the Malay Archipelago to Australia and New Guinea. In the S.W.P. recorded from Micronesia, Bismarck Archipelago, Solomon Isls., Santa Cruz Isls., and New Caledonia.

Pectoral Sandpiper (*Calidris melanota* Vieillot): Extremely similar to preceding species, but differs by "a very sharp line of demarcation between dark upper breast and remainder of white underparts." Prefers marshes to beaches. Recorded once from Micronesia (Ponape).

STILTS AND AVOCETS (FAMILY RECURVIROSTRIDAE)

White-headed Stilt (*Himantopus himantopus leucocephalus* Gould): Unmistakable. *See* key 3a.

From the Philippines to Australia and the Papuan region. In the S.W.P. recorded only from New Britain, where it seems to be an irregular winter visitor from Australia.

PHALAROPES (FAMILY PHALAROPODIDAE)

Northern Phalarope (*Phalaropus lobatus* Linnaeus): Small (7½). Usually found in large flocks on the open ocean, swimming high in the water (like corks). Circles like a merry-go-round while feeding. *See* key 15b.

Breeds throughout the Arctic; winters in tropical and subtropical seas. A favorite wintering ground is the sea north of New Guinea, from New Britain westward.

THICK-KNEES OR STONE-CURLEWS (FAMILY BURHINIDAE)

Reef Thick-knee (*Esacus magnirostris* Vieillot): *See* Figure 4. A very large (20), plump shorebird that looks more like a small heron than a wader. White patches and stripes on wing produce a pied pattern in flight. Frequents reefs and sandy outer beaches. *See* key 7c.

Fig 4. Reef Thick-knee (*Esacus magnirostris*)

Nonmigratory. Ranges from the Malay Archipelago and the Philippines eastward to New Caledonia, the Bismarck Archipelago, and the Solomon Isls. Not recorded from Micronesia or central Polynesia.

III

The Land and Fresh-Water Birds of the Southwest Pacific

Systematic Section

THE land birds of the Southwest Pacific include many types with which the bird student from Europe or North America is not familiar. To be sure, he may encounter some species, like the Barn Owl, the Osprey, or the Goshawk, that are also members of the bird fauna of his home country. In other cases, he will find close relatives of familiar European or North American birds, as occur among the swallows, thrushes, warblers, hawks, flycatchers, and other families. The dominant birds of the Southwest Pacific, however, belong to families that are peculiar to the Australian region or at least to the Old World tropics, and it will be of considerable importance to the student who is not acquainted with them to learn something about the typical characteristics of these families. The following section contains a short description of each of the families found in the Southwest Pacific.

Also treated in this systematic section are all the widespread species, mostly species that occur in three or more of the seven geographical subdivisions. Such species and genera are marked with an asterisk in the various geographical sections. In this way much repetition has been avoided. On the other hand, this abbreviated treatment makes it necessary that every visitor to a given island group study this systematic section before profitably starting to identify species listed in the geographical sections. The most important systematic literature on each family is listed.

CASSOWARIES (FAMILY CASUARIIDAE)

Of the 3 species of this ostrich-like family of running birds only one (*Casuarius bennetti*) reaches New Britain. The female is larger and more brightly colored, and the male takes care of incubation and raising of the young.

GREBES[1] (FAMILY PODICIPIDIDAE [COLYMBIDAE])

Grebes are duck-like, swimming birds, found in the S.W.P. only on lakes and ponds. They dive frequently and well, and can be distinguished from ducks by their slender appearance and by their apparent taillessness. The neck is held erect and the head turned frequently. The nest, containing 5–8 eggs, is built on floating vegetation. The grayish downy young have a series of longitudinal stripes on head and neck. Two very similar species are found in the S.W.P., the wings of both showing white in flight:

(1) Underparts mostly white; a chestnut brown stripe behind the eye separates the black crown and nape from the black chin and throat (breeding plumage) .... *Podiceps novaehollandiae*

(2) Underparts mostly blackish; entire throat except chin rufous brown (breeding plumage) .... *Podiceps ruficollis*

[1] Mayr, E. 1931. *Amer. Mus. Novit.*, no. 486:2–3. Mayr, E. 1943. *The Emu*, 43:3–7.

CORMORANTS OR SHAGS[2] (FAMILY PHALACROCORACIDAE)

This family is represented in the S.W.P. by a single species.

Little Pied Cormorant (*Phalacrocorax melanoleucus*): Swimming it might be confused with a large duck, but the neck is longer and the body lies deeper in the water. Small (21). Entire upperparts glossy black; underparts white. Often sits quietly in an upright position on rocks, sand bars, or on dead branches of forest trees. Prefers fresh to salt water. Nests in small colonies.

The subspecies *melanoleucus* Vieillot is known from Tasmania, Australia, East Indies west to Celebes and eastern Java, Palau Isls., New Guinea region, Solomon Isls., Santa Cruz Isls. (Tucopia), and New Caledonia.

HERONS AND BITTERNS[3] (FAMILY ARDEIDAE)

Long-legged, long-necked wading birds, usually standing quietly in shallow water, waiting for prey, or perched on trees in a somewhat hunched up position. Most of the species found in the S.W.P. are rather wary and secretive. Only 3 species (*Butorides, Demigretta,* and *Nycticorax caledonicus*) are wide ranging.

Little Mangrove Heron (*Butorides striatus*): *See* Plate 1: 6. *Adult.* Small (14). Crown black; back and wings dark gray. Underparts dirty gray washed with ocher; middle of upper

[2] Amadon, D. 1942. *Amer. Mus. Novit.*, no. 1175:1–2.

[3] Mayr, E. 1940. *Amer. Mus. Novit.*, no. 1056:4–7 (*Butorides*). Mayr, E. and Amadon, D. 1941. *Amer. Mus. Novit.*, no. 1144:1–11 (*Demigretta*). Amadon, D. 1942. *Amer. Mus. Novit.*, no. 1175:2–8 (*Notophoyx, Nycticorax*).

throat white with a blackish or dark gray line along the center. Iris yellow; feet olive to reddish orange. *Immature.* Dark grayish brown above with rufous or whitish spots and streaks; underneath buffy ocher, streaked with blackish or gray.

Throughout the Solomon Isls., Santa Cruz Isls., western Fiji Isls., New Hebrides, and New Caledonia. Absent from Tonga, Samoa, and Micronesia. In mangroves and along lowland streams. In habits and appearance much like the American races of the species (Green Heron).

Reef Heron (*Demigretta sacra*): Large (20). Occurs in 3 color phases: (1) blackish gray (with a white stripe along the middle of the throat); (2) pure white; and (3) mottled. Most birds in a partly white and partly gray plumage are immatures of the white phase, but mottled adults occur in Fiji, Solomon Isls., and Micronesia. Iris yellow; bill black and yellowish; legs pale green.

Occurs on all islands of the S.W.P. (*sacra* Gmelin). Birds from New Caledonia and the Loyalty Isls. are larger (*albolineata* Gray). To record the exact number of gray, mottled, and white individuals on each island is an important task of the field observer. Conspicuous along beaches, in tidal pools, on coral rocks, etc. Nests in small colonies more or less throughout the year. Occasionally up to 5 or 6 miles from the coast on lowland streams.

Rufous Night Heron (*Nycticorax caledonicus*): *Adult.* A medium-sized (22) heron with a black crown, rufous back and wings, and whitish underparts. Iris yellow; bill black; feet dull yellow to reddish orange. One or two long occipital plumes, which are white or rufous white with black tips. *Immature.* Dark brown above, heavily spotted with buffy white;

underneath buffy white with grayish streaks. Differs from the young *Butorides* by much larger size, by the rufous, not greenish gray, wings and tail, by the paler underparts, and by the different habitat.

Four subspecies in the S.W.P., all except *mandibularis* with a rufous-white superciliary. A fairly common bird along lowland streams, also in mangrove swamps. Nests in the true forest. Feeds on fish and crabs.

IBISES (FAMILY THRESKIORNITHIDAE)

Rennell Isl. is the only locality in the S.W.P. where a species of this family (*Threskiornis aethiopicus*) occurs. It is a more or less white stork-like bird with a long, curved, black bill.

SPOONBILLS (FAMILY PLATALEIDAE)

Rennell Isl. again is the only place of occurrence (*Platalea leucorodia regia*).

DUCKS[4] (FAMILY ANATIDAE)

The ducks of the S.W.P. belong to 3 subfamilies, which differ in their habits as follows. The surface-feeding ducks (Anatinae), to which belong such familiar species of the Northern Hemisphere as the Mallard, Shoveller, and Widgeon, do not dive. When swimming they keep their tails above the water line. Surprised on a small pond or river, they jump into the air with a loud splashing. The diving ducks of the pochard group (Nyrocinae) try to escape danger by diving. If taking flight, they first run a stretch along the surface of the water.

[4] Ripley, D. 1942. *The Auk*, 59:90–99 (*Anas gibberifrons*). Amadon, D. 1943. *Amer. Mus. Novit.*, no. 1237:1–5 (*Anas superciliosa*).

Their colors are plain, mostly browns, blacks, and grays, and they lack a metallic wing speculum. The Australian White-eyed Duck (*Nyroca australis*) is perhaps the only species of diving duck occurring in the S.W.P. The third subfamily is that of the tree ducks (Dendrocygninae). The loud whistles of these long-legged, long-necked ducks are diagnostic. In spite of their much smaller size, there is something goose-like in their swimming posture and slow wing beat. They are most active at night and rarely perch in trees, notwithstanding their name. The nest, however, may occasionally be in hollow trees. They are reported to be expert divers.

Whistling Tree Duck (*Dendrocygna arcuata*): Size of a teal (14). Breast pale brown (with fine black bars); throat whitish. Side of wing (when swimming) rufous chestnut; lower back black; upper back barred black and golden brown; crown blackish; sides of face buffy. Under tail-coverts whitish, contrasting with rufous chestnut belly. Differs from *Anas superciliosa* by the lack of a superciliary, by the rufous wing and underparts, and by the whitish under tail region and flanks. Differs from *Dendrocygna guttata* (Australian region, New Britain) by smaller size, by the blackish lower back, by the absence of light spots on breast and flanks, and by the rufous on wing and abdomen. In flight the underwing is blackish in both species of *Dendrocygna*.

From the Philippines and Sunda Isls. to Australia. In the S.W.P. found in New Caledonia, Fiji Isls., and New Britain (*arcuata* Horsfield).

Australian Gray Duck (*Anas superciliosa*): *See* Plate 1: 7. The common duck of the South Sea Isls. and Papuan region. Similar to a dark female mallard or to a North American

Black Duck. Swimming it appears as a dark brown duck with a glossy green and black wing-bar and a conspicuous facial pattern (a broad blackish brown line from the bill through the eye is separated from the dark crown by a buffy white line; another dark line beginning at the gape separates the buff cheeks from the buff throat). The white underwing is conspicuous in flight.

Widespread and common. In the mountains, in the lowlands, and even on salt water. Occasionally feeds on outer reefs. Nest often situated quite a distance from water.

HAWKS, KITES, AND EAGLES[5] (FAMILY ACCIPITRIDAE)

The species of this family that are found in the S.W.P. belong, with 2 or 3 exceptions, to types with which the student of European or American birds is familiar. Most common, although perhaps least conspicuous, are small and large Accipiters, cousins of the Goshawk. In the more westerly islands there are also found crested hawks (*Aviceda*), eagle-kites (*Haliastur*), and sea eagles (*Haliaeetus*).

Swamp Harrier (*Circus approximans*): Large (22–23). This species is very close to the European Swamp Harrier and in habits and flight similar to the North American Marsh Hawk. Usually seen flying low over grasslands and other open areas, with the wings held somewhat above the horizontal (giving it a slightly V-shaped flight silhouette). Tail and wings long.

Coloration variable. Immatures blackish brown above, rufous brown below. Adult males with a white rump, gray-

[5] Amadon, D. 1941. *The Emu*, 40:365–384 (*Haliastur sphenurus, Circus approximans*).

ish wing and tail, whitish underparts (with brown streaks), and brown back and mantle. Other birds intermediate, with light (ocher) rump, pale brown underparts, and a heavily barred tail.

Known from the Society Isls. (introduced), Tonga, Fiji, New Hebrides, Loyalty Isls., and New Caledonia (*approximans* Peale). Found in marshes and all open country, lowlands and highlands, but not in the forest. Feeds on frogs, lizards, mice, grasshoppers, and other insects, occasionally on birds. Nests on the ground in cane grass or in marshes.

OSPREYS OR FISH HAWKS[6] (FAMILY PANDIONIDAE)

Osprey (*Pandion haliaetus*): The white underparts, the whitish head, and the dark brown upperparts are diagnostic. Usually perched on dead branches of tall trees near the seashore or along rivers. In flight somewhat similar to a large gull. Feeds on fish, which it catches by plunging into the water, also on sea snakes.

In the S.W.P. found on New Caledonia, the Solomon Isls., the Bismarck Archipelago, and Palau Isls. (Micronesia) (*melvillensis* Mathews 1912).

FALCONS[7] (FAMILY FALCONIDAE)

Rapid, powerful strokes of the long, pointed wings are diagnostic of falcons. Soar infrequently. The only widespread, al-

[6] Amadon, D. 1941. *The Emu,* 40:375–377.

[7] Mayr, E. 1941. *Amer. Mus. Novit.,* no. 1133:1–2.

though rare, falcon of the S.W.P. is the Peregrine Falcon (Duck Hawk of American bird students).

Peregrine Falcon (*Falco peregrinus*): The only large falcon in the S.W.P. Above blackish, below dark rufous (gray) with black crossbars. About the size of a crow.

The native Peregrine Falcons are, on the whole, restricted to the vicinity of cliffs. Winter visitors of the Siberian races are most likely encountered near the seashore of Palau and other islands in the western part of the S.W.P. The resident races of the S.W.P. are *ernesti* Sharpe (New Britain, New Ireland) and *nesiotes* Mayr 1941 (New Caledonia, Loyalty Isls., New Hebrides, and Fiji Isls.).

MEGAPODES,[8] BRUSH TURKEYS (FAMILY MEGAPODIIDAE)

The members of this curious family of fowl-like birds of the Australian region do not incubate their eggs. Instead, the female deposits them in the soil, in sand, in hot volcanic ashes, or in big scratched-together heaps of decaying leaves and forest litter. The "incubation period" of more than 40 days is extraordinarily long, but the newly hatched young are completely independent of their parents. They dig themselves out, and can fly as soon as their plumage is dry. Not knowing their parents, they are independent from the day of their birth. Much is still to be learned about the habits of the megapodes. There is only one group of geographically representative species in the Pacific, belonging to the genus *Megapodius*.

[8] Mayr, E. 1938. *Amer. Mus. Novit.*, no. 1006:1–15 (*Megapodius*). Amadon, D. 1942. *Amer. Mus. Novit.*, no. 1175:9.

Incubator Bird (*Megapodius freycinet*): A dull-colored ground bird of the size (11–15) and behavior of a chicken. Upperparts dark brown; underparts sooty gray. Males, females, immatures alike. Two races in the S.W.P.

layardi Tristram (northern New Hebrides, from Efate northward, and Banks Isls.) back blackish, only slightly tinged with brown; crown with a short crest; forehead and throat bare with the skin red; legs red.

eremita Hartlaub (Bismarck Archipelago and Solomon Isls.) small and very dark; bare forehead red; crest very short; legs and feet dusky olive green.

Does much calling at night. Small parties often undertake roosting flights from the mainland to small offshore islets. It is of interest to take detailed notes on such roosting flights and on the circumstances of every nest. Two other species of the genus are found in Micronesia (*lapérouse*) and in central Polynesia (*pritchardii*).

QUAILS AND PHEASANTS[9] (FAMILY PHASIANIDAE)

There are only 2 representatives of this family in the S.W.P., a dwarf quail (*Excalfactoria*) [*see* Figure 5], which is found in the grasslands of New Britain and was introduced into Guam, and the ubiquitous domestic fowl.

Domestic Fowl (*Gallus gallus*): The sea-faring Polynesians took chickens on many of their colonization trips. They kept them in a semidomesticated condition and some became wild on nearly all the islands. These feral chickens are very similar

[9] Ball, S. C. 1933. *Bernice P. Bishop Mus. Bull.*, 108:1–122 (*Gallus*).

FIG. 5. Head of Pigmy Quail (*Excalfactoria chinensis lepida*) (New Britain).

to the original jungle fowl but are larger. More recently they have freely interbred with many modern breeds. Feral fowl have been reported from Samoa, Tonga, Fiji, New Caledonia, and the Micronesian Isls.

BUTTON-QUAILS OR HEMIPODES (FAMILY TURNICIDAE)

These secretive birds, which look like dwarf quail, have a very restricted distribution in grassland areas. The females are larger and more brightly colored than the males, who take care of the duties of incubation. Each female lays several sets of eggs to be attended by different males. Two species occur in the S.W.P.: *Turnix maculosa* (*see* Figure 6) in the Bismarck Archipelago and on Guadalcanal; and *Turnix varia* on New Caledonia. Most field naturalists will look in vain for these elusive birds, even in their proper habitat.

Fig. 6. Button-Quail (*Turnix maculosa salomonis*)

RAILS AND GALLINULES[10] (FAMILY RALLIDAE)

Sixteen species of rails are known from the S.W.P., but 11 of these have been reported from only a single island group of the S.W.P. We associate rails generally with swamps or thick reed beds along the edge of lakes or slow-flowing rivers, and this, no doubt, is the customary habitat of most of them. Many of the South Sea Isls. rails, however, are forest birds; others frequent the dense second growth of abandoned native plantations or impenetrable cane-grass thickets. The nest is usually built on the ground or, in a few species, in low bushes a foot or two above the ground. Most rails have very short tails. They fly only reluctantly, and some species seem to have

[10] Amadon, D. 1942. *Amer. Mus. Novit.*, no. 1175:10–11 (*Porzana tabuensis*). Mayr, E. 1938. *Amer. Mus. Novit.*, no. 1007:4–13 (*Rallus, Porphyrio*).

lost the power of flight entirely. Rails are champion skulkers and usually manage to keep out of sight of even the most skillful observer. Frequent calls, particularly at night, reveal their presence, but calls of the S.W.P. species have not yet been described adequately. The downy young of all species are black. Four species are widespread in the S.W.P.

Banded Rail (*Rallus philippensis*): A large (11), slender rail, a little smaller than a chicken, with long legs and a strong bill. Crown, nape, and a broad stripe through the eye rufous brown. A conspicuous whitish gray eyebrow. Upper throat whitish, lower throat gray. Flanks barred black and white; lower belly unbarred buffy white. Entire back and mantle blackish to olive brown, more or less barred and spotted with white; wings with chestnut bars. Some birds have a conspicuous rufous-ocher band across the breast. Iris reddish; bill flesh color; feet greenish gray.

There are 9 races in the S.W.P., but the differences between them are not sufficient to serve as field marks.

This rail is quite common on most islands. It is more secretive than shy, and a quiet observer may watch it from a close distance. Like all rails, it feeds entirely on the ground. It is found in almost any kind of habitat, usually far away from water in native gardens or second growth, sometimes even in very dry areas. Escapes by running rather than by flying, the tail being cocked up and flicked nervously.

Sooty Rail (*Porzana tabuensis*): A small (6), short-legged rail. Head and underparts sooty black, underneath with a gray tinge. Mantle and wings dark walnut brown; lower back fuscous; tail blackish. A few inconspicuous white spots on under tail-coverts and under wing-coverts. Eyes and feet red;

bill black. The black (with a greenish gloss) downy young have a white stripe along chin and throat.

Of wide distribution in the Pacific (*tabuensis* Gmelin), but not yet reported from the Solomon Isls. and Micronesia. In the S.W.P. usually found in the swamp vegetation surrounding ponds and lakes. Generally overlooked.

White-browed Rail (*Poliolimnas cinereus*): A small (7), long-legged rail. Above light brown, below whitish gray. A dark gray line from the gape through the eye to the nape. Lores and short eyebrow (ending over the eye) white, also a white line between the gray ear-coverts and the dark eye-stripe. Flanks and under tail-coverts ocher. Iris reddish; bill yellowish brown; feet greenish olive. Immatures are ochraceous brown with throat and belly white and an indistinct facial pattern. The species is easily recognized by its light underparts and the absence of white spots and bars except on the face.

Breaks up into 4 or 5 races in the S.W.P. which are indistinguishable to the field observer. Not yet reported from Santa Cruz and Solomon Isls. Lives in (?) mangrove swamps and marshy places. Call: *cutchi-cutchi-cutchi.*

Purple Swamphen (*Porphyrio porphyrio*): *See* Plate 1: 10. Large (14–15). The purplish blue coloration, the red bill and frontal shield, and the long, red legs characterize this unmistakable species. The short tail is usually held cocked up and is nervously flicked up and down by the walking bird, the white under tail-coverts flashing at the same time. Back, mantle, wings, and tail are dark olive brown. The throat is blue; flanks, sides of throat, and hind-neck are dark purplish blue.

Found throughout the S.W.P. Size and coloration vary

geographically and have led to the description of a number of subspecies. In the S.W.P. not at all restricted to swamps. Often found at the edge of the true forest, even more often in second growth and in native gardens, where it may do considerable damage by digging out and eating batatas and taros. Also feeds on snails, insect larvae, and worms. Most active at dusk and during the night, but its weird cry may be heard by day or night. It has been variously described as having the quality of a whistle (*kway-kway*) or more of a cackle: "*KEE-Rer-r-r-r-r-r*, or *OO-Reek-k-k-k-k*, with a vibrant, resonant, and sometimes explosive quality" (Beecher). The nest is a bulky, loose structure placed on the ground or in a low bush.

PIGEONS AND DOVES[11] (FAMILY COLUMBIDAE)

With about 50 species this family is better represented in the S.W.P. than any other. This rich number includes beautiful fruit doves, big pigeons, long-tailed pheasant doves, ground doves, and a number of aberrant types like the Choiseul Pigeon or the Tooth-billed Pigeon of Samoa. In spite of this superficial diversity the pigeon family is rather compact and uniform. All the species seem to feed on fruits and berries; they all lay one or 2 white eggs; the male shares the duties of incubation, particularly during the day; the nest is an untidy structure of sticks; and the voice has a cooing quality. Many of the species are partly migratory in their search for ripe

[11] Ripley, S. D. and Birckhead, H. 1942. *Amer. Mus. Novit.*, no. 1192:1–14 (*Ptilinopus*). Amadon, D. 1943. *Amer. Mus. Novit.*, no. 1237:5–22 (*Ptilinopus, Ducula, Columba vitiensis, Macropygia mackinlayi, Chalcophaps indica, Gallicolumba stairii*).

fruits of favorite food plants. Identification is not always easy since many pigeons, particularly the fruit doves of the genus *Ptilinopus,* are birds of the treetops and are generally well concealed in the luxurious foliage of towering fruit trees. A gunshot may scare 50 birds out of a tree where not one had been previously visible. It seems that each species has a specific call note, but accurate information has never been published.

Crimson-crowned Fruit Dove (*Ptilinopus porphyraceus*): Small (9). Male and female alike. Mantle, wings, and tail dark green, a terminal tail-bar yellowish or gray. Crown crimson. Hind-neck, throat, and breast pale greenish or yellowish gray. Middle of abdomen usually with a dark purple spot; flanks green; lower belly and under tail-coverts yellow, orange, or red. Immatures entirely green with the feathers of back, wings, and underparts edged with yellow.

There are in the S.W.P. 6 geographic races of this fruit dove, which differ in important details of the adult plumage. *Ptilinopus greyii* and *richardsii* are additional geographical representatives, but they are different enough to be considered separate species. The range of *porphyraceus* overlaps partly with that of other similar species, *perousii,* and *luteovirens.* The diagnostic differences are given under the island groups (Samoa, Fiji, etc.) where the overlap occurs.

This bird lives singly or in small flocks. It feeds in high forest trees, particularly on fruits of the fig family. There is considerable seasonal wandering, including even interisland flights. Call: *coo-coo-coocooroo* (2 long and 3 short notes).

Red-bellied Fruit Dove (*Ptilinopus greyii* Bonaparte): Small (8). Green except for the crimson crown, a purplish red patch in the middle of the underparts, and for the pinkish orange under tail-coverts. A terminal tail-band grayish. Underside of wing and tail gray. Immatures like those of *porphyraceus*. Bill gray green; legs red; iris yellow brown.

The identification of this species is simplified by the fact that over most of its range it is the only greenish fruit dove. It shares the northern New Hebrides with *Ptilinopus tannensis*. Reported from New Caledonia, Loyalty Isls., New Hebrides, Banks, Torres, Santa Cruz, Reef Isls., and Gower Isl. In habits like any *Ptilinopus,* but perhaps even more apt to fly from one island to another.

Pacific Pigeon (*Ducula pacifica*): *See* Plate 2: 13. A large (15) pigeon with gray crown and upper back, pinkish gray (vinaceous) underparts, dark chestnut under tail-coverts, and dark glossy green or blue-green mantle, wings, back, and tail. There is a fold of black skin ("knob") at the base of the bill followed by a narrow white line across the forehead. Bill black; feet red.

Widespread in the Pacific: Cook Isls., Samoa, Tonga, Union, Phoenix, Ellice, Fiji, Santa Cruz, Banks, New Hebrides, Loyalty Isls., New Caledonia, Solomon Isls. (*pacifica* Gmelin); Bismarck Archipelago (*sejuncta* Amadon 1943).

Gathers in considerable flocks, which fly from island to island feeding on the fruit of various trees. Voice: a loud, barking *kao-kao*. Others describe it as a deep cooing *pr-rrr-oo,* followed after a pause by a very deep *oooo*.

White-throated Pigeon (*Columba vitiensis*): A large (16), dark pigeon with a white or whitish throat. Upperparts blackish or dark gray with a more or less pronounced greenish or purplish gloss; wings and tail grayish black or brownish black. Breast and abdomen in some races chestnut, in others slate gray with a green gloss. Feet bright red.

Five rather distinct races in the S.W.P. (*see* geographical sections). Often flies in large flocks. Voice: a booming *hoo-hoo*. Nest, with single egg, about 10–20 feet above the ground in fairly heavy timber.

Rufous-brown Pheasant Dove (*Macropygia mackinlayi*): *See* Plate 2: 14. A rufous or cinnamon-brown dove with a very long tail. Total length 11–12½. Tail and particularly wings much darker. Throat often sprinkled with black, particularly in females. Iris and feet red; bill black.

Ranges in several subspecies from the New Hebrides and Santa Cruz Isls. to the Solomon Isls. and the Bismarck Archipelago. Prefers the substage in the true forest. It announces its presence by a melodious cooing and can be approached rather closely. Feeds on various small fruits.

Malay Turtle Dove (*Streptopelia chinensis tigrina* Temminck): Medium (12) with a rather long tail. Upperparts earth brown; head gray with a pink hue. A broad black band (patch), from one side of the neck to the other and across the upper back, finely spotted with white. Underparts grayish pink (vinaceous), whitish on upper throat and lower belly. Lateral tail-feathers with broad white tips. Iris light brown; bill black; feet pinkish red.

Feeds mostly on the ground, flies up to trees when disturbed. Call: a soft *coo*. Very tame. Native in the Indian region. Introduced on Viti Levu and New Britain (Rabaul).

Ground Doves (*Gallicolumba*): Seven species of this genus occur in the S.W.P. They belong to 2 groups, the bronze-winged or *beccarii* group, with *beccarii* (*see* Plate 2: 15), *canifrons, sanctaecrucis,* and *stairii,* and the purple-winged or *erythroptera* group, represented in the S.W.P. with *xanthonura, jobiensis,* and *salamonis* (the species *erythroptera* being extralimital in this book). All 7 species differ only in coloration; the habits seem to be essentially the same. They feed entirely on the ground, but fly up when disturbed and occasionally perch on low branches. Males and females are usually found together but do not gather in flocks. The nest, with one or 2 white eggs, is built 4–10 feet off the ground.

Nicobar Pigeon (*Caloenas nicobarica*): A heavy-bodied, large (14) bird with short tail and legs. Tail white; remainder of plumage dark. Feathers of hind-neck long, ribbon-like, forming a mane. Head and throat grayish black; rest of body and wings glossy green, sometimes bluish or coppery. Iris brown; bill black; feet purplish red. Immatures with a dark tail.

Of extremely wide distribution from the Indian Ocean through the entire Indo-Malayan Archipelago to the Solomon Isls. and Palau. Mostly terrestrial; can run with great speed. Breeds on small coral islands, but feeds sometimes on the mainland of larger islands. The nests are built in low trees, often in small colonies. Roosts in trees.

PARROTS, COCKATOOS, AND LORIES[12]
(FAMILY PSITTACIDAE)

The members of this family are unmistakable. They are all brightly colored, either uniformly green, or red, or patterned with blue and yellow. The cockatoo is entirely white. There

[12] Amadon, D. 1942. *Amer. Mus. Novit.*, no. 1176:1–12 (*Vini, Phigys, Prosopeia*).

are no clear-cut subdivisions of the family, but for the sake of convenience the following groups are recognized:

1. The brush-tongued lories, which feed on the nectar of flowers and on soft fruit, like bananas, paw-paw. In the S.W.P. this group includes the genera *Eos, Trichoglossus, Lorius, Phigys,* and *Vini*. They are mostly small to medium in size (never as large as a pigeon), swift fliers, and generally found in flocks. Their voices are squeaky or shrill.

2. The pigmy parrots of the genus *Micropsitta*. These dwarfs of the family are no bigger than a thumb. As in woodpeckers, the stiffened shafts of their tail-feathers help to keep the birds propped up when they are feeding on termite nests. They frequently fly in little flocks, which are hard to see in the dense forest even when their whispering call notes are heard all around. The nesting hole is excavated from the nest of tree termites. Their food is still uncertain, either the soft abdomen of termites or certain fungi.

3. The cockatoos. The big, noisy, and conspicuously white cockatoos are unmistakable. When a flock descends on a native garden, it can do a lot of damage to bananas, paw-paw, and other fruit.

4. Parakeets. This includes the somewhat heterogeneous residue of species with a normal, not brush-like, tongue. Most species are rather large with powerful bills. They are found more often in pairs than in flocks. The group is rather poorly represented in the S.W.P. The species found in this area belong to the genera *Larius, Geoffroyus, Prosopeia, Loriculus* (Bismarcks), *Eunymphicus,* and *Cyanorhamphus.*

In woodpecker fashion all eastern parrots excavate holes in trees or in the nests of tree termites. The eggs are white. Several of the species make good pets and may be taught to talk.

Coconut Lory (*Trichoglossus haematodus*): *See* Plate 2: 16. Size of a small dove or big thrush (10). Green, except head and breast. Head dark, variegated blue, green, and purple. A yellow-green collar across the hind-neck. Upper throat purplish black; lower throat and breast bright red, feathers edged with black, giving them a scaly appearance. Belly green; lower belly and under tail-coverts mixed with yellow. A broad yellow bar across underside of the wing. Iris yellow; bill red; feet blue gray.

Occurs in a number of races throughout the Papuan region to the Solomon Isls., Santa Cruz Isls., New Hebrides, Loyalty Isls., and New Caledonia.

A very numerous parrot, found in nearly every coconut plantation, as well as in the true forest. Often in large flocks, visiting flowering or fruiting trees. In the evening sometimes seen flying to communal roosts; they are also known to fly from one island to another, covering up to 40 miles on such roosting flights. Shrieking, high-pitched call note.

CUCKOOS AND COUCALS[13] (FAMILY CUCULIDAE)

In the S.W.P. (including the Bismarcks) are found 5 native and 2 visiting species of parasitic cuckoos, as well as 3 species of coucals, representing 2 rather different branches of the family. Even the true cuckoos have few diagnostic features in common, since they range from the small Shining Cuckoo (*Chalcites*) to the large Channel-billed Cuckoo (*Scythrops*

[13] Amadon, D. 1942. *Amer. Mus. Novit.*, no. 1176:15–21 (*Cacomantis*). Mayr, E. 1932. *Amer. Mus. Novit.*, no. 520:1–9 (*Chalcites lucidus*). Bogert, C. 1937. *Amer. Mus. Novit.*, no. 933:1–12 (*Eudynamis taitensis*).

FIG. 7. Buff-headed Coucal (*Centropus m. milo*)

[Bismarcks]). Cuckoos have, on the whole, slender bodies and long tails. They like to sit in tall trees where they sometimes repeat their melodious whistling call notes in endless succession. They fly straight and with a rapid wing beat. Caterpillars are their preferred food, but other insects are also taken as well as occasional berries and other fruits.

The coucals (genus *Centropus*) live in the dense cane grass or in the forest undergrowth. They look like large, clumsy magpies with round wings and long tails. They hop up a tree, branch by branch, and then plane across to the next one, like some surviving *Archaeopteryx*. The nest is a bulky, roundish structure with a lateral entrance, usually placed in a small bush in the cane grass. The 2–3 eggs are incubated by their own parents with the male assuming the greater share. Their voice is an oft-repeated raucous *ko-ko-ko*. One species is found in the Solomon Isls. and 2 in the Bismarck group. *See* Figure 7.

Fan-tailed Cuckoo (*Cacomantis pyrrhophanus*): Medium (9–10). Rather similar to the European Cuckoo, but uniformly dark slate gray or deep bronze brown above. Underparts rufous (adults), barred black and buffy white (immatures), or sooty black (color phase on Fiji). Tail long, blackish; tail-feathers with narrow white tips and notched with white on the margin; lateral feathers with white bars. Iris red brown; bill black above, brown below; feet yellow.

Three subspecies in New Caledonia, Loyalty Isls., New Hebrides, Banks Isls., and Fiji Isls.

This species parasitizes *Petroica,* also *Rhipidura, Myiagra, Lalage,* and other small songbirds. Caterpillars seem to be the preferred food. A good description of the call note of the species is lacking. It is referred to as a "shrill trilling 3-syllabic whistle." Calls much at night.

Shining Cuckoo (*Chalcites lucidus*): Small (6½). Glossy green above, with or without coppery tones on head and tail. Underparts white, finely barred with glossy green. Lateral tail-feathers barred with white.

Occurs in several races (one of which is a winter visitor from New Zealand and one from Australia) on New Caledonia, Loyalty Isls., New Hebrides, Banks Isls., Santa Cruz, Solomons, and Bismarck Archipelago. Parasitizes mainly a small warbler (*Gerygone flavolateralis*). "The call consists [of] a series of double notes, upward slurs, often repeated, followed by fewer downward slurs, the whole in a musical whistle with ventriloquistic effects" (Oliver). During this performance the bird will sit quietly in the dense foliage of a treetop. Feeds usually only 5–10 feet above the ground.

Long-tailed New Zealand Cuckoo (*Eudynamis taitensis* Sparrman): *See* Figure 8. A fairly large, slender, long-tailed bird (with tail 16). Upperparts dark brown with white spots on head, back, and wings, and rufous crossbars, particularly on tail. Underparts white or buffy rufous with few or many dark brown shaft streaks, particularly on the breast. The species is sometimes separated in a special genus, *Urodynamis*. The brown upperparts, mottled and barred with rufous, and the buffy white underparts with longitudinal blackish streaks are diagnostic. Can be confused only with the immatures of some species of hawks.

Breeds in New Zealand; on migration found throughout Polynesia, Micronesia, and occasionally in the Solomon Isls. and the Bismarck Archipelago. Generally silent in its winter

FIG. 8. Long-tailed New Zealand Cuckoo (*Eudynamis taitensis*)

quarters, but has a magpie-like chattering note. Often "mobbed" by small songbirds. Flight fairly rapid and straight with continuous wing beats. Most common in Polynesia during the southern winter, i.e. May to September.

OWLS (FAMILIES TYTONIDAE AND STRIGIDAE)

Barn owls have habits much like other owls, but they differ by certain anatomical features as well as by their facial appearance. They are very long-legged. In addition to the almost world-wide common Barn Owl (*T. alba*), the Grass Owl (*T. longimembris*) is found in the S.W.P. Two very localized species occur in the Bismarck Archipelago.

Each of the species of true owls of the S.W.P. is restricted to a single island or island group. The range is diagnostic of most of these, since only *Nesasio* (large size) overlaps the range of any of the other species.

Barn Owl (*Tyto alba*): *See* Figure 9. A very light-colored owl (12). Underparts usually snow white, occasionally with a few dark spots. Heart-shaped facial disk white. Upperparts and wings a variegated pattern of pale gray and buffy cinnamon with numerous small white and blackish brown spots. No ear tufts. Bill and feet yellowish horn color.

Occurs in 4 or 5 races in the S.W.P. Partial to limestone caves, but also found nesting in hollows of large forest trees. Feeds on rats, mice, and small birds, also on lizards, beetles, and other insects.

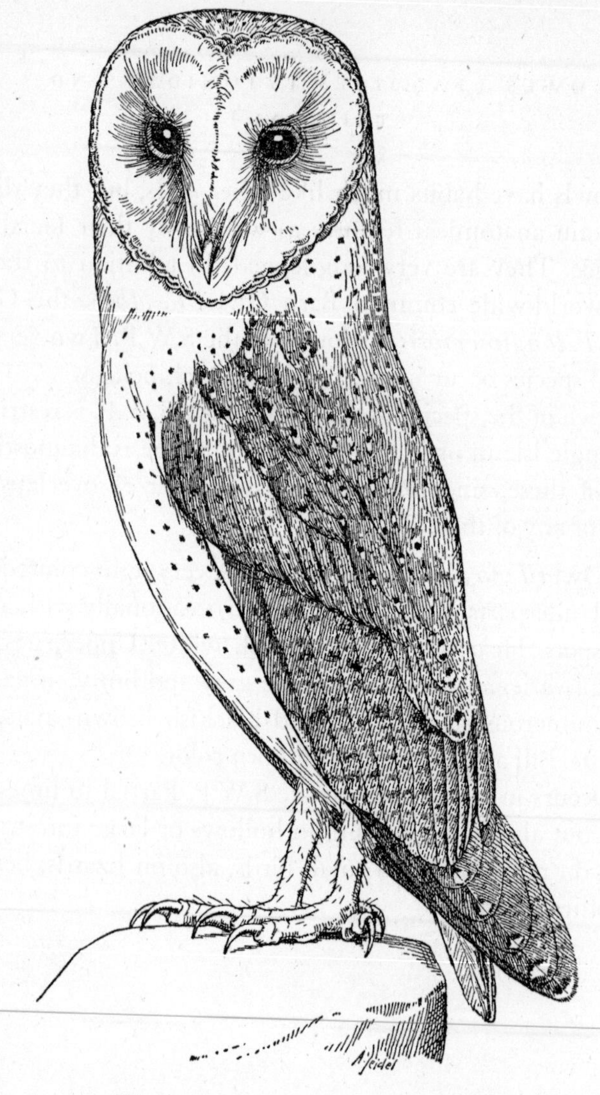

FIG. 9. Barn Owl (*Tyto alba lulu*)

FROGMOUTHS (FAMILY PODARGIDAE)

OWLET-NIGHTJARS (FAMILY AEGOTHELIDAE)

NIGHTJARS (FAMILY CAPRIMULGIDAE)

The members of these families, in spite of many anatomical and other differences, are nocturnal, insect-eating birds of owl-like coloration, but of the body build of large swallows. The frogmouths and owlet-nightjars are more or less arboreal, even their nests are in trees, and usually they perch sideways like most birds. The true nightjars (*Eurostopodus* and *Caprimulgus*) are more or less terrestrial, and if they perch on trees, they sit lengthwise on branches. The 5 species of these 3 families that occur in the S.W.P. (including the Bismarcks) are rare and restricted in their ranges. They feed at dusk or during the night primarily or exclusively on insects that they obtain by cruising around like swallows. Their beaks can be opened very wide.

SWIFTS[14] (FAMILY APODIDAE)

The only true native swifts of the S.W.P. are a number of species of cave swiftlets (*Collocalia*). These are swallow-like birds, which differ from true swallows by their manner of flight. The wings are long, stiff, and in flight held in a characteristic, curved position. The wings are beaten rapidly, but the amplitude of each wing beat is shallow. Between spurts of fluttering, they sail short stretches with outstretched wings,

[14] Mayr, E. 1937. *Amer. Mus. Novit.*, no. 915:1–19 (*Collocalia*).

but the wings are not folded against the body as with the swallows. They are often found in openings in the forest.

Some of the Malayan species of cave swiftlets build edible nests, which are the chief ingredient of the famous "swallow nests' soup" of the Chinese. The nests of the S.W.P. species are composed of moss and vegetable fibers glued against the walls of caves with varying amounts of hardened saliva. Most species nest in caves, sometimes far from the entrance and apparently in complete darkness. *C. esculenta* is less discriminating and also nests on overhanging cliffs and under the boughs of forest giants. *C. vanikorensis, C. spodiopygia,* and *C. esculenta* are the only 3 widespread species.

Key to the Genus Collocalia

(1) Plumage mainly a dull black: *whiteheadi* (Solomon Isls.), *inexpectata* (Palau, Guam), *inquieta* (Carolines), and *vanikorensis* (New Caledonia to Bismarck Archipelago).

(2) Plumage dull black with a white rump: *spodiopygia.*

(3) Plumage glossy blue with more or less white on belly and sometimes with a white rump: *esculenta.*

Vanikoro Swiftlet (*Collocalia vanikorensis*): Size of a small swallow (4½). Above sooty black with a faint greenish gloss; rump colored like back; tail slightly forked. Underparts gray; throat more silvery.

New Hebrides, Banks Isls., Santa Cruz Isls., Solomon Isls., and Bismarck Archipelago, westward to Celebes. Nest and nest location (probably always in caves) are insufficiently described. Hawks fairly high, above the smaller species of *Collocalia* and in more open localities. Is more solitary in nesting and hunting than *spodiopygia* and *esculenta.*

PLATE III—For the common and scientific names of the birds shown here see page vii

White-rumped Swiftlet (*Collocalia spodiopygia*): *See* Plate 2: 20. Smaller (4) than the Vanikoro Swiftlet. Blackish above with a faint bluish gloss, and a white bar across the rump. Underparts grayish. Tail furcation slight.

Occurs throughout Melanesia and central Polynesia in a number of races that are indistinguishable to the field observer. They are mentioned under the respective island groups. Differs from the white-rumped races of *Collocalia esculenta* by the black, not glossy blue, of back and wings and by the absence of white on the underparts. Nests in large colonies in limestone caves, which often open in cliffs along the seashore.

Glossy Swiftlet (*Collocalia esculenta*): Small (3¾). Back with a bluish or bluish green gloss. The rump is white in the race *uropygialis* from New Caledonia and the New Hebrides. Throat dark gray; belly white or whitish mixed with gray.

Hawks mostly low down among trees or in open patches of the forest, rarely in open grassland or high in the sky. Nests not only in caves but also on shady cliffs, or among the roots or in cavities of banyan trees. Nests, with 1–2 white eggs, constructed of moss and fibers. Colonies usually consist of 6–10 pairs, occasionally 40–50 or even larger.

Very widespread and common, from the Malay Archipelago to the Bismarck Archipelago, Solomon Isls., Santa Cruz, New Hebrides, Loyalty Isls., and New Caledonia. Absent from central Polynesia.

Large Swifts

Two large Asiatic swifts that winter in Australia may migrate through Micronesia and the Bismarck Archipelago, although there are no definite records yet. Both these species fly high.

(1) Brownish or sooty black; a white band across the rump; tail deeply forked: *Apus pacificus.*

(2) Brown; chin, throat, and under tail-coverts white; wings and tail with metallic green or steel-blue gloss; tail short and square: *Chaetura caudacuta.*

CRESTED SWIFTS (FAMILY HEMIPROCNIDAE)

These are large swifts with long, slender wings. They like to sit on dead branches of tall trees along the edge of the forest and in clearings. From these lookouts they fly out in search of flying insects. Dawn and dusk are their periods of greatest activity. The small nest, shaped like a shallow cup, is glued to the side of a branch and the single egg glued with saliva to the bottom of the nest. Call: a ringing *kek-kek-kek-kee-kee-kee-ee.* Only one species in the S.W.P. (*see* Figure 10).

KINGFISHERS (FAMILY ALCEDINIDAE)

Kingfishers occur in the New Guinea region in a greater variety of forms than anywhere else in the world. During the course of their evolutionary development about 7 lines have radiated from here into the S.W.P. where they are now represented by 11 different species and 4 additional ones in the Bismarck Archipelago. They belong to 2 subfamilies.

The water kingfishers (Alcedininae), which include the European Kingfisher, consist of rather small brightly colored species with sharp, narrow bills. They are blue or green above, and white, orange, or rufous ocher below. The food consists

Fig. 10. Whiskered Tree Swift (*Hemiprocne mystacea*)

of fish, crustaceans, and water insects, obtained by plunging into the water (or to the ground) from an exposed perch. The nest is placed at the end of a tunnel excavated by the birds in a river bank or steep slope. The voice is a shrill whistle, usually repeated. This group includes the genera *Alcedo* and *Ceyx*.

The tree kingfishers (Daceloninae) are rather puzzling to the bird student who is familiar only with the European or the American kingfisher. Most of the species have the habits of flycatchers. They dart out from a branch in pursuit of a flying insect and, after catching it, return gracefully to their perch. Others pounce down on grasshoppers, lizards, or even small birds, very much like shrikes. The nest is always in a hollow, either in a decaying tree trunk or in the nest of tree termites. The eggs are white. The call notes are noisy, rattling, and often repeated. This group is represented in the S.W.P. by the genus *Halcyon*. Two species (*Halcyon chloris* and *H. sancta*) are widespread and common; all other species are more local and rarer at a given locality.

All kingfishers can be recognized by their upright posture and by their habit of sitting motionless on an exposed lookout (tree, post, telephone wire). The bill is long, the tail short.

White-collared Kingfisher (*Halcyon chloris*): *See* Plate 2: 22. This species extends from the coast of Africa along the coast of India and through the Indo-Australian Archipelago as far east as Samoa. Its 40 odd subspecies are so different that no single description can cover them all. Distribution and races are discussed under each island group. A general description would be about as follows.

Medium (8½). Underparts white or buffy cinnamon. Upperparts bluish or dusky bottle green. A black or blue band encircles the back of the neck from gape to gape. Behind it, across the upper back, is a (buffy) white collar. On the nape is frequently a (buffy) white spot, which may or may not be connected with the white lores through the eyebrow. If there is any buff or rufous in the plumage, the males tend to have more on the eye-stripe, nuchal collar, and the flanks than females. Habits characteristically those of a tree kingfisher.

Sacred Kingfisher (*Halcyon sancta*): Very similar to *chloris*. It is fortunate for the field student that *chloris* is absent from New Caledonia and the Loyalty Isls., where *sancta* occurs. However, as a winter visitor this Australian species is found in the Bismarck Archipelago and the Solomon Isls., where it might be confused with *chloris*. The general coloration of the 2 species is the same, but *sancta* is considerably smaller with a more slender bill. It always has a rufous-buff wash on the underparts, which are pure white in many races of *chloris*. The upperparts are paler, more greenish olive. The white or buff spot on the nape is small or absent.

Similar to *chloris* in food habits and behavior, but in its winter quarters much quieter, calling only rarely. Most common around the coast and near human habitations. Usually perches much lower, on fence posts, low trees, telephone wires. A few remain in the Solomon Isls. and the Bismarck Archipelago throughout the year; most of them arrive in February–March and depart in September–October.

BEE-EATERS (FAMILY MEROPIDAE)

This African-Indian group is represented in the Australian region by only 2 species. *Merops philippinus* nests in the Bismarck Archipelago and the Australian *Merops ornatus* reaches the Bismarck Archipelago and the Solomon Isls. as a winter visitor.

Bee-eaters are social birds. They nest colonially in steep banks in which they excavate their nesting holes. The food consists exclusively of insects caught by hawking to and fro. Even on migration they appear in flocks, which make themselves conspicuous by their melodious call notes (*trrrii*). The prevailing color is green.

FIG. 11. Dollar Bird (*Eurystomus orientalis solomonensis*)

ROLLERS (FAMILY CORACIIDAE)

The Dollar Bird (*Eurystomus orientalis*) is the only representative of this family in the S.W.P. (*see* Solomon Isls.). *See* Figure 11.

HORNBILLS (FAMILY BUCEROTIDAE)

Only a single species of this family reaches the S.W.P.

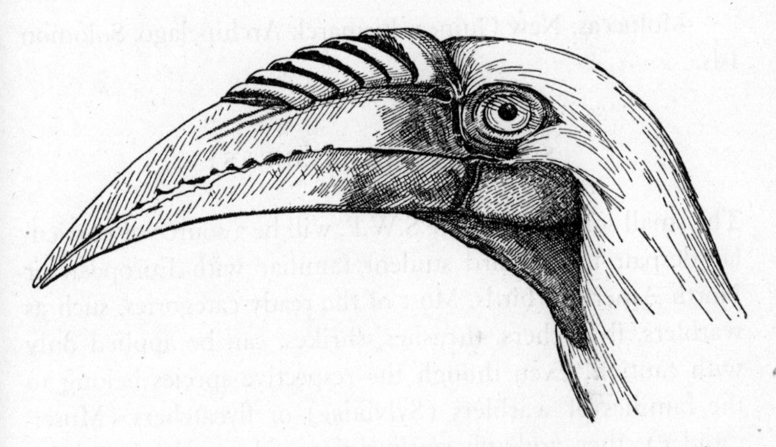

FIG. 12. Papuan Hornbill (*Rhyticeros plicatus mendanae*)

Papuan Hornbill (*Rhyticeros plicatus*): *See* Figure 12. This large (2½′) bird with its grotesque ivory yellow beak is unmistakable. Tail white; back, wings, and abdomen black with a slight greenish gloss. Female entirely black; male has head, hind-neck, throat, and upper breast golden buff to chestnut. Upper throat naked, reddish, basal part of bill red. Iris reddish orange; feet blackish. Adult males have 4–8 folds, adult females 4–6 folds, on the casque on the head. First-year birds have 2 or 3 folds; immatures have none or one.

Unmistakable in size, bill, and color characters. Very noisy in flight, almost like a passing steam engine. Feeds on fruits and undertakes long roosting and feeding flights. Has a loud, croaking call note. The female is walled into a hollow tree during incubation and is fed by the male through a small opening. The young are able to fly as soon as they leave the nest.

Moluccas, New Guinea, Bismarck Archipelago, Solomon Isls.

SONGBIRDS (PASSERES)

The small songbirds of the S.W.P. will be a source of particular despair to the bird student familiar with European or North American birds. Most of the ready categories, such as warblers, flycatchers, thrushes, shrikes, can be applied only with caution. Even though the respective species belong to the families of warblers (Sylviidae) or flycatchers (Muscicapidae), they are sufficiently different from the European types not to be recognized readily. In addition, there are represented in the S.W.P. a number of Australo-Papuan or Indian families that have no counterpart in Europe or North America. This includes the Campephagidae (cuckoo-shrikes), Artamidae (wood-swallows), Dicruridae (drongos), Nectariniidae (sunbirds), Zosteropidae (white-eyes), Dicaeidae (flower-peckers), Estrildinae (weaver-finches), and the important family of Meliphagidae (honey-eaters).

The subsequent characterizations of these various families are intended to convey a picture of the most important features of each family. The student should familiarize himself with these characterizations before attempting to identify individual species.

PITTAS OR JEWEL-THRUSHES (FAMILY PITTIDAE)

These chunky, thrush-like birds are not true songbirds, if one wants to be technical. Still they are closely related to them and have a pleasing, loud, whistled call note. They are seldom seen, even in places where the frequency of their whistles indi-

FIG. 13. Black-faced Jewel-thrush (*Pitta anerythra nigrifrons*)

cates that they are common. However, if the observer sits motionless on a log and imitates their call, he may see the bird cautiously approaching under cover.

Pittas are strictly terrestrial; they rarely fly or perch in shrubs, never in trees. Species of the S.W.P. are found only in the dark true rain forest. The call is low-pitched, a 2-syllabled *kree-kreeee-o*. The nest is a bulky structure of leaves and moss on or near the ground, usually with one egg only. Pittas feed on worms, snails, and insects. The heavy, long legs, and plump body with short wings and shorter tails are diagnostic. *See* Figure 13.

SWALLOWS[15] (FAMILY HIRUNDINIDAE)

The swallows (so familiar to everybody) can be mistaken in the S.W.P. only for swiftlets. They can be told by their more deliberate wing beats, by their way of pressing the wings to the body in flight more often, by their staying closer to the vicinity of human habitations, and by their perching frequently.

The single breeding species is widespread and common (*H. tahitica*). In addition, there is a winter visitor from Asia to Micronesia (*H. rustica*), and a rare winter visitor from the south to the Bismarck Archipelago and the Solomon Isls. (*H. nigricans*).

Pacific Swallow (*Hirundo tahitica*): *See* Plate 3: 23. Small (5). Above metallic blue black. Forehead and throat rufous chestnut; breast and belly (brownish) gray. Tail moderately

[15] Mayr, E. 1934. *Amer. Mus. Novit.*, no. 709:11–13 (*H. tahitica*). White, C. M. N. 1936. *Bull. Brit. Orn. Club*, 56:90–92 (*H. nigricans*).

forked. The subspecies *subfusca* Gould ranges from the Fiji Isls., New Caledonia, Loyalty Isls., New Hebrides, Santa Cruz Isls., Solomon Isls., to the northern islands of the Bismarck Archipelago. Replaced on New Britain by *ambiens,* often with white in the tail.

In some places almost entirely restricted to the vicinity of houses; otherwise found in swamps, along the shore, and along rivers. Voice and nesting habits like those of the common Barn Swallow. Places nest occasionally under the limbs of trees, in shallow caves, on cliffs, and similar locations.

CUCKOO-SHRIKES[16] (FAMILY CAMPEPHAGIDAE)

This family of curious birds has nothing to do either with cuckoos or with shrikes. It consists of a group of medium-sized, soft-plumaged birds that are a conspicuous element in the bird fauna of the S.W.P. even though they are represented by only a few species. The prevailing colors are light and dark gray, more rarely black and white; one species is brownish, and the female of another is rufous chestnut. A few species show conspicuous barring.

All species are arboreal, although the Polynesian Triller sometimes feeds on the ground. A few species are restricted to the true forest; the others are most common on the edge of the forest, in second growth, native gardens, coconut plantations, and in the coastal vegetation. The call notes are loud, either whistles or rather disagreeable screechy squawks. They feed on caterpillars, other insects, and on fruits.

[16] Mayr, E. and Ripley, D. 1941. *Amer. Mus. Novit.*, no. 1116:1–18 (*Lalage*). Ripley, D. 1941. *The Auk,* 58:381–395 (*Coracina*).

Long-tailed Triller (*Lalage leucopyga*): Size of a sparrow (6–7). White or buffy white underneath. *Male.* Blue black above with a white, grayish white, or buffy white rump. Lateral tail-feathers tipped with white. Some white on wing. *Female.* Like male except upperparts blackish brown or rufous brown. A buffy white patch on wings. Iris brown; bill and feet black.

From Norfolk Isl. and New Caledonia to the New Hebrides, and San Cristobal (Solomon Isls.). Six subspecies in the S.W.P. (one of them extralimital, on Norfolk Isl.), which differ in size, in the color of the rump, the presence or absence of a white eyebrow, and the tone of brown in the females.

Usually in pairs or in small flocks. Often in rather tall trees. Likes to perch in conspicuous locations on the top of trees or bushes. From sealevel to the mountains. Prefers open country to the solid forest. Nest (with 2 eggs) a cup of rather coarse weed stalks and plant wool, usually some 20–30 feet up, on horizontal branch of large tree. Feeds on caterpillars, other insects, and small fruits. Has a loud, pleasing, trilling song, but generally uses a single note call, *cheerk.*

Polynesian Triller (*Lalage maculosa*): *See* Plate 3: 24. Size of a sparrow (6–7). Black and white. Upperparts black or brownish black, rump grayish. White eyebrow and a white or rusty patch on the wing. Underparts white, sometimes with a buffy wash or lightly barred with black (in the Fijian races). Tail-feathers tipped with white. Iris brown; bill black; lower mandible sometimes yellow. Females and immatures duller and browner.

There are 16 subspecies, which differ in the amount of

white mottling on the back and the black barring of the underparts. They are discussed under the geographical subdivisions. Samoa, Tonga, Fiji, Santa Cruz Isls., and northern New Hebrides, south to Efate.

Common and conspicuous in most of its range. Lowland forest, second growth, gardens in towns and villages. Feeds in little parties in trees, but also feeds on the ground, hopping like a sparrow. Voice a chatter and a trill. Cup-shaped nest in trees, 5–15 feet off the ground.

Cicada Bird (*Edolisoma tenuirostre*). Size of a thrush (8–9½). Males a uniform dark blue gray. Lores, sides of head, and throat blackish. A white patch under the wing. Females deep ochraceous below; darker, more olive brown above. Crown blue gray; a pale eye-ring; sides of head mottled rufous and gray. Upperparts blue gray in one subspecies (San Cristobal). The males of the 8 or 9 subspecies (including the Bismarck races) are very similar. The females are either pale below or deep rufous, or barred with black. Iris brown; bill and feet black. In the S.W.P. found in the Solomon Isls., Bismarck Archipelago, and Micronesia.

A lively bird, seen either singly, in pairs, or occasionally in small parties (on food trees). The voice is loud, but not yet accurately described in the literature. Found in the deep forest as well as on the edge, in both small and high trees.

Melanesian Graybird (*Coracina caledonica*): A dark slate-gray bird the size of a large jay or small crow (12–14). Bill heavy, short. Tail long. Bill, feet, wings, and tail black. Iris brown or yellow. Male and female alike.

New Caledonia, Loyalty Isls., New Hebrides, and Solomon Isls. Usually in pairs. Frequent in well-wooded country, lowlands, or hills. Call note a whistle.

THRUSHES AND CHATS[17] (FAMILY TURDIDAE)

This family is very poorly represented in the S.W.P. In addition to the widespread Island Thrush (*see* below), there are only 2 species of ground thrushes of local distribution in the Bismarck Archipelago and the Solomon Isls. A black and white chat reaches New Britain. A few species of northern Asiatic thrushes have also been recorded from the Palau Isls. as stragglers.

Island Thrush (*Turdus poliocephalus*): A close relative of the European Blackbird and the American Robin. In size, habits, call notes, and flight very much like these 2 species. The striking geographical variation of this species makes a general description impossible. The most widely occurring color type is all black with bill and feet yellow. However, head and throat may be white, gray, or golden tawny. The belly may be black, chestnut, or gray.

Ranges throughout S.W.P., but not on all islands. In the Solomon Isls. only found on the high mountains, as on Bougainville, and Kulambangra. Occasionally on low, coralline islands (Rennell, St. Matthias).

Feeds on the ground on worms and snails. Usually restricted to the densest, most humid part of the forest or, in the mountain forms, to the upper tree line. Altitudinal range different on each island.

[17] Mayr, E. 1941. *Amer. Mus. Novit.*, no. 1152:3–6 (*Turdus poliocephalus*).

WARBLERS[18] (FAMILY SYLVIIDAE)

The warblers of the S.W.P. are a very diversified group consisting of species that do not seem to have much more in common with each other than small size and a thin bill. There are species that seem intermediate between warblers and babblers (*Ortygocichla* of New Britain, *Trichocichla* of Viti Levu, *Megalurulus* of New Caledonia, and *Cichlornis* of Espiritu Santo); there are typical leaf warblers (*Phylloscopus*), reed warblers (*Acrocephalus, ?Psamathia*), grass warblers (*Megalurus, Cisticola*), and Australian wren-warblers (*Gerygone, Vitia*).

All warblers are active, insect-eating birds, and most of them are good, or at least pleasing, singers. In other characteristics they show much divergence. Some frequent treetops (*Phylloscopus*), some the substage of the rain forest (*Vitia, Trichocichla, ?Cichlornis*), some the second growth (*Gerygone*, some *Acrocephalus* species), some the cane grass savannas (*Cisticola, Megalurus, ?Megalurulus*), and some the reed beds of swamps (*Acrocephalus arundinaceus*). All of the species are localized in restricted parts of S.W.P. and will, therefore, be discussed in the respective geographical sections.

FLYCATCHERS[19] (FAMILY MUSCICAPIDAE, SUBFAMILY MUSCICAPINAE)

This is the most richly developed family of songbirds in the S.W.P. and the various flycatchers are usually the most com-

[18] Mayr, E. 1936. *Amer. Mus. Novit.*, no. 828:15–18 (*Vitia, Phylloscopus*).

[19] Mayr, E. 1931. *Amer. Mus. Novit.*, no. 502:1–21 (*Rhipidura*); 1933. *Amer. Mus. Novit.*, no. 628:1–21 (*Clytorhynchus*); 1933. *Amer. Mus. Novit.*, no. 665:1–5 (*Neolalage*); 1934. *Amer. Mus. Novit.*, no. 714:1–19 (*Petroica*).

mon and conspicuous birds in the substage of the forest and along its edges. Most of the flycatchers of the S.W.P. belong to the genera *Rhipidura, Monarcha* (and allies), and *Myiagra*.

The fantails (*Rhipidura*) are small flycatchers with short, rounded wings and very long tails. Gray, brown, rufous, and white are the dominant colors. They often have a tinkling call note and a short melodious song, which they repeat frequently. They like best either the substage of the forest, where they flit from branch to branch, or the thickets along the forest edge. Most species are very confiding and inquisitive and may follow the observer for long distances. The nest is a well-built cup, 2–5 feet off the ground, with fibers trailing off the bottom like a tail. The fantails, with their drooping wings and cocked up and more or less fanned tails and their restless movements, are easily identified. They respond readily to squeaking. The 2 sexes are colored alike in all S.W.P. species. The slightly different habits of the Willie Wagtail (*Rh. leucophrys*) are discussed in the Solomon Isls. section.

The monarch flycatchers (*Monarcha*) are far less active birds and rarely (if ever) sally out from a branch after a flying insect. They rather gather their insect food by hopping through the branches and gleaning them from the leaves and twigs. They often sit motionless on a twig with the tail drooping down vertically. The females, and more often birds in the immature plumage, are frequently colored very differently from the adult males. The song, slightly different in every species, is a whistled trill. The warning note is a disagreeable, harsh *tjaij* or *kwaich*. The birds are usually seen singly or in pairs in the substage or "middle layer" of the deep forest. A cup-shaped mossy nest, with 2 eggs, is placed in the upright fork of a twig 2–15 feet above the ground. The naked young seem to have a blue-black skin. No significant differences are as yet known among the habits of the 7 species that occur in S.W.P. (including the Bismarcks). Closely related and similar in habits are the genera *Mayrornis, Neolalage, Metabolus,* and *Clytorhynchus,* which are discussed in the respective geographical sections.

The broad-billed flycatchers or broadbills (*Myiagra*) have typical flycatcher habits. They sit upright on branches and dart out after flying insects. They have the habit of twitching the tail nervously. Nest, with 2 eggs, suspended from horizontal fork of tree, 5–15 feet above the ground. Call notes a twitter and a whistle.

The Yellow Robin (*Eopsaltria*) is restricted in the S.W.P. to New Caledonia.

Scarlet Robin (*Petroica multicolor*): *See* Figure 14. Small (4) with a short bill. Males and females very different. *Adult male* (typical): Upperparts sooty black, except for white forehead and wing patch; upper throat black, *remainder of underparts scarlet red. Female* and *young*. Rufous brown above (forehead with or without white); underparts paler (pinkish) scarlet; upper throat whitish. Females black backed, like males, in Samoa and on San Cristobal (Solomon Isls.). Males brown-backed and dull like females on several islands of the New Hebrides and Banks Isls.

Occurs in Australia and, in 13 races, on the islands from Norfolk Isl. to the New Hebrides, Fiji, Samoa, and Solomon Isls. In most localities restricted to the mountain forest.

Usually singly or in pairs, rarely in parties. Pairs defend their territories against neighboring pairs, and males often sit on exposed perches. Nests, with 3 eggs, are neat little cups, well disguised with lichens, usually in the fork between a

FIG. 14. Scarlet Robin (*Petroica multicolor*)

side branch and the main trunk or in an upright fork, often less than 10 feet above the ground. Song "a series of sweet whistles running down the scale in quick succession." Males and females join in rearing the young.

WHISTLERS[20] (FAMILY MUSCICAPIDAE, SUBFAMILY PACHYCEPHALINAE)

The whistlers are often united in one family with the shrikes, but they are actually shrike-billed flycatchers, distantly related to the Australo-Papuan robins (*Poecilodryas, Petroica,*

[20] Mayr, E. 1932. *Amer. Mus. Novit.*, no. 522:1–22 (*Pachycephala*, Solomon Isls.); no. 531:1–23 (*Pachycephala*, Polynesia).

and allies). Their bright plumage, melodious calls, and bold spirit makes them at once a favorite with the bird student.

Whistlers are characterized by their round, thick head (hence also called "thick-heads"), by their robust body, and by their short, thick, shrike-like bill. They have a loud whistle, *huid-huid,* each call with a rising inflection; also a warning note. They readily respond to an imitation of their call note or to squeaking. Females tend to be rather silent, but during the mating season they call *chip-chip* or answer the whistle of the male with *witchoo.* The nest is a substantial structure of fine twigs, fibers, and leaves. It is built by the female alone. The clutch consists of 2 or 3 eggs. Whistlers are usually found singly or in pairs in the substage of the forest where with quick movements they search for their insect prey on twigs and branches. They seem to be territorial, but are apt to wander after the breeding season. Differences in habits between the various species have not yet been worked out.

Golden Whistler (*Pachycephala pectoralis*): *See* Plate 3: 29, 30. This species, in the widest sense of the word, extends from Java to the Loyalty Isls. and Fiji and breaks up into about 80 geographical races or subspecies. No single description can adequately apply equally to all of them. The basic plumage of the species is: *Adult male.* Crown black; remainder of upperparts olive green; a black collar separates the white throat from the golden-yellow breast and belly. *Adult female.* More or less brownish or olive green. *Immature.* Similar to female, often with more rufous in the wing.

The various races, which differ by having the back, wing, or tail black or the throat yellow, or the breast band lacking, are described in the geographical sections. *Pachycephala me-*

lanops (Tonga), *P. flavifrons* (Samoa), and *caledonica* (New Caledonia) are geographical representatives of *P. pectoralis.*

WOOD-SWALLOWS OR SWALLOW-SHRIKES (FAMILY ARTAMIDAE)

The Artamidae are neither swallows nor shrikes, but a peculiar family that seems to have originated in Australia and whose nearest relatives are unknown. Wood-swallows usually sit quietly on an exposed dead branch of a tree from which they pursue insects in the manner of flycatchers. They are partial to telegraph wires where these exist. Their flight is exceedingly graceful and often interrupted by long periods of gliding, for which they are well adapted with their long, pointed wings. The larger species are even able to soar on thermic upcurrents. Of all songbirds they are in my opinion the best fliers. Male and female are colored alike. The color of all species (except a partly chestnut Australian one) is a mixture of black or gray and white.

White-breasted Wood-Swallow (*Artamus leucorhynchus*): *See* Plate 3: 31. Size of a small starling (6½). Legs short, wings long. Upperparts black. Rump white; upper or entire throat dull black, rest of underparts white. Tail-feathers in some races faintly tipped with white; tail slightly forked. Iris dark brown; bill blue; legs and feet gray black. There are 4 races in the S.W.P.

Feeds on flying insects; is never seen on the ground. Nest a shallow, loosely built cup of fibers and weed stems, placed either in a fork or in the cavity of a broken branch, 5–40 feet off the ground. The 2–3 eggs are creamy white with a circle of spots. Both parents take part in the rearing of the young. Voice twittering.

STARLINGS AND MYNAS[21] (FAMILY STURNIDAE)

The majority of the starlings of the S.W.P. belong to the genus *Aplonis* and are not unlike the familiar Starling of Europe and North America. They are usually glossy black and short-tailed. There are also a few large, grackle-like, long-tailed species. In the Solomon Isls. and the Bismarck Archipelago, the Papuan Myna (*Mino dumontii*) [*see* Plate 3: 33] is found as a native species, while the Indian Myna (*Acridotheres tristis*) has been introduced on many islands of the S.W.P.

Most starlings nest in hollow trees, others build stick nests, while at least one species (*Aplonis metallicus*) builds a large hanging nest like weaver birds. They are largely arboreal and feed on fruit and insects. Some species are very social.

Indian Myna (*Acridotheres tristis* Linnaeus): Size of a small jay (10). Bill and feet yellow. Head black with a short crest. Throat blackish gray. Back, breast, and flanks vinaceous brown. Lower belly white. Wings and tail blackish. Tip of tail and a broad band across the wings white. Naked skin around the eye orange.

Introduced on many islands of the S.W.P. (Solomon Isls., New Caledonia, Fiji, and others). A common and noisy bird. Partial to coconut plantations. Feeds much on the ground,

[21] Mayr, E. 1931. *Amer. Mus. Novit.*, no. 504:19–22 (*Aplonis grandis*); 1942. *Amer. Mus. Novit.*, no. 1166:1–6 (Polynesian *Aplonis*).

particularly near cattle (New Caledonia). The nest is a big pile of twigs, etc., in coconut trees or in hollow trees. It is a serious competitor of several species of native birds. The dark rump and the white tips of the tail distinguish this species from the Papuan Myna. Rapid sequence of calls, like *AhCHOOkee-AhCHOOkee-AhCHOOkee,* or *ooEEcheK-ooEEcheK-ooEEcheK.*

DRONGOS (FAMILY DICRURIDAE)

This Indian-African family barely reaches the S.W.P. Most drongos are the size of magpies or grackles. The S.W.P. species are glossy black; the tail is moderately or enormously elongated. They are arboreal and usually restricted to the true forest. Their song is loud and musical. The nearest relatives are unknown; jays (Corvidae) and birds of paradise have been suggested. The nest, which is a well-built shallow cup, is usually placed rather high and in the fork of a tree. The food consists of insects. In the S.W.P. found only in the Solomon Isls. (Guadalcanal, San Cristobal) and in the Bismarck Archipelago (New Britain, New Ireland). *See* Figure 15.

CROWS (FAMILY CORVIDAE)

Typical crows of the genus *Corvus* are the only members of this family that reach the S.W.P. All 5 species are rather small and have a glossy black plumage. They live in pairs or small flocks and are omnivorous, their food ranging from carrion cast up on the beach to insects and fruit. Their noisy caw-caw make them conspicuous even in the dense forest.

Crows are found in the S.W.P. in New Caledonia (*mone-*

duloides), the Solomon Isls. (*woodfordi, meeki*), the Bismarck Archipelago (*orru*), and Guam (*kubaryi*). Large cuckoo-shrikes (*Coracina*), starlings (*Aplonis*), and the giant

Fig. 15. Spangled Drongo (*Dicrurus bracteatus longirostris*)

honey-eaters (*Gymnomyza*), have occasionally been confused with crows.

SUNBIRDS (FAMILY NECTARINIIDAE)

The sunbirds are "the hummingbirds of the Old World tropics." They are small, active birds showing some metallic colors and feeding on nectar and insects in flowering trees. The 2 species that reach the S.W.P. are most common along the coast, near native villages and gardens, and in other open localities of the lowlands. They occur only rarely in the closed forest or far inland, and are absent in the mountains. The voice is a metallic twitter. The nest, somewhat like that of a Penduline Tit-mouse, is a pear-shaped soft structure of spider webs, lichens, and plant-down woven onto a branch. It contains 2 or 3 eggs. The females have a drab yellow-olive or olive-gray plumage, very different from that of the males. Two species occur in the Bismarck Archipelago (*Nectarinia jugularis* [*see* Plate 3: 34, 35] and *N. sericea*), the former extending as far as the Solomon Isls.

HONEY-EATERS[22] (FAMILY MELIPHAGIDAE)

The honey-eaters, a family restricted to the Australo-Papuan region, are represented in the S.W.P. by a number of common and conspicuous species. They range in size from that of a small warbler to that of a grackle or jay. A curved bill and the habit of visiting flowers are common to all of them. Fe-

[22] Mayr, E. 1932. *Amer. Mus. Novit.*, no. 516:1–30 (Polynesian and Solomon Isls. honey-eaters).

males are much smaller than the males in most of the species and apparently much rarer or at least less conspicuous. Honey-eaters are treetop birds in the primeval forest but can be observed within easy range of field glasses along the edge of the forest, in native plantations, or in other open formations. The cup-shaped nest, containing 2–3 eggs, is usually placed fairly high in a tree in the fork of a branch. Both parents share in the duties of raising the young. Most honey-eaters have loud and musical calls. Even the small *Myzomela* have a distinctive song. *See* Figure 16.

FIG. 16. Heads of honey-eaters (Meliphagidae)—*Foulehaio c. carunculata* (top), *Myzomela lafargei* (middle left), *Lichmera incana flavotincta* (middle right), *Gymnomyza v. viridis* (bottom).

Cardinal Honey-eater (*Myzomela cardinalis*): *See* Plate 3: 36
Small (4–5). Bill long and curved. *Adult male.* Head, breast, and middle of back scarlet; rest of plumage black. *Female* and *immature.* Black replaced by olive gray or olive brown, lighter

below, darker above. The scarlet is duller and is also partly or entirely replaced by olive brown, depending on age, sex, and subspecies.

Ranges in a number of subspecies from Samoa (but not Tonga or Fiji) to the New Hebrides, Loyalty Isls., eastern Solomon Islands, and Micronesia.

Males seem to outnumber females by about 4:1. Feeds in treetops or lower, on about 60 per cent nectar and 40 per cent insects. Nest a neat, small cup of fine roots and fibers, placed in a small fork, from 10 feet up. Lays 2 eggs, rarely 3. Has a characteristic, short song strophe and a twittering call note.

FLOWER-PECKERS (FAMILY DICAEIDAE)

The flower-peckers reach their peak of abundance and diversification in the Indo-Malayan region. Only a single branch of the family reaches the Bismarck Archipelago and the Solomon Isls. in the S.W.P. (including the Bismarcks). It is comprised of 3 species of the genus *Dicaeum,* which are of very small size (3–4) with short tails and rather thick, slightly curved bills. The male is usually much more brightly colored than the female. Flower-peckers inhabit treetops and usually travel in small flocks. The voice is a frequently uttered sharp twitter or *chip-chip.* They can be observed more easily along the edge of the forest, in native gardens, and in second growth than in the true forest. Berries of various species of tropical mistletoe (*Loranthus*) are the favorite food, but small insects are also part of the diet. The nest is a tiny, deep cup of plant down and fibers attached to a twig. *See* Plate 3: 37.

WHITE-EYES[23] (FAMILY ZOSTEROPIDAE)

This family is composed of many small birds whose prevailing color is olive green. They resemble superficially the American vireos, but are not related to them. The conspicuous circle of white feathers around the eye, which gave the family its name, is missing in some species. There are about 25 species known from the S.W.P., but most of them are of very localized occurrence and rarely more than 2 species are found on a single island.

White-eyes have a slender, pointed, slightly curved bill and strong, usually blue-gray legs. They are extremely active and restless birds, generally traveling in small flocks, except during the breeding season. They are found in the treetops of the true forest, but more commonly in second growth, at the edge of the forest, in plantations, and in native gardens. They have a twittering call note, as well as a house sparrow-like *chilp-chilp* in some species. The melodious, often-repeated short song strophe may be diagnostic for each species but is not yet sufficiently described. The food consists of insects, berries, and other small fruits. The nest is a neat little cup, usually woven onto the fork of a branch, fairly high up in a tree. The full clutch consists of 2, 3, or 4 eggs. Male and female are colored alike. Except for song and habitat preference (some lowlands, some mountains), there are no known differences in the behavior of the various species. This statement applies equally to the closely related genera *Woodfordia* and *Rukia.*

[23] Murphy, R. C. and Mathews, G. M. 1929. *Amer. Mus. Novit.*, no. 356:1–14 (Zosteropidae from Polynesia). Murphy, R. C. 1929. *Amer. Mus. Novit.*, no. 365:1–11 (Zosteropidae from Solomon Isls.). Stresemann, E. 1931. *Mitt. Zool. Mus. Berlin*, 17:201–238 (revision).

Gray-backed White-eye (*Zosterops lateralis*): Small (4–5). Head, rump, wings, and tail yellowish olive; mantle gray; breast and belly dirty white; flanks with a brownish wash. Broad white eye-ring, bordered by blackish feathers. Iris light brown; bill brown; feet grayish or brown. Found in about 6 races from New Caledonia to the Banks Isls. and Fiji.

WEAVER-FINCHES[24] (FAMILY PLOCEIDAE, SUBFAMILY ESTRILDINAE)

This subfamily, with about 110 species, ranges from Africa to Australia. It is composed of small birds, with thick finch-like bills and with conspicuous color patterns. The globular nest is placed in cane grass or reeds and contains 4–8 white eggs. The nestlings have a peculiar set of dark spots and lines on the inside of the mouth. These are different in nearly every species.

The native species of the S.W.P. belong to 2 rather distinct groups, the bamboo-finches or parrot-finches (genus *Erythrura*) and the mannikins (genus *Lonchura*). The bamboo-finches frequent the edge of the forest and glades in the forest, feeding on bamboo seeds and other grass seeds, as well as on buds, flowers, and apparently on small fruit. Females are similar to or indistinguishable from males. Green, red, and blue colors dominate in the plumage. The mannikins are typical grasslands birds. They are usually encountered in small or large flocks in the savanna or in rushes surrounding swamps. The prevailing color is rufous brown with white and black patterns; no red, green, or blue

[24] Mayr, E. 1931. *Amer. Mus. Novit.*, no. 489:1–10 (*Erythrura*). Delacour, J. 1943. *Zoologica*, 28:69–86 (revision of subfamily).

in plumage. In addition to these native weaver-finches, a few species have been introduced, which belong to the group called waxbills (*Estrilda*).

Blue-faced Parrot-Finch (*Erythrura trichroa*): *Adult.* Small (4½). Bright green; face blue; tail rust red. Bill black; feet horn brown. *Immature.* Dull olive green, more grayish on breast, and lacking the blue in the face.

Seven subspecies in the S.W.P. (including the Bismarcks) which do not differ by field identification marks. They occur in Micronesia, Bismarck Archipelago, Solomon Isls., New Hebrides, and Loyalty Isls.

Red-browed Waxbill (*Estrilda temporalis* Latham): Small (4½). Crown and tail dark gray; mantle and wings grayish olive. Rump and eyebrow scarlet red. Underparts pale gray. Iris and bill scarlet; feet yellow. The Red-browed Waxbill is a native of Australia but has been introduced to a number of South Sea Isls.

Astrild (*Estrilda astrild* Linnaeus): Small (4) with a rather long tail. Gray brown above, grayer on the crown. Underparts pale gray, slightly washed with pink. Entire plumage finely barred with blackish brown. A stripe through the eye and a patch in the middle of the belly crimson. Vent and under tail-coverts black. Bill red; iris brown; legs black. Differs from the Red-browed Waxbill by the brown rump, by the lack of greenish olive on back and wings, by the barred plumage, and by the black vent. Lives in small or large flocks in the grassland. Introduced on New Caledonia and perhaps other islands (?Fiji).

Part Two

GEOGRAPHICAL SECTION

IV

The Land and Fresh-Water Birds of Samoa

THE identification of birds is rather easy in the Samoan Islands. None of the islands has more than 30 species of resident, native species, to which will have to be added about a dozen winter visitors and introduced species.[1]

The Samoan group can be subdivided, according to its bird fauna, into 4 parts: (a) Upolu-Savaii—2 islands that harbor the bulk of the avifauna, (b) Tutuila, (c) the Manua Islands (Tau, Ofu, Olosinga), and (d) Rose Island, which is not inhabited by any land birds. Aside from the widespread species of rails, ducks, and herons only 10 species of resident land birds are known from the Manua Islands and the same number from Tutuila. About 24 such species are known from Upolu-Savaii.

Most of the Samoan species are widespread in the Southwest Pacific and have been described in the systematic section (Chapter 3, "The Land and Fresh-Water Birds of the Southwest Pacific"). All such species and genera are marked with an asterisk. This includes *Demigretta, Anas, Rallus, Porzana, Poliolimnas, Porphyrio, Ptilinopus porphyraceus, Ducula, Columba, Tyto, Collocalia, Halcyon, Eudynamis, Turdus,*

[1] Armstrong, J. S. 1932. *Hand-List to the Birds of Samoa.* London: J. Bale Sons & Danielsson, Ltd. 91pp. Incomplete and lists at least 3 species that do not occur in Samoa.

Petroica, Aplonis tabuensis, Myzomela cardinalis, and *Erythrura cyanovirens.*

HERONS

***Reef Heron** (*Demigretta s. sacra* Gmelin): Found throughout Samoa, including Rose Isl. About 25 per cent or fewer of the birds seem to be white.

DUCKS

***Australian Gray Duck** (*Anas superciliosa pelewensis* Hartlaub and Finsch): *See* Plate 1:7. Reported from Upolu and Tutuila.

PHEASANTS

***Domestic Fowl** (*Gallus gallus*): A fairly conspicuous member of the Samoan fauna.

RAILS

Five species of rails are found on the Samoan Isls. They can be distinguished as follows:

Key to Samoan Rails

(1) Small, smaller than a starling 2
Large, much larger than a starling 3

(2) Head and underparts sooty black; bill black; feet red .... *Porzana*
Upperparts light grayish brown; underparts grayish white; bill yellow brown; feet light gray green .... *Poliolimnas*

(3) Conspicuous whitish stripe above the eye; back and flanks narrowly barred blackish and white .... *Rallus*
Plumage entirely dark (brown, blue, or gray); bill and feet red 4

(4) Larger; under tail-coverts white; underparts more or less purplish blue .... *Porphyrio*
Smaller; under tail-coverts brownish black like belly; underparts blackish, with a blue-gray tinge on throat and breast .... *Pareudiastes*

The downy young of all species are apparently black.

***Banded Rail** (*Rallus philippensis goodsoni* Mathews): Recorded from Savaii, Upolu, Tutuila, and the Manua Isls. Native name: *Veha.*

***Sooty Rail** (*Porzana t. tabuensis* Gmelin): Recorded from the Manua Isls.

***White-browed Rail** (*Poliolimnas cinereus tannensis* Forster): Recorded from Savaii and Upolu. Native name: *Vai.*

***Purple Swamphen** (*Porphyrio porphyrio samoensis* Peale): *See* Plate 1: 10. Recorded from Savaii, Upolu, Tutuila, and the Manua Isls. Native name: *Manu-alii.*

Samoan Wood Rail (*Pareudiastes pacificus* Hartlaub and Finsch): Upperparts olive black; face and upper throat pure black; lower throat and breast dark bluish slate. Remainder of underparts black. Base of upper bill broadened to a frontal shield, as in a gallinule. Bill and feet yellow in dried skins, but probably red in life.

This species, which has been found with certainty only on Savaii, has not been recorded for more than 50 years and may be extinct. The softness of the wings and the reduced size of the tail indicate that it is flightless. Native name: *Punaë.*

Has been reported to live in the mountains in self-excavated holes, but obviously confused with some species of Tubinares.

PIGEONS AND DOVES

Six species of pigeons occur in the Samoan Isls. They belong to rather different subdivisions of the pigeon family. Three are fruit pigeons (*Ptilinopus, Ducula*), one (*Columba*) is an ordinary pigeon related to the domestic kind, one (*Gallicolumba*) is a ground dove, and, finally, the sixth one (*Didunculus*), which is endemic on Samoa, is a highly peculiar type without known close relatives.

Key to Samoan Pigeons

(1) Size small, about that of a large thrush or smaller 2
Size larger, as large or larger than a domestic pigeon 4

(2) Terrestrial; upperparts more or less rufous brown .... *Gallicolumba*
Arboreal; top of head red; back and wings with much green .... 3 (*Ptilinopus*)

(3) Under tail-coverts red; adult males have underparts largely yellowish white, and a broad red band across the back .... *perousii*
Under tail-coverts yellow; tail-feathers green, with pale yellowish gray tips; throat and breast much lighter than abdomen .... *porphyraceus fasciatus*

(4) Back, wings, and tail dark, blackish, with a more or less pronounced greenish, bronze, or blue-green gloss 5
Back, tail, and most of wing chestnut brown; head, upper

back, and breast dark bluish gray with a green gloss ....
.... *Didunculus*

(5) Sides of head and upper throat white; rest of underparts dark gray .... *Columba*
Entire underparts pale gray, liberally washed with vinaceous or pinkish brown .... *Ducula*

***Crimson-crowned Fruit Dove** (*Ptilinopus porphyraceus fasciatus* Peale): Recorded from Savaii, Upolu, Tutuila, and Manua Isls. Very common on all of the islands, inland and on the coast. Less social than *perousii*. Native name: *Manu-tagi*.

Many-colored Fruit Dove (*Ptilinopus perousii*): *Adult male* (8½). Crown and broad bar across upper back, from shoulder to shoulder, lavender red; nape, sides of head, and underparts yellowish white; a pinkish spot in middle of breast and throat. Back and rump yellowish green; wings dark glossy green; wing-coverts and tail gray with greenish yellow edges. *Female* and *immature*. More similar to *fasciatus* than to adult male *perousii*, but the under tail-coverts are red and there is no terminal yellow bar on the tail. Iris yellow.

Recorded from Savaii, Upolu, Tutuila, and Manua Isls. (*perousii* Peale). Usually in the very tops of fruiting banyan fig trees. Lives in flocks, but is hard to see. Its call consists of a quickly repeated *hoo-hoo-hoo-hoo*. Native name: *Manu-ma* (male), *Manu-lua* (female).

***Pacific Pigeon** (*Ducula pacifica*): *See* Plate 2: 13. Throughout Samoa. Native name: *Lupe*.

***White-throated Pigeon** (*Columba vitiensis*): The subspecies *castaneiceps* Peale occurs on Savaii and Upolu; crown purplish chestnut. Native name: *Fiaui*.

Friendly Ground Dove (*Gallicolumba stairii*): Medium (10½). Appears all brown from a distance. Adult males (and some females) with a lighter (vinaceous-gray) throat and breast shield, which is conspicuously set off from the brown belly by a whitish border. Upperparts with a faint bronze-green gloss. Shoulder patch glossy purplish. The breast shield is rufous cinnamon in the immatures and some females. Iris brown; bill black; feet dark red.

With the habits of the genus.* Has difficulty in balancing when perching on a small twig. Native name: *Tu-tautifa* (ad. male), *Tu-aimeu* (imm.).

Restricted to Savaii and Upolu (*stairii* Gray).

Samoan or Tooth-billed Pigeon (*Didunculus strigirostris* Jardine): This remarkable pigeon is easily identified by the characters given in the key above. The powerful, curved, owl-like bill is orange; feet and naked skin around the eye are red. Found only on Savaii and Upolu.

Feeds on the ground, but flies off with a loud clapping of wings when alarmed. Like all terrestrial pigeons, it is very agile in flying through the undergrowth. Likes to perch in low trees, but is reported to roost in high ones. Voice not adequately described.

PARROTS

Only a single species, a small lory, occurs on Samoa. Natives, of course, keep as pets additional species that have been introduced from other islands.

Blue-crowned Lory (*Vini australis* Gmelin): Small (7). More or less green (including forehead) but cheeks and throat red, crown blue, the tail partly yellow, the middle of the belly red, and the lower belly dark purple. Bill and feet orange red. Abundant on Savaii, Upolu, and the Manua Isls.

Lives in flocks, feeding on the flowers of coconut and other trees. Said to fly from one island to another (?in its search for food?). Nests in holes in trees, or in hollow dead coconuts that have stayed on the trees. Voice a shrill whistle. Native name: *Senga.*

CUCKOOS

***Long-tailed New Zealand Cuckoo** (*Eudynamis taitensis* Sparrman): *See* Figure 8. Throughout the Samoan group.

OWLS

***Barn Owl** (*Tyto alba*): *See* Figure 9. Known from Savaii, Upolu, Tutuila, and Manua Isls. (*lulu* Peale). Native name: *Lulu.*

SWIFTS

***White-rumped Swiftlet** (*Collocalia spodiopygia*): *Cf.* Plate 2: 20. Unmistakable, since there is no other swift or swallow on the Samoan Isls. Known from Savaii, Upolu, Tutuila, and Manua Isls. (*spodiopygia* Peale).

KINGFISHERS

The 2 species of kingfishers found in the Samoan Isls. complement each other geographically.

Flat-billed Kingfisher (*Halcyon recurvirostris* Lafresnaye): Small (7). The buffy (or cinnamon) white underparts and the greenish blue upperparts (with a buff collar across the upper back) are diagnostic. Lores buff. Bill and feet blackish.

Restricted to Savaii and Upolu. Habits like those of *Halcyon chloris*. Native name: *Tiotala.*

***White-collared Kingfisher** (*Halcyon chloris*): *See* Plate 2: 22. Two rather distinct subspecies occur in eastern Samoa.

Tutuila (*pealei* Finsch and Hartlaub). The blue (in males) or greenish blue (in females) of the crown is largely replaced by white. The white of head and underwing often washed with ochraceous in males.

Manua Isls. (*manuae* Mayr 1941). Like typical *chloris,* but upperparts rather dark greenish blue, underparts usually pure white.

SONGBIRDS

Only 15 species of songbirds are known from Samoa, but they belong to 8 different families or subfamilies. To facilitate identification for beginners, particularly those who are not familiar with the Old World families of songbirds, I have constructed an artificial key. It will be well to read the general remarks on each family in the systematic section (Part I, chapter 3) as well as the detailed description in the subsequent pages.

Key to Samoan Songbirds

(1) With red in plumage 2
No red in plumage 4
(2) Bill heavy; back and underparts green or green blue ....
.... *Erythrura*
No conspicuous green in plumage 3

(3) Head and upper throat red; breast and belly grayish or black .... *Myzomela*
Some red on breast and belly; back blackish .... *Petroica*

(4) Plumage with white, black, gray or gray-brown colors only 5
Plumage with chestnut, yellows, or olive greens 10

(5) Upperparts black or brown; underparts white with or without narrow dark bars .... *Lalage* (2 species)
Underparts not prevailingly white 6

(6) Entire plumage sooty black; bill and feet yellow .... *Turdus*
Plumage more or less dark gray or fuscous brown 7

(7) Small body, long fan-tail. Total length 6. Sooty brown; inconspicuous white marks above and behind the eyes .... *Rhipidura*
Larger, no white on face 8

(8) Large, size of a grackle or jay; wings and tail dark brown; rest of plumage blackish with a green gloss; feet and rather long bill black .... *Aplonis atrifuscus*
Medium, size of a starling; underparts paler than upperparts 9

(9) Iris yellow; tail, bill, and feet short; crown and sometimes upperparts with a purplish gloss .... *Aplonis tabuensis*
Iris brown; tail and bill fairly long; upperparts dull sooty brown; tips of lateral tail-feathers white .... *Clytorhynchus*

(10) Belly white; throat tawny; without olive colors ... *Myiagra*
With yellow, green, or olive in plumage 11

(11) Belly bright yellow; upperparts sooty or olive black .... *Pachycephala*
Belly not bright yellow 12

(12) Warbler size; upperparts olive; underparts pale greenish white; inconspicuous white eye-ring; bill yellow brown .. .. *Zosterops*

Not so 13

(13) Thrush size; all olive, darker above, more yellowish below; a yellow line from the gape to the ear region; a naked wattle below base of the bill .... *Foulehaio*
Size of a large jay; a long curved beak; head and underparts blackish; wings, back, and tail olive .... *Gymnomyza*

CUCKOO-SHRIKES

Two species of trillers represent this family in the Samoan Isls. In the smaller species (*sharpei*) the iris is white, the bill is yellow, the upperparts are brown, and the underparts faintly, or more strongly, barred with brown. In the larger species (*maculosa*) the iris is brown, the bill is black, the upperparts are black or dark gray mixed with white, and the underparts are almost pure white.

***Polynesian Triller** (*Lalage maculosa*): *See* Plate 3: 24. Females and immatures have brownish black upperparts, the white pattern tinged with buff, and the lower mandible yellow. Common and tame in the lowlands and around the villages of Savaii and Upolu (*maculosa* Peale).

Samoan Triller (*Lalage sharpei*): Males and females colored alike. No white in the wing. Upolu (*sharpei* Rothschild) and Savaii (*tenebrosa* Mayr and Ripley 1941, darker and more heavily barred underneath). Apparently restricted to the mountain forest. Habits unknown.

THRUSHES

***Island Thrush** (*Turdus poliocephalus*): The Samoan race (*samoensis* Tristram) is restricted to Savaii and Upolu. It is all sooty black. Found in the deep forest, particularly in the mountains between 1200 and 2500 feet. Native name: *Tutumalili.*

FLYCATCHERS

This rich and diversified family (and its subfamily of whistlers) is represented on Samoa by 5 different species, each belonging to a different section of the family. These species have become adapted to such different ways of living that their ultimate relationship is not apparent to the casual observer.

Samoan Fantail (*Rhipidura nebulosa*): The behavior of this species is more diagnostic than its simple coloration. The only white marks of its otherwise dull sooty-gray plumage are above and behind the eye and on the tips of the tail-feathers.

Savaii birds (*altera* Mayr 1931) are somewhat lighter than Upolu birds (*nebulosa* Peale). Very tame; hops from branch to branch with fanned tail and drooping wings. Likes to follow the observer. Utters a short twittering note at frequent intervals. Native name: *Sehoo.*

Samoan Broadbill (*Myiagra albiventris* Peale): The combination of dark upperparts, orange-brown throat, and white abdomen is completely diagnostic. Females are more grayish above. Known from Savaii and Upolu. Lives in the forest. Catches insects in typical flycatcher fashion. Native name: *Tolai-ula* or *Tolai-fatu.*

Fiji Shrikebill (*Clytorhynchus vitiensis*): *See* Fiji. The endemic Manua Isls. subspecies (*powelli* Salvin) is very dark. Absent from the western isls. *Aplonis* and *Foulehaio* are the only other 2 songbirds of the Manua Isls.

***Scarlet Robin** (*Petroica multicolor*): *See* Figure 14. The subspecies *pusilla* Peale is restricted to Savaii and Upolu. The white spot on the forehead of the male is rather small; the female is sooty black above. Native name: *Tolai-fatu* or *Tagi-Tagi.*

WHISTLERS

Samoan Whistler (*Pachycephala flavifrons* Peale): The bright orange-yellow belly is diagnostic. There are 3 color phases in this species: (1) forehead and throat yellowish; (2) forehead yellow, throat whitish; (3) forehead and throat whitish. Females are less blackish above and lack the well-defined yellow areas on the forehead.

Known from Savaii and Upolu. Common in the sub-stage of the forest, also in coconut groves and native gardens. Native name: *Vasa-vasa.*

STARLINGS

Two species of this widespread and successful family have reached the Samoan Isls.

Polynesian Starling (*Aplonis tabuensis*): Small (7½). Upperparts dark brown or sooty black, darker and with a greenish purple gloss on the crown. Underparts much lighter, almost buffy white on throat and under tail-coverts; rest of underparts grayish with indistinct whitish streaks. There is a whitish line on the blackish wing formed by the pale edges of the secondaries. Tail short. Iris yellow.

Three races in the Samoan Isls. The above description is based on the subspecies *brevirostris* Peale of Savaii and Upolu. The Tutuila race (*tutuilae* Mayr 1942) is similar but darker. The Manua race (*manuae* Mayr 1942) is much darker, glossy black above and darker below without pale shaft streaks.

With the typical habits of the genus.* Common and widespread, singly or in small flocks. In the forest as well as along the shore and near human habitations. Either in rather tall trees, particularly in bread fruit and coconut trees, or in the substage of the forest. Has a rather musical whistle or song. Nest with 2 eggs placed in hollow trees. Native name: *Miti-vao.*

Samoan Starling (*Aplonis atrifuscus* Peale): Iris brown; females much smaller than males. Occurs on Savaii, Upolu, Tutuila, and Manua Isls. Common in the forest and around villages. Feeds on fruit and does much damage in gardens. Call note loud. Nothing known of its nesting except that the eggs are pale blue. In pairs or flocks. Native name: *Fuia.*

HONEY-EATERS

This family is represented on Samoa by 3 very dissimilar species, one as large as a grackle (*Gymnomyza*), one the size of a small thrush (*Foulehaio*), and one the size of a warbler (*Myzomela*). However, all 3 have long, curved bills and visit flowering trees to feed on insects and nectar. The 2 larger species are very vocal. *See* Figure 16.

Mao (*Gymnomyza samoensis* Hombron and Jacquinot): Males larger than females. An olive stripe along the cheeks separates the blackish crown from the blackish throat. Iris brownish gray; bill black; feet blackish gray. Found on Savaii, Upolu, and Tutuila. Frequents the treetops in the deep forest. Has a loud wailing call note.

Wattled Honey-eater (*Foulehaio carunculata*): Iris brown. Female like male but smaller. The subspecies *carunculata* Gmelin is found on Savaii, Upolu, Tutuila, and Manua Isls.

An abundant and noisy bird. Is very pugnacious and fights with species twice its size. Feeds on nectar and insects. Inland and along the coast, particularly in coconut trees. One of the few good singers of Polynesia. Song: *ti-ti-tui-tui-tur-twee*. Strictly territorial, but lives in flocks between breeding seasons. Native name: *Jao*. *See* Fig. 16.

***Cardinal Honey-eater** (*Myzomela cardinalis*): *Cf*. Plate 3: 36. Small (5). Adult males, with only 2 contrasting colors of scarlet and black, are easily identified. Females and immatures have the black replaced by grayish olive underneath, and by sooty olive above. Immatures have a scarlet head; females have scarlet only on lower back and rump.

Found on Savaii, Upolu, and Tutuila in the subspecies *nigriventris* Peale. Most common near villages, in native gardens, and along the edge of the forest. Native name: *Tolaiula*.

WHITE-EYES

Samoan White-eye (*Zosterops samoensis* Murphy and Mathews 1929): Small (4½). Sexes alike. Iris yellowish white. Known only from Savaii Isl., probably restricted to the mountains.

WEAVER-FINCHES

Red-headed Parrot-Finch (*Erythrura cyanovirens*): Small (4). Crown, cheeks, and tail red. Wings olive green, remainder of body olive green or more or less washed with blue. Young have partly yellow bill, dull blue cheeks, and a duller plumage throughout. Known from Savaii and Upolu (*cyanovirens* Peale). This is not a grass, but a tree, finch. Feeds on flowers and buds. Wanders much from place to place; usually found in the true forest, but occasionally in flowering trees near the coast, such as *Erythrina* and *Casuarina.* Nothing is known of its reproduction. Singly or in pairs, rarely in parties. Native name: *Sega-sega-manu.*

V

The Land and Fresh-Water Birds of Fiji, Tonga, and Neighboring Islands[1]

THE Fiji Islands consist of 4 or 5 large and hundreds, if not thousands, of smaller islands. On the whole the fauna of the smaller islands is very much poorer than that of the large mountainous ones (Viti Levu, Ovalau, Vanua Levu, Taviuni). Kandavu Island, in the southwest, has 2 endemic species (*Rhipidura personata* and *Xanthotis provocator*), but at the same time it lacks a number of species found on the other mountainous islands. All of the eastern islands, the so-called Lau Archipelago, have a much-impoverished fauna, but they do have 2 species, *Vini australis* and *Mayrornis versicolor,* not found elsewhere in the Fiji group. The fauna of the Tonga Islands, about 200 miles east of Fiji, is similar to that of the Lau Archipelago but still poorer. The Tonga Whistler (*Pachycephala melanops*) is the only endemic bird of the Tonga Islands.

Not far from Fiji and Tonga are a number of scattered, isolated coral or volcanic islands. Six of these are known to be inhabited by land birds: Rotuma, Fotuna (or Futuna) and Alofa (Horne Islands), Niue (Savage Island), Uea (Wallis

[1] No book on the birds of Fiji or Tonga has been published. The following important reports appear in the periodical literature: Layard, E. L. 1875. "Notes on Fijian Birds." *Proc. Zool. Soc. London,* p.423–42. Layard, E. L. 1876. "Notes on the Ornithology of Fiji." *Ibis,* p.137–57. Wood, C. A. and Wetmore, A. 1925. "A Collection of Birds from the Fiji Islands." *Ibis,* p.814–55; 1926, p.91–136. Gräffe, E. 1870. "Die Vogelwelt der Tonga Inseln." *Jour. f. Orn.,* 18:401–20.

Island), Keppel (or Niuatobutabu) and Boscawen (or Tafahi), and Niuafou. The Incubator Bird (*Megapodius pritchardii*), endemic on Niuafou, is the only species peculiar to these islands. In the subsequent text, these 6 islands or groups of islands, are referred to as the "isolated [central Polynesian] islands."

Gräffe, Kleinschmidt, and Layard undertook a fairly thorough exploration of the main islands of the Fiji group during the 1870's. Other naturalists have gathered much additional information during the past 60 years. The Whitney South Sea Expedition made the first thorough survey of the Lau Archipelago, of the Yasawa group, and of other smaller outlying islands. *Trichocichla rufa,* described in 1890, and *Mayrornis versicolor,* discovered in 1924, were the last species of birds to be added to the Fiji list. Although the faunistic exploration of the Fijian avifauna can be considered to be nearly complete, little is yet known about the ecology and life history of most Fijian birds.

All species and genera marked with an asterisk are treated in more detail in the systematic section (Chapter 3, "The Land and Fresh-Water Birds of the Southwest Pacific") of Part I.

HERONS

***Reef Heron** (*Demigretta s. sacra* Gmelin): Common throughout Fiji, Tonga, and adjacent islands. Among adults, about 65 per cent are in the gray phase, 20 per cent in the white phase, and 15 per cent in a mottled white and gray phase.

***Little Mangrove Heron** (*Butorides striatus*): *See* Plate 1: 6. Recorded from Kandavu, Ovalau, Viti Levu, Ngau, and

Vanua Mbalavu. These birds from western Fiji may be referred to *diminutus* Mayr 1940, the grayish subspecies of the Santa Cruz Isls. The species is absent from eastern Fiji, Tonga, Samoa, and from the isolated islands.

DUCKS

*__Whistling Tree Duck__ (*Dendrocygna a. arcuata* Horsfield): Recorded from Viti Levu and Vanua Levu, but not recently. Apparently now extinct in this region.

*__Australian Gray Duck__ (*Anas superciliosa pelewensis* Hartlaub and Finsch): *See* Plate 1: 7. Throughout the Fiji Isls. (from Kandavu and Viti Levu to Ono Ilau), Tonga Isls., Niuafou, and Uea.

HAWKS

Fiji Goshawk (*Accipiter rufitorques* Peale): Female medium (16), male small (12). *Adult.* Upperparts ash gray, with a rufous collar across the hind-neck; no bars on wings or tail. Underparts rufous (dark vinaceous). Sides of head gray; middle of upper throat whitish. Iris (? and eyelid), cere, and feet orange yellow; bill black. *Immature.* Dark brown above, feathers edged with dark rufous. Underparts profusely marked with drop-shaped, dark brown streaks on a white background. Thighs rufous. Iris brown.

Widespread on Fiji. Recorded from Kandavu, Mbengha, Yasawa group, Viti Levu, Ovalau, Ngau, Koro, Vanua Levu, Taviuni, and adjacent islands; northern Lau Archipelago (Thithia, Avea, Vanua Mbalavu), and south-central Fiji (Matuku, Totoya, Moala). Possibly also Rotuma.

Feeds on lizards, insects, and occasionally on birds. Breeds February–June.

***Swamp Harrier** (*Circus a. approximans* Peale): Large size, brownish coloration and light rump, as well as manner of flight, distinguish this species from goshawk and falcon. Found throughout the Fiji Isls., from Kandavu to the Lau Archipelago. Straggles occasionally to Uea and other isolated islands of central Polynesia.

FALCONS

***Peregrine Falcon** (*Falco peregrinus nesiotes* Mayr): This dark falcon has been recorded with certainty only from Viti Levu and Taviuni, but may occur near cliffs on all the larger islands. Flight pattern, blackish upperparts, and rusty underparts are diagnostic.

MEGAPODES

Niuafou Incubator Bird (*Megapodius pritchardii* Gray): A small (11), light-colored megapode. Head, upper back, throat, and breast dark gray; chin and sides of head pale gray. Lower abdomen pale ash gray. Lower back and wings rufous brown. Some white in wings and tail. Bill and legs brownish yellow. Buries its eggs in hot volcanic ashes. Habits those of *M. freycinet.**

PHEASANTS

***Domestic Fowl** (*Gallus gallus*): Feral fowl are found on many islands of the Fiji group and Tonga. The mongoose has decimated it on Viti Levu and Vanua Levu.

RAILS

Of the 5 species of rails that occur on Fiji and Tonga, 4 are widespread in the Pacific and one is endemic. For a comparative description of the 4 widespread species, *see* New Hebrides. The ground dove (*Gallicolumba*) is the only bird of Fiji and Tonga that might be confused with rails. Birds described by natives as "nesting in holes in the ground in the mountain forest" are not rails, but petrels or shearwaters (Tubinares). On Viti Levu and Vanua Levu all rails have been more or less exterminated by the mongoose.

*__Banded Rail__ (*Rallus philippensis*): Two races, both with reduced or absent breast band: *sethsmithi* Mathews 1911 (throughout Fiji, Rotuma), bold black bars below, little white spotting above; *forsteri* Hartlaub (Tonga, Keppel, Uea, Niuafou), lighter above and below.

Barred-wing Rail (*Nesoclopeus poecilopterus* Hartlaub): A large (13) rail with a powerful bill. Upperparts plain walnut brown. Underparts dark ash gray; middle of upper throat whitish. Flight feathers bright chestnut with black bars. Iris light brown; bill orange and yellow; legs yellowish. Large size and absence of any pattern on upper- and underparts (except wing-feathers) are diagnostic.

Restricted to Viti Levu and Ovalau. Inhabits taro beds and swamps. Not found for more than 50 years and possibly now extinct through depredation by the mongoose. Probably the *Sasa* of the natives.

*__Sooty Rail__ (*Porzana t. tabuensis* Gmelin): Recorded from Fiji (Viti Levu, Ovalau, Ngau, Kandavu), Tonga (Tongatabu, Late, Honga Hapai, Fanua Lai), and Niue.

***White-browed Rail** (*Poliolimnas cinereus*): Rare in Fiji. Recorded from Viti Levu, Ovalau, and Ngau (*tannensis* Forster).

***Purple Swamphen** (*Porphyrio porphyrio*): *See* Plate 1: 10. The subspecies *vitiensis* Peale is rather large and has a bright blue breast shield. Found throughout the Fiji Isls., also on the Tonga Isls., Niue, Uea, Rotuma, and ?Niuafou. Widespread and common, except on those islands where recently exterminated by the mongoose.

PIGEONS AND DOVES

This family is represented in the Fijian area by 8 species or groups of species, 3 fruit doves (*Ptilinopus*), 3 large pigeons (*Ducula, Columba*), one ground dove (*Gallicolumba*), and one introduced turtledove (*Streptopelia*). There are thus no serious identification difficulties.

***Crimson-crowned Fruit Dove** (*Ptilinopus porphyraceus*): The subspecies *porphyraceus* Temminck differs by having no reddish on the abdomen. There is a dark bluish purple patch in the middle of the abdomen, and a subterminal gray tail-bar. Found on Keppel and Boscawen, Niue, throughout the Tonga Isls., Rotuma, Lau Archipelago, and on smaller islands throughout the Fiji group, but apparently absent from the larger islands. The subspecies *graeffei* Neumann 1922 (Uea, Fotuna, Niuafou) is intermediate between *fasciatus* and *porphyraceus*.

Many-colored Fruit Dove (*Ptilinopus perousii*): *See* Samoa. The Fiji-Tonga race *mariae* Jacquinot and Pucheran is a little less yellow than the Samoan race; it is found throughout the

Fiji Isls. and on Tonga (Eua, Tongatabu, Tofua, and Late). Females differ from *porphyraceus* females by the uniformly lighter abdomen and the inconspicuous tail-bar; they differ from females of the *Pt. luteovirens* group by the red cap and the light-colored underparts. Adult males appear whitish in flight.

Ptilinopus luteovirens group: This consists of 3 geographically representative, small (8) species formerly united in the genus *Chrysoena*. The females are all very similar: dark green; head more yellowish; lower abdomen light green or yellowish; underwing and under tail-coverts yellow. The males are strikingly different. Bill and feet green. The habits of the 3 species appear to be the same. Call an explosive, barking *boo,* followed by a soft, clucking *oo-oo-oo.* The explosive sound is produced by expelling air from the fully inflated crop (? air sacs). Call on Kandavu supposedly a double whistle. Primarily a bird of the hill forest.

Velvet Dove (*Ptilinopus layardi* Elliot): Dark green except greenish yellow head (and upper throat). Under tail-coverts bright yellow. Kandavu group.

Orange Dove (*Ptilinopus victor*): A beautiful reddish orange; head and upper throat olive yellow. *victor* Gould (Vanua Levu, Taviuni, Kio, Rambi); *aureus* Amadon 1943 (Ngamia, Lauthala).

Golden Dove (*Ptilinopus luteovirens* Hombron and Jacquinot): Feathers of breast, back, and wings hackle-shaped (lanceolate), olive yellow. Head yellowish olive; abdomen and under tail-coverts bright yolk yellow. Viti Levu, Ovalau, Mbengha, Waia, Ngau.

***Pacific Pigeon** (*Ducula p. pacifica* Gmelin): *See* Plate 2: 13. Found throughout central Polynesia. Union, Ellice, Tonga Isls., all Fiji, and many isolated islands (Niuafou, Danger, Boscawen, Fotuna, Alofa, Uea, Niue).

Peale's Pigeon (*Ducula latrans* Peale): A large (16) fruit pigeon without a knob on the bill. Upperparts more or less gray; head and upper back pale ash gray, lower back and wings darker and more brownish. Tail dull chestnut brown, lighter and more reddish below. Underparts lighter; throat and breast vinaceous gray; lower abdomen and under tail-coverts rufous buff. Iris red; bill black; feet purplish. Differs from *pacifica* by larger size, lack of knob, gray back and brown tail, grayish breast, and pale under tail-coverts. Differs from *vitiensis* by black bill, pale underparts, pale head without a well-defined white throat.

Found on all the larger islands of the Fiji group, also central Fiji (Ngau, Koro, Matuku, Totoya, Moala) and northern Lau Archipelago (south to Naiau). Has a very loud, barking call. Lowland and mountain forest.

***White-throated Pigeon** (*Columba vitiensis*): The Fijian subspecies *vitiensis* Quoy and Gaimard has rather vinaceous or chestnut underparts; the flanks only are gray. White of throat washed with grayish in females. Found throughout the entire Fiji group from Kandavu to Taviuni and Ongea Levu.

Friendly Ground Dove (*Gallicolumba stairii*): Medium (10½). More or less brown throughout (*see* Samoa). A white border separates the vinaceous-brown breast shield from the earth-brown abdomen. The subspecies *vitiensis* Finsch is found throughout the Fiji Isls., Tonga Isls., and on Alofa (Horne Isls.).

***Malay Turtle Dove** (*Streptopelia chinensis tigrina* Temminck): Introduced on Viti Levu and other islands of the Fiji group.

PARROTS

This family is represented in the Fiji group by 3 small lories (*Vini, Phigys*) and by 2 large, long-tailed parrots (*Prosopeia*).

Red-throated Lorikeet (*Vini amabilis* Ramsay): Small (7), with a long, pointed tail. All green except cheeks, throat, and thighs, which are red. Tips of tail-feathers yellow. Iris yellow; bill and feet orange.

Found only on Viti Levu, Ovalau, and Taviuni. Probably restricted to the mountain forest where it lives in the tops of flowering trees, particularly on a species with white flowers. Usually in parties of 6 or 8.

Blue-crowned Lory (*Vini australis* Gmelin): *See* Samoa. Differs from *amabilis* by larger size and shorter tail (60 per cent, not 80 per cent of wing), the blue crown, and the large red and purple patch on the abdomen. Widespread through central Polynesia: Samoa, Fotuna, Niuafou, Keppel-Boscawen, Niue, Uea, Tonga Isls., and southern Lau Archipelago (Turtle Isl. to Oneata).

Collared Lory (*Phigys solitarius* Suckow): Medium (8). Bright crimson red below, except purplish black lower abdomen and green under tail-coverts; top of head and hindneck purplish black. Back, wings, and tail green. A double collar of bright green and red across the upper back. A concealed reddish orange band across base of tail; rump bright green. Iris brown or orange; bill and feet orange yellow.

Larger islands of the Fiji group, in the Lau Archipelago southward to Lakemba and Oneata (Kandavu, Ono, Viti Levu, Ovalau, Wakaya, Koro, Vanua Levu, Rambi, Taviuni, Yathata, Vatu Vara, Tuvutha, Lakemba, Oneata, Matuku). In flocks, visiting coconut and other flowering trees.

Red-breasted Musk Parrot (*Prosopeia tabuensis*): A large (18), long-tailed parrot with green back and wings and red head and underparts. The red parts are crimson in one subspecies (*splendens*) and maroon in the other 4. The flight- and tail-feathers are royal blue. In some races there is a bright blue collar across the hind-neck, in some the rump may be mottled with maroon. *Prosopeia t. tabuensis* Gmelin (Ngau and [introduced to] Tongatabu and Eua, Tonga); *atrogularis* Peale (Vanua Levu, Kio), blue collar present; *koroensis* Layard (Koro), blue collar lacking or narrow; *taviunensis* Layard (Taviuni, Ngamia) small, no blue collar; *splendens* Peale (Kandavu, introduced to Viti Levu and Ovalau), head and underparts crimson, blue collar conspicuous.

Feeds on various kinds of wild or planted fruits. In pairs or small flocks. Learns to speak, hence a favorite pet. In the wild has a harsh, loud call note. Plumage has a peculiar musky odor.

Yellow-breasted Musk Parrot (*Prosopeia personata* Gray): Large (19), long tailed. Mostly green. Face black; outer tail-feathers bluish; middle of breast yellow; middle of abdomen deep orange; underside of tail black. Iris orange; bill and feet black. Endemic on Viti Levu and ? formerly Ovalau.

CUCKOOS

*__Fan-tailed Cuckoo__ (*Cacomantis pyrrhophanus*): The only native resident cuckoo of the Fiji Isls. The Fijian subspecies (*simus* Peale) is rufous below, slate gray with a greenish gloss above. The tail is blue black, barred with white. Some adults are more or less all sooty black.

Occurs on Kandavu, Viti Levu, Ovalau and adjacent islands, Vanua Levu, and Taviuni. Lowland forest and open country.

*__Long-tailed New Zealand Cuckoo__ (*Eudynamis taitensis* Sparrman): *See* Figure 8. May be expected on any island in central Polynesia.

BARN OWLS

The only 2 owls found in central Polynesia belong to the genus *Tyto*. They can be differentiated by the key characters given in the New Caledonian section.

*__Barn Owl__ (*Tyto alba*): *See* Figure 9. The subspecies *lulu* Peale is found throughout central Polynesia (Samoa, Tonga, all Fiji, Niue, Rotuma, Fotuna and Niuafou).

Grass Owl (*Tyto longimembris*): *See* New Caledonia. The subspecies *oustaleti* Hartlaub has been recorded from the grasslands of Viti Levu.

SWIFTS

*__White-rumped Swiftlet__ (*Collocalia spodiopygia*): *See* Plate 2: 20. This is the only swift in central Polynesia. The whitish rump, the dull upperparts, and the uniform dusky gray underparts distinguish it from the Pacific Swallow. The subspecies *assimilis* Stresemann 1912 occurs on all Fijian islands and on Fotuna; *townsendi* Oberholser on the Tonga Isls.

KINGFISHERS

***White-collared Kingfisher** (*Halcyon chloris*): *See* Plate 2: 22. The only kingfisher in central Polynesia. Five subspecies: *vitiensis* Peale (all Fiji, except the ranges of the 2 following subspecies and Matuku-Totoya-Moala where the species is absent); *eximia* Mayr 1941 (Kandavu group); *marina* Mayr 1941 (Lau Archipelago), less ochraceous underneath; *sacra* Gmelin (Tonga), very blue above; little buff underneath, female none; *regina* Mayr 1941 (Fotuna), very deep ocher underneath. Along the seashore and inland. Most common in second growth, gardens, and other open situations. Breeding season, November–January.

SWALLOWS

***Pacific Swallow** (*Hirundo tahitica*): *See* Plate 3: 23. The subspecies *subfusca* Gould is found throughout the Fiji Isls. and has been recorded at least once from the Tonga Isls. (Kelefesia).

CUCKOO-SHRIKES

***Polynesian Triller** (*Lalage maculosa*): *Cf.* Plate 3: 24. Two subspecies in Tonga, 5 in Fiji, and 4 in the outlying islands. *Whitmeei* Sharpe (Niue) and *futunae* Mayr and Ripley 1941

(Fotuna) are similar to *maculosa* (*see* Samoa), but with a darker rump; *keppeli* Mayr and Ripley 1941 (Keppel, Boscawen), *vauana* Mayr and Ripley 1941 (northern Tonga), *tabuensis* Mayr and Ripley 1941 (central and southern Tonga), and *nesophila* Mayr and Ripley 1941 (Lau Archipelago) have pronounced white tips to the feathers of the back, often a white nuchal collar, and the females have more brownish backs; *woodi* Wetmore 1925 (Ngamia, Taviuni, Vanua Levu) and *rotumae* Neumann 1927 (Rotuma) have V-shaped bars on sides of neck and flanks; *mixta* Mayr and Ripley 1941 (Ovalau and adjacent islands), *pumila* Neumann 1927 (Viti Levu), and *soror* Mayr and Ripley 1941 (Kandavu) have a rather brownish back and pronounced barring of the underparts, particularly in females.

BULBULS (FAMILY PYCNONOTIDAE)

Red-vented Bulbul (*Pycnonotus cafer*): Medium (8). Head, throat, and breast black; back sooty brown with wavy gray lines. Rump white; tail black with white tip. Abdomen gray, under tail-coverts red. Iris brown; bill and feet black. An Indian species introduced on Viti Levu and other islands (*bengalensis* Blyth). Common in gardens. Has a pleasant call note.

THRUSHES

***Island Thrush** (*Turdus poliocephalus*): This species reaches its greatest diversification in the Fiji Isls. The 5 recognized races are as different as 5 species. There is, however, no identification problem, since it is the only thrush in the Fijis. The subspecies are *ruficeps* Ramsay (Kandavu) black, with ocher head and throat; young all rufous underneath, with black spots; *layardi* Seebohm (Viti Levu, Ovalau, Yasawa, Koro) dusky gray above, with an ash-gray throat and chestnut abdomen and flanks; *vitiensis* Layard (Vanua Levu) entirely gray, almost blackish above, female sometimes with a rufous wash on the abdomen; *tempesti* Layard (Taviuni) black, except head and throat gray in males, blackish gray in females; *hades* Mayr 1941 (Ngau) all jet black. Immatures of all races tend to be lighter underneath and are usually somewhat spotted.

UNCERTAIN FAMILY

Silktail (*Lamprolia victoriae*): A beautiful, small (5) bird. Mostly black; top of head glossy green blue; throat with glossy blue spangles; back and wings velvety black with a slight violet gloss. Upper tail-coverts and tail snow white; feathers with a silky gloss and structure. Tips of tail-feathers glossy purplish black. Iris brown; bill and feet black. Two subspecies: *victoriae* Finsch (Taviuni) and *kleinschmidti* Ramsay (Vanua Levu).

This is one of the most puzzling birds of the world. It looks like a dwarf bird-of-paradise and may well be related to that family. Song and habits are poorly known. It lives in the undergrowth of the mountain forest. Clings to vines and saplings when feeding. Hops about on the ground or on branches with drooping wings and cocked up tail. Call note a sharp twitter. Feeds on termites and small beetles. The mouth of the young is bright yellow inside. Known on Taviuni under the name Satin Flycatcher.

The nest, lined with feathers, is 4 to 5 feet above the ground, usually in the fork of a thin horizontal twig. The single egg is pinkish white with bold reddish brown spots.

WARBLERS

Fiji Warbler (*Vitia ruficapilla*): Small (5) with a long thin bill, long legs, and a long tail. Top of head rufous; back, wings, and tail brownish olive. Underparts whitish gray; sides of throat and breast gray; flanks brownish. Iris brown; bill brown, horn color below; feet flesh color. Apparently not uncommon in the dense undergrowth and substage of the forest, particularly in the mountains.

Four subspecies: *ruficapilla* Ramsay (Kandavu) with bright rufous on head and sides of head; back and wings rather olive gray; *badiceps* Finsch (Viti Levu) has a white eyebrow; sides of head gray, only top of head rufous; a dark line through the eye; *castaneoptera* Mayr 1935 (Vanua Levu) has a buff eyebrow; back, wings, tail, and flanks more brownish; *funebris* Mayr 1935 (Taviuni) very dark, with a buff eyebrow; wings and tail fuscous; top of head sepia.

Long-legged Warbler (*Trichocichla rufa* Reichenow): Large (7½). Dark rufous brown above with a conspicuous white, posteriorly buff eye-stripe. Middle of throat and breast white; sides and abdomen rufous brown. Tail long. Iris and bill brown; legs pink.

Habits unknown. Apparently an inhabitant of heavy undergrowth in the forest. Not found during the past 50 years and possibly extinct. Native name: *Manu Kalo*. Known from Viti Levu only.

FLYCATCHERS

This family is represented in the Fiji Isls. by more species than any other group of songbirds. There are 9 resident species with 29 subspecies.

Kandavu Fantail (*Rhipidura personata* Ramsay): A small (6) flycatcher with a long tail. Upperparts dark earth brown; tail black. A narrow white eyebrow and a white line back of the eye. Upper throat white; a black bar across lower throat; breast and abdomen whitish or buff. Outermost tail-feather with white edge. Iris brown; bill black; feet brown. With the habits of the genus.* This species is endemic on Kandavu and is the only fantail of that island.

Spotted Fantail (*Rhipidura spilodera*): *Cf.* Plate 3: 26. Small (6½). Back and wings brownish; top of head fuscous. Upper throat white; lower throat and breast streaked with dark or rufous brown; flanks rufous; abdomen buff. Tail black, outer feathers with white tips. A short white eyebrow and a white line behind the eye. Iris and feet brown; lower bill whitish horn color.

Three subspecies in the Fiji Isls.: *layardi* Salvadori (Ovalau and Viti Levu) with strong dark streaking on the breast; *erythronota* Sharpe (Vanua Levu, Yanganga, Kio) with very rufous back; *rufilateralis* Sharpe (Taviuni) with very rufous flanks. Gardens, lowland and mountain forest.

Slaty Flycatcher (*Mayrornis lessoni*): A small (5–5½), gray flycatcher with a black tail, the lateral tail-feathers broadly tipped with white. Upperparts slate gray; underparts pale gray; upper throat and lower abdomen whitish. A whitish eye-ring. Iris brown; bill black; feet dark gray.

Two subspecies: *lessoni* Gray (western and northern Fiji from Kandavu to Taviuni); *orientalis* Mayr 1933 (Moala and Lau Archipelago).

A bird of the substage in lowland and mountain forest. Habits apparently similar to those of *Monarcha,** but sometimes spreads the tail like a fan. Has a harsh rasping alarm note.

Versicolor Flycatcher (*Mayrornis versicolor* Mayr 1933): Small (5). Slate gray above, pale rufous below (between ochraceous buff and pinkish cinnamon); upper throat colored like the underparts. Iris brown; bill bluish black; feet gray. Found only on Ongea Levu.

Fiji Shrikebill (*Clytorhynchus vitiensis*): Mostly dark brown above, brownish gray below. Lateral tail-feathers sometimes with white or buffy tips. Peculiar, wedge-shaped, long bill, laterally compressed. Iris brown; bill black with whitish edge; feet bluish gray.

In addition to *powelli* (Manua, Samoa) there are 11 subspecies of this widespread species in central Polynesia: *compressirostris* Layard (Kandavu group); *vitiensis* Hartlaub (Viti Levu, Ovalau, Koro, Ngau, etc.); *buensis* Layard (Vanua Levu, Kio) less rufous above; *layardi* Mayr 1933 (Taviuni) underparts with an ocher wash; *pontifex* Mayr 1933 (Ngamia, Rambi); *vatuana* Mayr 1933 (northern Lau Archipelago) and *nesiotes* Wetmore 1919 (southern Lau Archipelago) larger and with grayer underparts; *heinei* Finsch and Hartlaub (central Tonga Isls.) light and grayish underneath with brownish flanks and white tips on the lateral tail-feathers; *wiglesworthi* Mayr 1933 (Rotuma); *fortunae* Layard (Fotuna and Alofa) smallest and lightest race; *keppeli*

Mayr 1933 (Keppel and Boscawen) very dark brown above, dark mouse gray below.

Feeds in the substage of darkest parts of the forest, gleaning insects from vines and branches (*see also* New Hebrides). Voice a series of whistles with a very human quality, like *wui-wui-wui-wee*. Warning note a quaking *gay-gay-gay*. Spreads the tail when excited and flicks it up and down.

Black-faced Shrikebill (*Clytorhynchus nigrogularis*): Large (8–8½). *Adult male*. Forehead, eye-stripe, face, upper throat black. A silver gray ear-spot. Underparts light gray, whitish on lower abdomen and on border of the black throat. Top of head dark gray; remainder of upperparts, wings, and tail dull olive brown with a gray tinge. Lateral tail-feathers with pale tips. Some birds washed with brown above and below. *Female* and *immature*. All brown, lighter below. Iris brown; bill blackish with white edges; feet gray. Females are apparently indistinguishable from *vitiensis* except for larger size and thicker bills.

The subspecies *nigrogularis* Layard occurs on the larger islands of the Fiji group (Taviuni, Vanua Levu, Viti Levu, Ovalau, and Kandavu). Possibly a bird of the mountain forest.

Vanikoro Broadbill (*Myiagra vanikorensis*): Small (5½). *Adult male*. Head and throat black with greenish blue gloss; wings and tail blackish; back dark gray; breast and abdomen ochraceous buff, richer on the breast. *Female*. Top and sides of head dark gray with a greenish blue gloss; back gray; upper throat whitish, remainder of underparts pale rufous or ocher. Iris brown; bill and feet blue black.

Four subspecies in the Fiji Isls.: *rufiventris* Elliot (northern and northwestern Fiji); *kandavensis* Mayr 1933 (Kandavu group, Mbengha, Vatu Leile) darker; *dorsalis* Mayr 1933 (south-central Fiji and northern Lau group) and *townsendi* Wetmore 1919 (southern Lau group) larger, more richly colored, males more glossy on back and breast.

Common in the lowlands, particularly in second growth and in gardens. Tame. Habits those of the other species of the genus.*

Blue-crested Broadbill (*Myiagra azureocapilla*): Small (6). A pretty flycatcher with white breast and abdomen, an orange bill and a light, sky-blue crest. *Male*. Back and wings bluish slate; tail black, with or without white tips. Upper throat chestnut or golden brown. Forehead and broad band from bill through eye to hind-neck black. Earpatch light blue like top of head. *Female*. Crown dark gray, back rufous brown. Maxilla brownish, mandible orange. Iris brown; feet grayish green. Females differ from *vanikorensis* by the white abdomen, orange mandible, chestnut throat, brownish back, and by having chin, lores, a ring around the eyes, and a patch on the side of the hind-neck white.

Three subspecies: *whitneyi* Mayr 1933 (Viti Levu) and *castaneigularis* Layard (Vanua Lavu) males with golden brown throats and white tips to the tail-feathers; *azureocapilla* Layard (Taviuni) with deep chestnut throat and little white on tail.

Mountain forest, apparently not found below 600 feet. Solitary or in pairs.

*Scarlet Robin (*Petroica multicolor*): *See* Figure 14. Two subspecies in Fiji: *kleinschmidti* Finsch (Viti Levu and Vanua Levu; ? subspecies, Taviuni) and *becki* Mayr 1934 (Kandavu). Pronounced sexual dimorphism in both subspecies.

WHISTLERS

***Golden Whistler** (*Pachycephala pectoralis*): *Cf.* Plate 3: 29, 30. This species is exceedingly diversified in the Fiji Isls. In 3 races the throat is white, separated by a black collar from the lemon-yellow breast and abdomen: *kandavensis* Ramsay (Kandavu group and Mbengha) females ochraceous below, back and tail olive; *vitiensis* Gray (Ngau) black breast collar broad, tail black; females richer ochraceous below; *lauana* Mayr 1932 (Ongea Levu, Fulanga, Wangava) males with a blackish back, females pale underneath.

The males have a black breast band and yellow throat in 5 subspecies: *bella* Mayr 1932 (Vatu Vara) with yellow spot on either side of forehead and golden-yellow abdomen; *koroana* Mayr 1932 (Koro) and *torquata* Layard (Taviuni) no yellow on forehead, females very rufous; *ambigua* Mayr 1932 (Rambi, Kio, and eastern Vanua Levu) and *optata* Hartlaub (Ovalau and easternmost Viti Levu) males with narrow or partly interrupted breast band, females variable, underneath either plain rufous ocher or more or less streaked.

In 2 subspecies the males have no breast band, but yellow foreheads; the females are grayish underneath with fuscous mottling: *graeffii* Hartlaub (Viti Levu, Waia) and *aurantiiventris* Seebohm (Yanganga and most of Vanua Levu).

Habits those of the genus.* Clutch consists of a single egg.

Tonga Whistler (*Pachycephala melanops* Pucheran): Medium (7). *Male.* Head and throat black; remainder of underparts bright golden yellow. Back olive, with a yellow ring across the hind-neck. Tail black, tips of tail-feathers yellow. *Female.* Crown pale gray brown, back and tail olive; throat buffy white; abdomen pale yellow. Iris brown; bill black; feet grayish.

Vavau group and Late, Tonga Isls. Lives in the substage of the true forest. Has a pretty song strophe.

WOOD-SWALLOWS

***White-breasted Wood-Swallow** (*Artamus leucorhynchus*): *Cf.* Plate 3: 31. The black on the throat is restricted to a bib on the upper throat; white tips of tail-feathers conspicuous. The subspecies *mentalis* Jardine is restricted to northern Fiji from Yasawa and Viti Levu to Taviuni and Ngamia. Absent from the Kandavu group, Koro, and the Lau Archipelago.

STARLINGS

Polynesian Starling (*Aplonis tabuensis*): *See* Samoa. Small (7½) with dark gray-brown upperparts and pale gray underparts with whitish streaks. Upper throat and lower belly whitish.

Many subspecies:[2] *brunnescens* Sharpe (Niue) rather brownish, iris ?yellow; *tabuensis* Gmelin (Tonga Isls.) streaks underneath inconspicuous, iris brown, yellow on Turtle Isl. and Ono Ilau; *tenebrosus* Mayr 1942 (Keppel, Boscawen) upperparts sooty, underparts fuscous gray; iris yellow; *nesiotes* Mayr 1942 (Niuafou) large and dark, iris yellow; *fortunae* Layard (Fotuna, Alofa, Uea) iris yellow; *rotumae* Mayr 1942 (Rotuma) pale above and below, iris

[2] For detailed descriptions of these 7 races, *see* Mayr. 1942. *Amer. Mus. Novit.*, no. 1166, p.2–5.

yellow; *vitiensis* Layard (entire Fiji group from Kandavu and Viti Levu to Ongea Levu) iris yellow in eastern Lau Archipelago, brown in western Fiji.

***Indian Myna** (*Acridotheres tristis* Linnaeus): Introduced on many islands of the Fiji group.

HONEY-EATERS

Orange-breasted Honey-eater (*Myzomela jugularis* Peale): Very small (4). Black and scarlet above; scarlet, orange, and whitish below. Nape, rump, and chin scarlet; remainder of upperparts black; lower throat and breast orange or yellow. Flight feathers edged with olive, tail tipped with white. Females duller; immatures without red above. Iris brown; bill and feet red.

Habits those of all small honey-eaters.* Call: *tweet-tweet.* Endemic on Fiji, but found throughout the archipelago, from Kandavu and Yasawa to the Lau group and Turtle Isl. Common everywhere, including gardens in towns and villages.

***Cardinal Honey-eater** (*Myzomela cardinalis*): *Cf.* Plate 3: 36. The strikingly distinct subspecies *chermesina* Gray is restricted to Rotuma. Throat, breast, upper belly, flanks, middle of back, and upper tail-coverts scarlet. Rest of plumage black. Females and immatures duller, more brownish, and with less red in plumage.

Wattled Honey-eater (*Foulehaio carunculata*): *See* Figure 16. Medium (7½). Olive with a short, slightly curved bill. Upperparts darker, top of head somewhat scaly; underparts paler, grayish on the breast, yellowish white on lower abdomen. Females much smaller. Iris brown; bill black; feet blue gray.

Three subspecies: *caruncalata* Gmelin (Samoa, Fotuna and Alofa, Tonga, and Lau Archipelago, eastern Fiji) with an orange wattle on the side of the neck and a tuft of yellow feathers in the ear region; *taviunensis* Wiglesworth (Vanua Levu, Taviuni, and adjacent islands) much darker and grayer, wattle small; *procerior* Finsch and Hartlaub (Ovalau, Viti Levu, and adjacent islands; ?Kandavu) much darker and with a scaly pattern. A stripe of bare skin from the bill to the side of the throat, bordered with black. Inconspicuous yellowish olive ear-patch. For habits, *see* Samoa.

Kandavu Honey-eater (*Xanthotis provocator* Layard): A medium-sized (7½) honey-eater with a golden yellow area around the eye. Top of head dark olive gray, back more brownish with light shaft-streaks. Underparts streaky gray, washed with yellowish on the lower throat, with brownish on the belly. A blackish line separates the yellow eye-patch from the gray upper throat. Iris brown; bill black; feet gray green. A bare fold of skin borders the eye. On the coast and inland. The nest contains one egg only. Endemic on Kandavu Isl.

Giant Forest Honey-eater (*Gymnomyza viridis*): *See* Figure 16. Very large (10½). Olive throughout, wings and tail brighter; a long, curved bill. Iris brown. Two subspecies: *viridis* Layard (Taviuni, Vanua Levu) with bill and legs yellow; *brunneirostris* Mayr 1932 (Viti Levu) with bill and legs blackish brown.

Call: a ringing *kikoo-kikoo-kikoo* or *geeow-geeow*. Restricted to the tall forest, particularly in the mountains. Feeds on nectar, caterpillars and other insects, and on fruit. Shy, usually in high treetops.

WHITE-EYES

The 2 species of white-eyes that occur in the Fijis are rather similar. Both have a brown iris and a well-developed eye-ring; both are small (4–4½). They differ as follows:

Entire upperparts yellowish olive; throat and breast lemon yellow; lores yellow .... *explorator*
Body encircled by a gray belt (darker on back); upper throat greenish yellow; flanks clay color; lores black .... *lateralis*

Layard's White-eye (*Zosterops explorator* Layard): Restricted to the larger islands (Kandavu, Viti Levu, Ovalau, Vanua Levu and Taviuni). Possibly a bird of the hill forest.

***Gray-backed White-eye** (*Zosterops lateralis*): The subspecies *flaviceps* Peale occurs on the main islands from Kandavu to Taviuni and on all the adjacent smaller islands, also on Ngau, Koro, and Moala, but is absent from the entire Lau Archipelago.

WEAVER-FINCHES

Red-headed Parrot-Finch (*Erythrura cyanovirens*): Small (4). Top and sides of head crimson red; rump and tail scarlet. Back, wings, and abdomen grass-green. Upper throat black, lower throat bluish. For habits, *see* Samoa. The subspecies *pealii* Hartlaub is found on Kandavu, Yasawa group (west of Viti Levu), Viti Levu, Vanua Levu, and Taviuni.

Pink-billed Parrot-Finch (*Erythrura kleinschmidti* Finsch): Small (4½) with a large, swollen pinkish yellow bill; face blue black; top of head dark blue; rump and upper tail-coverts light scarlet. Remainder of plumage olive green, lighter below, very bright behind the eye. Iris brown; bill and feet pinkish yellow (flesh color).

Nothing is known about the habits of this highly peculiar bird. It may feed on flower buds and is probably a bird of the true forest (in the mountains?). Endemic on Viti Levu. Rare.

***Red-browed Waxbill** (*Estrilda temporalis*) or ***Astrild** (*Estrilda astrild*): One or the other of these 2 species seems to have been introduced on Viti Levu.

VI

The Land and Fresh-Water Birds of New Caledonia and Loyalty Islands

New Caledonia, with about 68 species of native land and fresh-water birds, has a richer bird fauna than any other island east of the Solomon Islands. Although some of the species represent types widely distributed in the Southwest Pacific, the wealth of the fauna is mostly due to the comparative vicinity of Australia. In addition, there are 18 endemic species not found outside New Caledonia and the Loyalty Islands. This includes the famous Kagu, only representative of a special suborder, perhaps the most peculiar bird of the Southwest Pacific.

The bird fauna of the Loyalty Islands is much like that of New Caledonia but much poorer, with only about 40 species, 2 of which are endemic. Two other Loyalty Islands species, *Hirundo tahitica* and *Erythrura trichroa,* are not known to nest in New Caledonia. It has been decided to combine New Caledonia and the Loyalty Islands in one section, considering the similarities of their faunas.[1]

All species and genera marked with an asterisk are

[1] The most important publications on New Caledonia and the Loyalty Islands are: (1) Layard, E. L. and Layard, E. L. C. 1880. "Notes on the Avifauna of the Loyalty Islands." *Ibis*:220–34. (2) Layard, E. L. and Layard, E. L. C. 1882. "Notes on the Avifauna of New Caledonia." *Ibis*:493–546. (3) Mayr, E. 1940. "On the Birds of the Loyalty Islands." *Amer. Mus. Novit.*, no.1057:1–3. (4) Sarasin, F. 1913. "Die Voegel Neu-Caledoniens und der Loyalty Inseln." In *Nova Caledonia, Zoologie*, 1:1–78.

treated in more detail in the systematic section (Chapter 3, "The Land and Fresh-water Birds of the Southwest Pacific") of Part I.

GREBES

***Australian Dabchick** (*Podiceps novaehollandiae*): New Caledonian grebes are probably representatives of the subspecies *leucosternos* Mayr 1931. Not recorded for more than 50 years. Probably more secretive than rare.

CORMORANTS

***Little Pied Cormorant** (*Phalacrocorax melanoleucus*): The posture, when swimming or resting, at once distinguishes this black and white waterbird from ducks. New Caledonia.

HERONS AND BITTERNS

Five species of this family are found in New Caledonia. They can be separated with the help of the following key:

Key to New Caledonia and Loyalty Isls. Herons and Bitterns

(1) All white, possibly with a few dark gray feathers .... *Demigretta* (white phase)
Not so 2

(2) Grayish black, with white line along throat .... *Demigretta* (normal phase)
Not so 3

(3) Back plain gray 4
Back rufous, brown, or spotted 5

(4) Crown black; underparts grayish .... *Butorides* (ad.)
Face white; neck grayish; abdomen vinaceous rufous ......
.... *Notophoyx*

(5) Underparts streaked 6
Underparts white; rufous brown on throat and breast; crown and hind-neck black; upperparts plain rufous chestnut; rufous or whitish eye-stripe .... *Nycticorax*

(6) Back with whitish spots or streaks; underparts covered with conspicuous well-defined blackish stripes 7
Very large (30). Underparts ocher buff, with brown vermiculation or indistinct streaking. Crown plain dark brown. Middle of back blackish; neck and wings of a fine, salt-and-pepper pattern of buff and brown .... *Botaurus*

(7) Small (14). Very dark; streaks of upperparts fine; streaks below very dense .... *Butorides* (juv.)
Large (21). Dark rufous brown above with large, whitish drop-like spots. Buffy white below with numerous blackish streaks .... *Nycticorax* (juv.)

White-faced Heron (*Notophoyx novaehollandiae*): A medium-sized heron (23). Gray above, with short plumes on the back. Forehead, areas surrounding eye, throat, and middle of fore-neck white. Hind-neck and sides of neck gray. Breast and abdomen vinaceous, deepest (grayish rufous) on breast. Iris pale yellow; bill greenish black, yellow at the lower mandible; feet yellow brown.

Common on tidal flats and along rivers right up to their headwaters, 15–20 miles inland. Call note a noisy croak. Nest usually rather high up in trees, with 3–6 pale green eggs. Feeds as much on insects of all sorts as on crabs and other water animals. Usually feeds along rivers, but during floods also on grass flats. The subspecies *nana* Amadon 1942 is restricted to New Caledonia and Lifu Is.

***Little Mangrove Heron** (*Butorides striatus*): *Cf.* Plate 1: 6. Rare on New Caledonia. Subspecific identification doubtful (?*macrorhynchus* Gould).

***Reef Heron** (*Demigretta sacra*): Occurs on New Caledonia and all 3 Loyalty Isls. (*albolineata* Gray). White individuals of this race are very rare.

***Rufous Night Heron** (*Nycticorax caledonicus*): The New Caledonian subspecies *caledonicus* Gmelin is dull rufous chestnut above. The 2 long white plumes are not worn by all individuals.

Australian Bittern (*Botaurus poiciloptilus* Wagler): Top of head, hind-neck, middle of back, and long stripe along side of head (from bill to neck) blackish brown. A broad ocher eyebrow continues along the neck. Wings and lower back a fine pepper-and-salt mottling of clay color and brownish black. Underparts clay colored with brownish streaks, most pronounced on throat and flanks. Little is known about the habits and distribution of this species on New Caledonia. Probably restricted to lowland marshes and to the reed beds of lakes. Calls much at night.

DUCKS

***Whistling Tree Duck** (*Dendrocygna a. arcuata* Horsfield): Recorded from New Caledonia.

***Australian Gray Duck** (*Anas superciliosa*): *See* Plate 1: 7. Birds from New Caledonia and the Loyalty Isls. are best referred to *pelewensis* Hartlaub and Finsch, although slightly larger. This is the only common duck in New Caledonia. On inland waters, as well as on the seacoast and outlying islands.

Gray Teal (*Anas gibberifrons*): A medium-sized duck (16). More or less brown above, dirty brownish gray below. Throat whitish. Sides of head finely mottled brown and whitish. Wings brown, a conspicuous white patch in front of the black speculum. Iris red; upper bill bluish black, mandible gray with a broad orange patch; feet gray or black. Differs from the Australian Gray Duck by smaller size, by the more grayish, less brownish color, by the absence of an eyebrow, by the white patch on the wing, by the uniformly dark brown shoulder, by the narrow glossy green stripe across the black speculum, and by the black, not brownish or yellowish, feet. Birds from New Caledonia belong to *mathewsi* Phillips 1923. A surface-feeding duck of fresh-water lakes and ponds.

Australian Shoveller (*Spatula rhynchotis*): A rather large fresh-water duck (18), with a typical broadened "shovel" bill. Both male and female are very similar to the American Blue-winged Teal. *Adult male.* A white crescent separates the black forehead and chin from the blue-gray cheeks and sides of the head. Back dark. Underparts, chest, and breast spotted with black; throat blackish; under tail-coverts black. Wing pattern very striking: wing bend pale enamel blue, a white wing-bar, followed by a glossy green speculum. A white patch at the side of the base of the tail. Iris bright yellow; bill olive green; feet orange. *Adult female.* Like the female Australian Gray Duck, but with the bill longer than the head, lacking the striped pattern of the face, having the throat not pure buff, but slightly mottled with black, by having a pale bluish wing bend, and an inconspicuous speculum. New Caledonia (rare).

Australian White-eyed Duck (*Nyroca a. australis* Eyton): *See* New Hebrides. This is the only diving duck found on New Caledonia (rare).

HAWKS

Whistling Eagle-Kite (*Haliastur sphenurus* Vieillot): A large hawk (20–22), dark brown above, pale brown below. Hindneck and underparts with pale (buffy) streaks; lower abdomen dirty white. Iris gray; bill brown; feet yellowish.

Quite similar to the Swamp Harrier, but rump not appreciably lighter than back. Streaking of head and underparts pale, not dark brown. General color fawn brown, not rufous brown. Bars on tail indistinct or missing. Bill much heavier. Tail slightly wedge-shaped. New Caledonia. Most common near the coast and over open country, but found also in the mountains.

White-bellied Hawk (*Accipiter haplochrous* Sclater): A small (12½–15) black and white hawk. Upperparts, wings, tail, and throat blackish slate color. Remainder of underparts white. Iris red or orange; bill black with yellow cere; legs and feet yellow. *Immature.* Blackish above with inconspicuous rufous barring and a fairly conspicuous buff collar across the hind-neck. Underparts creamy white, with narrow black streaking on face and throat, with bold black spots on the breast, and with black bars across belly, flanks, thighs, and underside of the tail. New Caledonia. In the mountain and lowland forest. Feeds mostly on rather large birds, such as parrots, pigeons, and domestic poultry, but also on mice, lizards, grasshoppers, and other insects.

Australian Goshawk (*Accipiter fasciatus*): A medium-sized hawk, male 15, female 18. Upperparts dull gray-brown with an indistinct rufous collar across the hind-neck. Underparts pale grayish rufous, more gray on throat, more rufous on thighs, finely barred with white. Iris brown; bill black; cere greenish; legs and feet yellowish. Immatures are similar to *haplochrous,* but are rufous brown, not blackish, above, with brown, not black spots and bars below and with rather rufous thighs. Legs and feet greenish yellow. Occurs on New Caledonia, the Loyalty Isls., on Aneiteum and Rennell Isls. (*vigilax* Wetmore 1926). Prefers second growth, grasslands, and edge of forest to true forest. Feeds on birds, lizards, grasshoppers, and other insects. Wary and silent.

***Swamp Harrier** (*Circus approximans*): Could be confused with the Whistling Eagle-Kite. *See* that species for differential diagnosis. Common on New Caledonia and recorded from Lifu and Uvea (*approximans* Peale).

OSPREYS OR FISH HAWKS

***Osprey** (*Pandion haliaetus*): Recorded from New Caledonia. Usually nests on small offshore islands or near the coast. Breeds July–September.

FALCONS

***Peregrine Falcon** (*Falco peregrinus nesiotes* Mayr): The black upperparts and the buffy or rufous underparts, barred (adults) or streaked (immatures) with black, are diagnostic. Black "side-whiskers." New Caledonia and Uvea (Beaupré Isl.)

BUTTON-QUAILS

Painted Button-Quail (*Turnix varia*): A small (7), quail-like, terrestrial grassland bird. Upperparts blackish, mottled with chestnut, whitish, and gray. A chestnut patch on the sides of throat and breast. Upper throat white; breast pale gray with buff spots; abdomen buff. A gray-brown line along the middle of the head and a buffy white eye-stripe. Iris red; feet orange; bill slaty blue. The subspecies *novaecaledoniae* Ogilvie-Grant is found on New Caledonia only. Probably more elusive than rare.

RAILS[2]

***Banded Rail** (*Rallus philippensis*): The New Caledonian subspecies *swindellsi* Mathews 1911 is characterized by having the upperparts rather olive brown with little white barring. The rufous breast band is usually present. New Caledonia and all 3 Loyalty Isls. Also outlying islands, like Huon Isl. and Chesterfield Isls.

New Caledonian Wood Rail (*Tricholimnas lafresnayanus* Verreaux and des Murs): A large (17) rail with a long bill (2). Upperparts dull olive brown, deep chestnut brown on wings and tail. Indications of a buff eyebrow. Upper throat whitish; remainder of underparts dusky gray, blackish on

[2] *See* New Hebrides for a key of the 4 common species.

lower abdomen. Iris crimson; bill and legs dark brown. New Caledonia.

This woodland rail is almost or entirely flightless. It is nocturnal and feeds on worms and snails. All the records seem to be from southwestern New Caledonia. It may now be extinct, since it does not seem to have been collected during the past 50 years.

***Sooty Rail** (*Porzana tabuensis*): New Caledonia, not yet reported from the Loyalty Isls.

***White-browed Rail** (*Poliolimnas cinereus*): Recorded from New Caledonia and from Lifu (*tannensis* Forster).

***Purple Swamphen** (*Porphyrio porphyrio*): *See* Plate 1: 10. Found on New Caledonia and the 3 Loyalty Isls. (*caledonicus* Sarasin 1913).

KAGUS (FAMILY RHYNOCHETIDAE)

Kagu (*Rhynochetos jubatus* Verreaux and des Murs): Large (22–23). Upperparts light ash-gray, washed with brownish on back and wings, a conspicuous pale gray crest. Underparts pale buffy gray. Wing-feathers with broad black, white, and chestnut bars, which are very conspicuous when wing is spread. Iris red; bill and feet orange red.

Restricted to the large forests in the southern third of New Caledonia and threatened with extinction. Being flightless and confiding, Kagus fall easy prey to marauding dogs. Nest with single egg on the ground; breeding season from August to January. Voice *ua-ua-ua,* resembling the barking of a small dog, also a deep *gooo.* Most active at night, lying concealed and asleep during the day in its rocky retreats. Feeds on worms and snails.

PIGEONS AND DOVES

Six species are known from the New Caledonian area; 2 predominantly green doves (*Ptilinopus* and *Drepanoptila*), 2 large fruit pigeons (*Ducula*), a true pigeon (*Columba*), and a small ground dove (*Chalcophaps*).

*****Red-bellied Fruit Dove** (*Ptilinopus greyii* Bonaparte): Recorded from New Caledonia, Uvea, and Lifu. Possibly only a visitor on most of New Caledonia. Seasonal movements poorly known. Breeds in August.

Cloven-feathered Dove (*Drepanoptila holosericea* Temminck): A large (10–11), green fruit dove. Middle of upper throat white. A black bar separates the green breast from the yellowish olive abdomen. Vent and under tail-coverts bright yellow. A few indistinct whitish gray bars across wing and tail. Female like the male but smaller with most of abdomen greenish. Iris brown or crimson. Bill blackish green; legs dark carmine. The most beautiful of the endemic New Caledonian pigeons. Mountain forest and savanna forest. Habits poorly described. Has a loud booming call, but is otherwise very inconspicuous.

*****Pacific Pigeon** (*Ducula p. pacifica* Gmelin): *See* Plate 2: 13. Rather rare on New Caledonia and the Loyalty Isls. (Lifu). Casual visitor to Uvea. Not definitely known to nest in the area.

Giant Pigeon (*Ducula goliath* Gray): A very large (20), long-tailed pigeon. Throat, breast, and upperparts blackish slate gray. Tail partly blackish, partly chestnut. Abdomen chestnut; vent and under tail-coverts buffy white. Iris orange; bill and feet deep crimson. Owing to steady persecution more and more restricted to the mountain forests and other remote locations. Loud booming voice. Food, nesting, etc., like other *Ducula*. Endemic on New Caledonia.

***White-throated Pigeon** (*Columba vitiensis*): *Adult male.* Throat and cheeks white; top of head, hind-neck, and underparts purple chestnut; rest of plumage blackish slate gray. *Female.* Grayish below, even throat sometimes grayish. New Caledonia, Lifu, and Uvea (*hypoenochroa* Gould). Seems to migrate between these islands.

Green-winged Ground Pigeon (*Chalcophaps indica*): *See* New Hebrides. Birds from New Caledonia belong to the subspecies *chrysochlora* Wagler; those from the Loyalty Isls. (Uvea, Lifu, Maré) seem to belong to *sandwichensis* Ramsay.

PARROTS AND LORIES

Four species of this family are known from New Caledonia.

Key to New Caledonia and Loyalty Isls. Parrots and Lories

(1) Underparts mostly green 2
Breast red, barred with blackish; a pale green collar across the hind-neck .... *Trichoglossus haematodus*

(2) Small (7–8). All green; vent red; top of head bluish .... *Vini*
Large (11–13). Crown partly red; wings and tail partly bluish 3

(3) Cheeks and chin green; no crest; red spot behind the eye;

hind-neck green .... *Cyanorhamphus novaezelandiae*
Cheeks and chin blackish; a crest of a few elongated feathers; no red spot behind the eye, hind-neck yellowish or green .... *Eunymphicus cornutus*

***Coconut Lory** (*Trichoglossus haematodus*): *See* Plate 2: 16. New Caledonia, Lifu, and Uvea (*deplanchei* Verreaux and des Murs).

New Caledonian Lorikeet (*Vini diadema* Verreaux and des Murs): This small lorikeet is known only from 2 females, collected nearly 100 years ago. It lives presumably in the mountain forests of northern New Caledonia. In habits like the other species of *Vini*. Should be looked for in large flowering trees (*Erythrina,* etc.).

Red-fronted Parakeet (*Cyanorhamphus novaezelandiae*): Medium (11½). Dark green above; yellowish green below. Anterior part of head and spot behind the eyes crimson. Wings bluish; tail green, washed with blue. Iris red, bill blue gray; feet blackish. The subspecies *saisseti* Verreaux and des Murs lives in the mountain forests of northern New Caledonia. Feeds on seeds, often on the ground. A quiet and rather rare bird; usually seen singly or in pairs.

Crested Parakeet (*Eunymphicus cornutus*): The subspecies *cornutus* Gmelin (New Caledonia) has a crest of 2 black feathers tipped with red. The ear region and the hind-neck are yellowish. The entire forepart of the crown is red and the face is sooty black. The subspecies *uveaensis* Layard (Uvea Isl.) has a crest of 6 green feathers; ear region and hind-neck are green; only the middle of the forehead is red and the face is blackish green. Iris orange; bill blue with black tip;

feet black. Partial to tall forest, particularly the Kauri pine forests of north-central New Caledonia. Feeds on various kinds of flowers, nuts, and seeds. Generally seen in pairs or small family parties. Rather silent and wary.

CUCKOOS

*__Fan-tailed Cuckoo__ (*Cacomantis pyrrhophanus*): The subspecies *pyrrhophanus* Vieillot breeds in New Caledonia and the Loyalty Isls. (Uvea, Lifu, Maré). Underparts deep rufous; upperparts black with a green gloss. Tail feathers notched with white along their edges. *Lalage, Pachycephala,* and *Myiagra* are the chief foster parents in the Loyalty Isls.

*__Shining Cuckoo__ (*Chalcites lucidus layardi* Mathews): New Caledonia and Loyalty Isls. (Maré, Lifu, Uvea). Breeding season, September–December (?). *See* New Hebrides.

*__Long-tailed New Zealand Cuckoo__ (*Eudynamis taitensis* Sparrman): *See* Figure 8. Passes through New Caledonia and the Loyalty Isls. on migration. Differs from the immature New Caledonian hawks by the prominent rufous bars of upperparts and tail, by being smaller and much more slender, and by being streaked below without any crossbars. Posture and behavior are, of course, also distinct.

BARN OWLS

Two species of barn owls are the only owls found on New Caledonia. The distinguishing features of the 2 species are about as follows:

(A) Very whitish below; prevailing color of upperparts pale grayish (with a little rufous and some black and white mottling). Near caves, cliffs, hollow trees, or human habitations .... *alba*

(B) Underparts more or less washed with buff or rufous. Upperparts dark, more or less brown with large orange-buff and small whitish spots. Legs very long. Lives in grasslands .... *longimembris*

***Barn Owl** (*Tyto alba*): *Cf.* Figure 9. The subspecies *lifuensis* Brasil 1916 is restricted to New Caledonia and the Loyalty Isls. (Uvea, Lifu, Maré).

Grass Owl (*Tyto longimembris*): Underparts with a scattering of black spots. Wings and tail barred dark brown and orange rufous. Facial disc buff. Iris brown; bill yellowish horn color; feet dirty white. A rare and elusive inhabitant of the grasslands. Nests on the ground. Reveals its presence by its harsh calls during the night (probably subspecies *oustaleti* Hartlaub).

OWLET-NIGHTJARS

New Caledonian Aegotheles (*Aegotheles savesi* Layard): A large (11) nightjar-like bird. Brownish black above, paler below, all feathers with numerous fine grayish bars. Top of head blackish; a pale grayish band across the hind-neck (i.e. nuchal collar). Known only from a single specimen collected on New Caledonia in 1880. Apparently a geographical representative of the Australian species *cristatus* and probably with similar habits.

NIGHTJARS

White-throated Nightjar (*Eurostopodus mystacalis*): Large (10). Upperparts dark; back gray with bold black, brown, and rufous spots and bars. Top of head black. Wing-feathers black with a white spot. Throat black with narrow rufous bars; a conspicuous white patch on either side of the throat. Rest of underparts barred black and rusty ocher. The subspecies *exul* Mayr 1941 is known from a single specimen from Tao, northwestern New Caledonia. Habits and call note probably similar to that of the Australian race *mystacalis* Temminck.

SWIFTS

***White-rumped Swiftlet** (*Collocalia spodiopygia*): *Cf.* Plate 2: 20. New Caledonia and all 3 Loyalty Isls. (*leucopygia* Gray).

***Glossy Swiftlet** (*Collocalia esculenta*): The subspecies *uropygialis* Wallace (New Caledonia and all 3 Loyalty Isls.) has a white rump like *spodiopygia,* but differs by the glossy blue color of the back and the white on the lower abdomen. It is more a bird of the edge of the forest and of clearings than of the open grasslands.

KINGFISHERS

***Sacred Kingfisher** (*Halcyon sancta*): The subspecies *canacorum* Brasil 1916 is restricted to New Caledonia, the subspecies *macmillani* Mayr 1940 to the Loyalty Isls. (Maré, Lifu,

Uvea). Both races have the same field characters as the species. Nesting season, November–January.

SONGBIRDS

Twenty-four species of native songbirds are known from New Caledonia and 19 species from the Loyalty Isls. Fourteen of these are common to both areas, although sometimes subspecifically distinct. Only on New Caledonia (and not in the Loyalty Isls.) are found the following species: *Coracina analis, Megalurulus mariei, Eopsaltria flaviventris, Clytorhynchus pachycephaloides, Pachycephala rufiventris, Corvus moneduloides* (introduced on Maré), *Gymnomyza aubryana, Guadalcanaria undulata, Myzomela dibapha,* and *Erythrura psittacea.* Only in the Loyalty Isls. (but not on New Caledonia) are found 5 species: *Hirundo tahitica, Myzomela cardinalis, Zosterops minuta, Zosterops inornata,* and *Erythrura trichroa.* In addition there are a few introduced species.

An artificial key for all these species would be cumbersome, particularly if the various subspecies, female and immature plumages are included. The following rough color key will narrow down the number of possible alternatives and will help the observer to speed up his identifications.

Color Key to New Caledonian Songbirds

Species with red (including pink or scarlet) in plumage: *Myzomela cardinalis, Myzomela dibapha, Erythrura trichroa, Erythrura psittacea, Estrilda temporalis.*

Species with yellow, green, or olive: *Gerygone flavolateralis, Eopsaltria flaviventris, Pachycephala pectoralis, Lichmera incana,*

Myzomela (2 species), *Zosterops* (4 species), *Erythrura* (2 species), *Estrilda temporalis.*

Species with dark gray, soft black, or glossy black: *Hirundo tahitica, Lalage leucopyga, Coracina* (2 species), *Turdus poliocephalus, Rhipidura* (2 species), *Myiagra caledonica* (♂), *Pachycephala* (♂) (2 species), *Artamus leucorhynchus, Aplonis striatus, Acridotheres tristis, Corvus moneduloides, Gymnomyza aubryana, Myzomela* (♂) (2 species), *Zosterops lateralis.*

Species with brown or rust color in plumage: *Hirundo tahitica, Lalage leucopyga* (♀), *Coracina analis, Turdus poliocephalus, Pachycephala pectoralis* (♀), *Pachycephala rufiventris, Acridotheres tristis, Philemon diemenensis, Megalurulus mariei.*

Species with white in plumage (including wing and tail): *Lalage leucopyga, Turdus poliocephalus pritzbueri, Megalurulus mariei, Rhipidura* (2 species), *Myiagra caledonica, Gerygone flavolateralis, Clytorhynchus pachycephaloides* (very small amount of white), *Eopsaltria flaviventris, Pachycephala* (2 species), *Artamus leucorhynchus, Philemon diemenensis* (very small amount of white), *Guadalcanaria undulata, Myzomela dibapha, Zosterops* (very small amount of white).

SWALLOWS

***Pacific Swallow** (*Hirundo tahitica subfusca* Gould): *See* Plate 3: 23. Common on Uvea, rarer on Lifu and Maré. A single sight record of a straggler from New Caledonia.

CUCKOO-SHRIKES

The family is represented on New Caledonia by 3 species, one black-and-white triller (*Lalage*) and 2 large graybirds

(*Coracina*). The triller and one graybird occur also in the Loyalty Isls.

**Long-tailed Triller* (*Lalage leucopyga*): Small (6½). The subspecies *montrosieri* Verreaux and des Murs is restricted to New Caledonia; *simillima* Sarasin 1913 occurs in the Loyalty Isls. (Maré, Lifu, Uvea) and southern New Hebrides (Aneiteum, Tanna, Erromanga). Very common and conspicuous. Breeds from August to November.

Mountain Graybird (*Coracina analis* Verreaux and des Murs): A rather large (11) gray bird with a heavy bill and a fairly long tail. Under tail-coverts chestnut brown. Iris brown; bill and feet black. A bird of the mountain forest, from 600 feet up; usually in rather high trees. Otherwise in habits much like the following species.

***Melanesian Graybird** (*Coracina caledonica*): The New Caledonian subspecies (*caledonica* Gmelin) is dark gray in the adult plumage; juveniles have wing and tail edged with white and the under tail-coverts barred with black and white. Iris yellow. Differs from *analis* by larger size (13) and the blackish gray under tail-coverts. The Loyalty Isls. subspecies *lifuensis* Tristram (on Lifu only!) is darker, more blackish slate. In the forest, both lowlands and mountains. Feeds mainly on large insects, particularly the coconut locust.

THRUSHES

***Island Thrush** (*Turdus poliocephalus*): The New Caledonian subspecies *xanthopus* Forster is a sooty brown bird with a peculiar deep vinaceous red wash of the underparts.

The head is paler brown. Bill and feet yellow. The 2 subspecies from the Loyalty Isls. are very different: Lifu Isl. (*pritzbueri* Layard) head and throat creamy or buffy white, rest of plumage sooty black, in adult males; in females head and throat are brownish gray; in immatures the whole body is brownish or rufous brown, often with spots on the underparts and with a whitish lower belly; probably now extinct. Maré Isl. (*mareensis* Layard and Tristram) sooty brown throughout, paler underneath, usually some white on lower belly; young like those of *pritzbueri;* probably now extinct.

WARBLERS

New Caledonian Grass Warbler (*Megalurulus mariei* Verreaux): Small (7) with a long tail. Upperparts brown; more rufous on crown, wings, and tail; more olive gray on back. A conspicuous white eye-stripe from bill to nape. Underparts white, flanks brown. Often a faint rufous breast band. Iris brown; bill black; feet yellowish horn color. Inside of mouth and throat black. Found on New Caledonia only. Lives in the grassland and open heathlands, lowlands, and hills. Calls not infrequently, either a sharp *tzik* or a note like the purr of a kitten. Breeding season probably October–November.

Fantail Warbler (*Gerygone flavolateralis*): *See* New Hebrides. The subspecies *flavolateralis* Gray (New Caledonia, Maré) has the same field characters as the New Hebrides race. Differs from the 3 species of *Zosterops* by much smaller size, the gray head, the grayish white throat, and the white spots on the tail-feathers. The abdomen is pale lemon yellow.

The subspecies *lifuensis* Sarasin 1913 (Lifu, Uvea) has less white on the tail. More common in open country than in mountains and true forest.

FLYCATCHERS

Spotted Fantail (*Rhipidura spilodera*): *Cf.* Plate 3: 26. *See* New Hebrides. Smaller (6½). Abdomen clay color; black spots on breast contrast with white throat; tips of lateral tail-feathers buffy, not white. These are the field characters of the New Caledonian subspecies *verreauxi* Marie in comparison with typical *spilodera.* Common throughout New Caledonia, Lifu, and Maré. Accidental on Uvea.

Collared Fantail (*Rhipidura fuliginosa*): *See* New Hebrides. Found on New Caledonia and Lifu (*bulgeri* Layard). Prefers to feed in fairly high trees. Often clings to the bark of big branches or tree trunks.

Broad-billed Flycatcher (*Myiagra caledonica*): The field characters of the following 3 subspecies are the same as of the New Hebrides races: (1) *caledonica* Bonaparte (New Caledonia), (2) *viridinitens* Gray (Uvea, Lifu), (3) *melanura* Gray (Maré). They differ slightly in size and in the width of the white margin of the tail-feathers.

Southern Shrikebill (*Clytorhynchus pachycephaloides*): *See* New Hebrides. The subspecies *pachycephaloides* Elliot (New Caledonia only) differs from *grisescens* by the dark gray lores and by the buffy, instead of pure white, tips of the tail-feathers. Under tail-coverts light buff.

Yellow-bellied Robin (*Eopsaltria flaviventris* Sharpe): Small (5½). Upperparts dark brownish gray, with an olive wash on back, wings, and tail. Throat and breast dirty white with indistinct grayish streaking. Lores whitish. Belly bright lemon yellow. Male and female alike. Differs from the male of *Pachycephala caledonica* by the lemon (not orange) belly, by lacking the black breast band, and by having back and tail dirty olive gray, not greenish olive.

A frequent and tame forest bird. Hops through low bushes with drooping wings and tail. Often feeds on the ground. Cup-shaped nest (2 eggs) on low bushes, ferns, etc.

WHISTLERS

New Caledonian Whistler (*Pachycephala caledonica* Gmelin): Medium (6–6½). *Adult male.* Head gray; throat white. Back, wings, and tail (brownish) olive; abdomen ocherish orange yellow. Narrow black breast band. *Female.* Grayish olive brown above; pale gray brown below; throat white. Juveniles with much rufous on wings. New Caledonia, lowlands and mountains. Habits like those of *Pachycephala pectoralis.*

***Loyalty Islands Golden Whistler** (*Pachycephala pectoralis littayei* Layard): *Cf.* Plate 3: 29, 30. Medium (7½). *Male.* Head black; throat white. Back, wings, and tail olive green; abdomen bright yellow. Black breast band. *Female.* Back olive; wings and tail brownish olive. Top of head dusky gray, sides hair-brown. A narrow greenish yellow band separates the white throat from the yellow breast and abdomen. Lifu and Uvea, in the true forest. A tree bird. Very fond of snails.

Rufous-bellied Whistler (*Pachycephala rufiventris*): Small (5½–6). *Adult male.* Upper side slate gray, more blackish on head, wings, and tail. White throat separated from rufous belly by black breast band. *Female* and *immature*. Paler gray above. Throat white; belly buff or pale rufous ocher; throat, breast, and flanks with narrow blackish streaks. Iris red brown; bill and feet black. The subspecies *xanthetraea* Forster is restricted to New Caledonia. A bird of the open country (heaths, etc.). Prefers low bushes to tall trees. Feeds occasionally on the ground or sallies out from a perch like a flycatcher. Voice like that of *caledonica,* but softer.

WOOD-SWALLOWS

***White-breasted Wood-Swallow** (*Artamus leucorhynchus*): *See* Plate 3: 31. The subspecies *melanoleucus* Wagler occurs in New Caledonia, Maré and Lifu.

STARLINGS

Glossy Starling (*Aplonis striatus*): Black with a bluish or blue-green gloss. Tail short; bill short, thick, and with a strongly curved culmen. Females grayish. Iris red orange; bill and feet black.

The New Caledonian subspecies *striatus* Gmelin is smaller (7), the males with a more greenish gloss, the females purer gray (very pale on lower abdomen, more blackish on head, wings, and tail). The Loyalty Isls. subspecies *atronitens* Gray is larger (7½), the gloss of the males is bluish, the females are darker slate gray, with a more pronounced gloss, particularly on the upperparts (Maré, Lifu, Uvea).

Typical starlings. In tall and low trees, in the true forest, and in gardens and plantations. Feeds on fruits, also on insects and on land snails. Rather musical call note ("flute-like whistle"). Usually in flocks of 8 or 10 birds. Nests in hollows in trees. Lays 2–4 eggs. The nesting season is from September to January.

*Indian Myna (*Acridotheres tristis* Linnaeus): Introduced on New Caledonia.

CROWS

New Caledonian Crow (*Corvus moneduloides* Lesson): An entirely black small crow. Female (15) smaller than male (17). Bill short, cone shaped. Entire plumage with a slight bluish or purplish gloss. Iris brown. New Caledonia and (introduced on) Maré. In pairs or small flocks, softly calling *wa-wa*. Feeds on insects, fruits, nuts, snails, and almost anything else that is edible. Breeding season, September–November. Nest usually contains only 2 eggs.

HONEY-EATERS

Scarlet Honey-eater (*Myzomela dibapha*): Small (4). *Male*. Head, middle of back, rump, throat, and breast scarlet red. Lores, wings, and tail black. Flanks and belly dirty white. Iris brown; bill and feet black. *Female* and *immature*. Brownish gray above with a slight olive tinge, grayish buff below, whiter on the belly. Rump cinnamon; forehead and throat washed with scarlet. The subspecies *caledonica* Forbes is restricted to New Caledonia. Habits like other *Myzomela*.*

***Cardinal Honey-eater** (*Myzomela cardinalis*): *Cf.* Plate 3: 36. The Loyalty Isls. subspecies *lifuensis* Layard is small (4½) and has the scarlet of the underparts restricted to the upper throat. In immature males the black parts are brownish, cream color, or gray. Females have no scarlet in plumage except an imperceptible wash on the top of the head. Upperparts dark olive gray. Throat grayish; breast and abdomen dirty cream white (or grayish). Maré, Lifu, Uvea.

Silver-eared Honey-eater (*Lichmera incana*): *Cf.* Figure 16. *See* New Hebrides. The subspecies *incana* Latham is smaller (5–6) than *flavotincta*. The greenish olive of wing and tail contrasts with the dark brownish olive of the back, the ash gray of the throat, and the yellowish white belly. Females slightly washed with greenish underneath. New Caledonia and Loyalty Isls. (Maré, Lifu, Uvea).

Barred Honey-eater (*Guadalçanaria undulata* Sparrman): Small (7–8). Upperparts grayish brown; underparts whitish with narrow gray-brown bars, particularly on the breast. Sides of head and neck brown with narrow white bars. Edge of wing-feathers olive. Iris brown; bill black (slender and well curved); feet blue gray. Differs from *Lichmera* by larger size, the white, crossbarred underparts, and the darker, less greenish upperparts. New Caledonia, particularly in the mountain forest. Singly or in small parties; call a flute-like whistle. In flowering trees.

Crow Honey-eater (*Gymnomyza aubryana* Verreaux and des Murs): Very large (16). Long, graduated tail; bill curved. Entirely black; naked skin around eye and a wattle back of it reddish orange to bright yellow. Young birds with a tuft of yellow feathers in the ear-region. Iris brown; bill black (grayish horn color below); feet yellowish horn color. Hill and mountain forests of New Caledonia. Has a ringing call note.

New Caledonian Friarbird (*Philemon diemenensis* Lesson): Large (11½). Brownish ash gray below; breast feathers long, narrowly pointed, silvery white. Back brown; edges of wings and tail-feathers pale bluish gray. Feathers on top of head with gray edging. A "moustache," as dark as upperparts. Eyes brown; bill black; feet dark gray blue or dark brown. Lives in the forest but visits gardens and open country. Feeds on fruits and insects. A bold, pugnacious bird with loud, varied calls. All New Caledonia, Maré, and Lifu.

WHITE-EYES

Four species are found in this area, 3 of which occur on Lifu, 2 on New Caledonia and Maré, and 1 only on Uvea. They may be distinguished by the following characters:

Key to New Caledonian and Loyalty Isls. White-Eyes

(1) Back yellowish green or olive; legs grayish; broad white eye-ring; brown of flanks inconspicuous 2
Back gray or dusky gray; legs yellowish or brown 3

(2) Forehead and upperparts dark olive green; throat, breast, and under tail-coverts yellowish green; abdomen dirty white . ... *Zosterops xanthochroa* (New Caledonia, Maré)
Forehead, throat, breast, middle of abdomen and under tail-coverts yellow; upperparts bright olive .... *Z. minuta* (Lifu only)

(3) Large (5½). White eye-ring missing. Top of head green; back dark gray; wings and tail green; throat pale greenish; breast greenish gray; abdomen dirty white; flanks grayish rufous .... *Z. inornata* (Lifu only)

Smaller (4½–5). Broad white eye-ring. Top of head olive or blackish. Back and mantle clear gray; wings and tail olive. Throat olive or yellowish olive; breast gray; abdomen and under tail-coverts white .... *Z. lateralis* (all islands)

Small Lifu White-eye (*Zosterops minuta* Layard): Small (4–4½). The yellowish color is characteristic for this species. It looks exactly like an intermediate between *xanthochroa* and the New Hebrides species *flavifrons*. Legs and feet gray brown. Lifu only.

Green-backed White-eye (*Zosterops xanthochroa* Gray): Small (4½–5). Ranges high into the mountains. New Caledonia and Maré. Feeds on insects and lantana berries.

***Gray-backed White-eye** (*Zosterops lateralis*): Three races of this widespread species occur in this area: *griseonota* Gray (New Caledonia) with breast rather grayish, brownish wash of flanks inconspicuous; *melanops* Gray (Lifu) with top and sides of head blackish, back rather dark gray, breast distinctly gray, the olive colors rather dark; *nigrescens* Sarasin 1913 (Maré, Uvea) intermediate between the other 2. Common in native gardens and other open country, also in the true forest.

Large Lifu White-eye (*Zosterops inornata* Layard): Large size, long bill, dark color, and absence of eye-ring are diagnostic. Upper bill black, mandible reddish horn color; legs yellowish flesh color. Fairly numerous. Differs from *Lichmera* by its heavier body, greenish throat and head, yellowish mandible and feet, less-curved bill, and shorter tail. Shy. "Call like that of a *Pachycephala*." A forest bird, rarely or never found in native gardens.

WEAVER-FINCHES

Red-throated Parrot-Finch (*Erythrura psittacea* Gmelin): Small (4½). Dark green, except for bright crimson head and throat, and scarlet rump and tail. Tail long; finch-like bill blackish brown; iris and feet dark brown. Female like male, but duller. Immatures pale gray green below, with a green head and with little scarlet on the throat. New Caledonia. Second growth, grassland, and other open country. Usually in flocks, but in pairs during the breeding season. Feeds mainly on grass seeds, also on *Casuarina* seeds. Breeding season, August–November. Seven to 8 white eggs are placed in large roundish nest.

***Blue-faced Parrot-Finch** (*Erythrura trichroa*): The subspecies *cyaneifrons* Layard occurs in the New Hebrides (for which *see*) and on Lifu, Loyalty Isls., but not on New Caledonia.

***Red-browed Waxbill** (*Estrilda temporalis* Latham): Introduced on New Caledonia. Common in grasslands.

VII

The Land and Fresh-Water Birds of the New Hebrides and Banks Islands[1]

THERE are about 54 native species of land and fresh-water birds known from this region. The Banks Islands belong zoologically to the New Hebrides; in fact not a single species of bird occurs on these islands that is not also known from the New Hebrides. However, both the Banks Islands and the southern New Hebrides (Erromanga, Tanna, Aneiteum) have a poorer fauna than the central islands (Efate and particularly Espiritu Santo).

All species and genera marked with an asterisk are treated in more detail in the systematic section (Chapter 3, "The Land and Fresh-Water Birds of the Southwest Pacific") of Part I.

GREBES

***Australian Dabchick** (*Podiceps novaehollandiae*): The New Hebrides subspecies (*leucosternos* Mayr 1931) has been recorded from Dolphin Isl., Espiritu Santo, and Gaua.

HERONS

Only 2 species are known from the New Hebrides. They cannot be mistaken for any other bird since no storks or cranes occur in the area.

[1] All literature on birds of the New Hebrides is either strictly technical or refers only to a single species; it has therefore not been listed.

***Little Mangrove Heron** (*Butorides striatus*): *See* Plate 1: 6. Seems to be rare in the New Hebrides and has been reported only from Santo and from the Torres group (Hiu) (probably *diminutus* Mayr 1940).

***Reef Heron** (*Demigretta sacra*): Occurs throughout the New Hebrides and Banks Isls. The white phase seems exceptional.

DUCKS

***Australian Gray Duck** (*Anas superciliosa pelewensis* Hartlaub and Finsch): *See* Plate 1: 7. This is the only common duck in the New Hebrides.

Australian White-eyed Duck (*Nyroca australis*): Head and breast chestnut brown; back and wings dull brown. White areas: a broad belly band, the under tail-coverts, and a wing-stripe. Iris white; bill bluish. Females are duller brown with a brown iris. Differs from the Australian Gray Duck by the uniformly rufous brown head, by the color of the speculum, and by its habits.

The subspecies *extima* Mayr 1940 has been recorded from the Banks Isls. (Gaua) and New Hebrides (Santo, Erromanga, Tanna). This diving duck seems to be restricted to a few fresh-water lakes and lowland streams.

HAWKS

Australian Goshawk (*Accipiter fasciatus*): *See* New Caledonia. Reported in the New Hebrides only from Aneiteum (*vigilax* Wetmore 1926).

***Swamp Harrier** (*Circus approximans*): The subspecies *approximans* Peale has been reported from Aneiteum, Tanna, Erromanga, Efate, and Santo.

FALCONS

***Peregrine Falcon** (*Falco peregrinus*): Recorded from Efate, Erromanga, and Tanna (*nesiotes* Mayr 1941).

MEGAPODES

***Incubator Bird** (*Megapodius freycinet*): The subspecies *layardi* Tristram occurs on the Banks Isls., northern and central New Hebrides, south to Efate.

RAILS

The 4 species of rails of the New Hebrides are easily told apart. The largest is the Purple Swamphen, of the size of a fowl, with a heavy red bill and red legs. The plumage is uniformly dark (purple or blackish) except for the white under tail-coverts. The Banded Rail has a whitish gray superciliary, black and white barred flanks, and mottled upperparts. The White-browed Rail is long-legged, but with a body the size of a thrush. The whitish gray underparts, brownish back, white eyebrow, and black line through the eye are diagnostic. The small Sooty Rail, not much bigger than a sparrow, is grayish black below and dark rufous brown above. No endemic rails are known from the New Hebrides in addition to these 4 widespread species.

***Banded Rail** (*Rallus philippensis*): The subspecies *seth-smithi* Mathews 1911 probably occurs on all the islands but has been reported so far only from Pentecost, Santo, Epi, Efate, Erromanga, Tanna, and Aneiteum.

***Sooty Rail** (*Porzana tabuensis*): This secretive rail has been recorded in the New Hebrides only from Tanna and Aneiteum (*tabuensis* Gmelin).

***White-browed Rail** (*Poliolimnas cinereus*): In the New Hebrides recorded only from Tanna (*tannensis* Forster).

***Purple Swamphen** (*Porphyrio porphyrio*): *See* Plate 1: 10. The subspecies *aneiteumensis* Tristram probably occurs throughout the Banks Isls. and New Hebrides, but has been recorded so far only from Santo, Malekula, Efate, Erromanga, Tanna, and Aneiteum.

PIGEONS AND DOVES

Eight species of this family are represented in the New Hebrides.

Key to New Hebrides and Banks Isls. Pigeons and Doves

(1) Small (8–9). Terrestrial or in low bushes 2
Small or large. Arboreal 3

(2) Mantle bright glossy green; no distinct breast shield; bill orange .... *Chalcophaps*
Mantle purplish brown or olive brown; throat and breast shield vinaceous white (♂), or tawny cinnamon (♀); bill black .... *Gallicolumba*

(3) Short-tailed. Small (7–11); prevailing color green 4

Rather long-tailed. Medium or large; prevailing color gray or brown 5

(4) Very small (7–9). Adults with red crown and spot on belly; reddish orange under tail-coverts .... *Ptilinopus greyii*
Larger (9½–11). Head yellowish olive; some inner wing-feathers with yellow tips; under tail-coverts pale yellow with green tips; no red in plumage .... *Ptilinopus tannensis*

(5) Bill red; cheeks and throat pure white .... *Columba*
Bill blackish; cheeks and throat not pure white 6

(6) Smaller. Tail as long as body; normally dark rufous brown above, cinnamon below .... *Macropygia*
Larger. Tail half as long as body; head grayish 7

(7) Head and neck ash gray. Mantle, wings, and tail dull glossy greenish or bluish black; underparts vinaceous gray; under tail-coverts chestnut. Large black knob at base of bill .... *Ducula pacifica*
Head, back, and wings blackish slate gray; collar across back and breast dark chestnut; abdomen rufous brown; under tail-coverts cinnamon. No knob at base of bill .... *Ducula bakeri*

***Red-bellied Fruit Dove** (*Ptilinopus greyii* Bonaparte): Throughout the area.

Tanna Fruit Dove (*Ptilinopus tannensis* Latham): Females are like the males, but lack the grayish white spots on the shoulders and have more yellow on the lower abdomen. Iris yellow; bill bluish; feet red. New Hebrides (except Aneiteum) and Banks Isls. (Gaua, Vanua Lava).

Voice unknown. Lives from sea level to mountaintops, in original forest and in wooded patches in the grasslands. Feeds on figs and other fruits.

***Pacific Pigeon** (*Ducula p. pacifica* Gmelin): *See* Plate 2: 13. Throughout the area.

Baker's Pigeon (*Ducula bakeri* Kinnear 1928): Large (15). Iris yellowish; bill black; feet red. No knob on bill. Differs from *D. pacifica* by the uniformly dark upperparts and by the dark throat and breast. Differs from *Columba vitiensis* by the blackish bill and gray upper throat. Larger islands of northern New Hebrides (Santo, Pentecost, Ambrym, Aurora) and Banks Isls. (Vanua Lava, Gaua, Bligh).

Frequents the mountain forest. Not known whether it also occurs in the lowlands. Has a characteristic single-noted ascending call.

***White-throated Pigeon** (*Columba vitiensis*): The New Hebrides race (*leopoldi* Tristram) is found in the southern and central New Hebrides (from Aneiteum to Ambrym, Malekula, Malo, and Santo) and in the Torres group (Lo, Hiu). Underparts grayish or chestnut. Throat of females dull white or grayish. Iris yellow, bill and feet red.

***Rufous-brown Pheasant Dove** (*Macropygia mackinlayi*): *Cf.* Plate 2: 14. The subspecies *mackinlayi* Ramsay is found throughout the New Hebrides and Banks Isls. Its uniform brown color (darker above) and the long tail are diagnostic. A peculiar dirty gray color phase (pale gray below) is rare on several islands but comprises about 30 per cent of the population on Tanna Isl.

Green-winged Ground Pigeon (*Chalcophaps indica*): Small (9–10). Head, upper back, and throat purplish rufous (vinaceous), abdomen paler and more grayish. Back and inner half of wing golden green; wing- and tail-feathers brown. Lower back blackish brown with 2 gray crossbars. A whitish gray spot on the wing-bend. Females duller, wing-bend grayish. Immatures are barred with black underneath and the wing-feathers are edged with rufous cinnamon. Iris brown; bill orange red; feet cherry red.

The subspecies *sandwichensis* Ramsay occurs in the Loyalty Isls., all the New Hebrides, Banks Isls., Torres group, and Santa Cruz group.

This terrestrial dove forages on the ground and settles only rarely on bushes or low trees even when flushed. The nest, containing 2 eggs, is generally about 4–15 feet up. Breeds from September to November. Flushed birds dart off with a startling and loud clapping of the wings, flying with great agility and rapidity through the tangled vines of the undergrowth.

Santa Cruz Ground Pigeon (*Gallicolumba sanctaecrucis* Mayr 1935): Small (9–10). Male and female very different. *Male.* Brownish black above with reddish purple gloss. A strongly glossy violaceous patch on wing-bend. Head grayish. A large white throat and breast shield, tinged with pinkish buff, more grayish on the side. Abdomen chocolate brown. Iris brown; bill black; feet purplish red.

Female. Lighter, more brownish. Head, neck, and breast shield tawny chestnut. Back, tail, and wings with a greenish gloss. Abdomen gray brown. Differs from *Chalcophaps* by the uniformly dull gloss of the upperparts (including rump and tail), by the rufous tawny, not vinaceous brown, head and throat, and by the black bill. Rare. Known only from Tinakula and Utupua in the Santa Cruz Isls. and from Espiritu Santo in the New Hebrides.

PARROTS

Two lories are the only representatives of this family in the New Hebrides, the red-breasted Coconut Lory, and a little, long-tailed, green lorikeet, the Palm Lorikeet.

***Coconut Lory** (*Trichoglossus haematodus*): *See* Plate 2: 16. The subspecies *massena* Bonaparte occurs throughout the entire New Hebrides and Banks Isls.

Green Palm Lorikeet (*Vini palmarum* Gmelin): Small (7) with a long tail. Entirely green; tip of tail yellow. Usually a few red feathers on chin and cheeks. Iris yellow; bill and feet orange yellow.

Santa Cruz Isls., Banks Isls., all New Hebrides. The green plumage makes this a hard bird to see. Lives in pairs or flocks in treetops, feeding on nectar, blossoms, and fruit. More common in the hills than in the lowlands. Call a shrill piping whistle. Might possibly be confused with the bamboo-finches (*Erythrura*), (for which *see*, for differences in color of head, tail, and bill).

CUCKOOS

There are 3 species in the New Hebrides, 2 of them resident and one a migrant visitor from New Zealand. The 3 are so different as not to be mistaken for one another.

*__Fan-tailed Cuckoo__ (*Cacomantis pyrrhophanus*): The subspecies *schistaceigularis* Sharpe has a gray throat contrasting with the deep rufous breast and abdomen. The barred immatures are very different. The slender body form, blackish upperparts, rufous breast, and white pattern on tail are diagnostic.

Ranges from Tanna northward through the entire New Hebrides to the Banks Isls. (Gaua and Valua).

*__Shining Cuckoo__ (*Chalcites lucidus*): The New Caledonian subspecies *layardi* Mathews 1912 ranges through the Loyalty Isls. and New Hebrides north to the Banks Isls. (Gaua and Vanua Lava) and Santa Cruz Isls. (Utupua). The distribution is closely correlated with that of its favorite foster species, *Gerygone flavolateralis.* Birds observed on Fotuna and Erromanga may have been visitors. Crown and nape of this race are dull purple with little gloss. Barring of throat inconspicuous and practically absent in immatures.

*__Long-tailed New Zealand Cuckoo__ (*Eudynamis taitensis* Sparrman): *See* Figure 8. Rather rare in the New Hebrides and not yet reported from the Banks Isls.

BARN OWLS

*__Barn Owl__ (*Tyto alba*): *Cf.* Figure 9. The subspecies *interposita* Mayr 1935, with buff or ochraceous underparts, is found in the Santa Cruz Isls. (Vanikoro), Banks Isls. (Vanua Lava), and northern New Hebrides (Pentecost, Santo, Malekula, Epi, and Efate). Birds from the southern New Hebrides (Erromanga, Tanna, Aneiteum) are more whitish.

No other nocturnal birds (owls or nightjars) have been recorded from the New Hebrides.

SWIFTS

***Vanikoro Swiftlet** (*Collocalia vanikorensis*): The subspecies *vanikorensis* Quoy and Gaimard is found throughout the New Hebrides and Banks Isls.

***White-rumped Swiftlet** (*Collocalia spodiopygia*): *Cf.* Plate 2: 20. The subspecies *leucopygia* Wallace is found throughout the New Hebrides, but is apparently not yet recorded from the Banks Isls. May have seasonal movements from island to island.

***Glossy Swiftlet** (*Collocalia esculenta*): The New Hebridean race *uropygialis* Gray differs from *leucopygia* by the characters mentioned in the key.* This is probably the most common of the 3 swiftlets. It has been recorded throughout the New Hebrides, Banks and Torres Isls.

KINGFISHERS

Only 2 species (*Halcyon*) are found in the New Hebrides:

(1) Upperparts greenish blue with a whitish or cinnamon collar. Underparts white or washed with ochraceous on flanks and belly .... *H. chloris*

(2) Crown black, back deep purplish blue; collar white; throat white; breast and abdomen deep tawny rufous . *H. farquhari*

***White-collared Kingfisher** (*Halcyon chloris*): *Cf.* Plate 2: 22. The 5 subspecies recognized in this area differ mainly in the extent of the rufous ocher wash of superciliary, nuchal collar, flanks, and abdomen. Beginning with the whitest and lightest race, the following sequence can be established: *torresiana* Mayr 1931 (Torres Isls.) very bright bluish or greenish; *santoensis* Mayr 1931 (Banks Isls. and northern New Hebrides) and *juliae* Heine (central New Hebrides, Efate to Malekula and Aoba) intermediate; *erromangae* Mayr 1938 (Erromanga, ?Aneiteum) flanks and abdomen in males washed with pale ochraceous; and *tannensis* Sharpe (Tanna) with the male deep ochraceous below.

Chestnut-bellied Kingfisher (*Halcyon farquhari* Sharpe): Small (7–8). Head black; a white spot on either side of forehead and a dark purplish blue eye-stripe continuing back of the eye. Back, wings, and tail dark purplish blue; rump brighter. Throat and nuchal collar white; breast and abdomen deep ocher to chestnut. Iris brown; bill black above, horn color below; feet black. Females have a white patch on the lower abdomen.

Known only from Malekula, Malo, and Espiritu Santo. Probably a bird of the true forest. Habits unknown.

SONGBIRDS

There are at least 24 species of native songbirds known from the New Hebrides and one or 2 introduced species. To make a key for all these species (including the 2 sexes, immature plumages, and geographical races) would be cumbersome. The following rough color key, however, will help in quick identification. It will assist in narrowing down the number of alternatives.

Color Key to New Hebrides Songbirds

Species with red (including pink or scarlet) in plumage: *Petroica multicolor, Myzomela cardinalis, Erythrura cyanovirens.*

Species with yellow, green, or olive in plumage: *Gerygone flavolateralis, Pachycephala pectoralis, Lichmera incana, Myzomela cardinalis* (♀, imm.), *Zosterops flavifrons, Zosterops lateralis, Erythrura trichroa, Erythrura cyanovirens.*

Species with dark gray, soft black, or glossy black in plumage: *Hirundo tahitica, Lalage maculosa, Lalage leucopyga, Coracina caledonica* (dark blue gray), *Turdus poliocephalus, Petroica multicolor, Neolalage banksiana, Rhipidura spilodera, Rhipidura fuliginosa, Myiagra caledonica, Pachycephala pectoralis, Artamus leucorhynchus, Aplonis zelandicus, Guadalcanaria notabilis, Myzomela cardinalis.*

Species with brown or rust color in plumage: *Hirundo tahitica, Lalage maculosa* (♀), *Lalage leucopyga* (♀), *Turdus poliocephalus, Cichlornis whitneyi, Petroica multicolor, Rhipidura spilodera, Rhipidura fuliginosa, Myiagra caledonica* (♀), *Clytorhynchus pachycephaloides, Pachycephala pectoralis* (♀), *Aplonis santovestris, Aplonis zelandicus, Guadalcanaria notabilis, Myzomela cardinalis* (♀). Immatures of some of these species are even more brownish than the adults, particularly in the species marked (♀).

Species with white in plumage (including wings and tail): *Lalage maculosa, Lalage leucopyga, Turdus poliocephalus* (Erromanga, Tanna only), *Gerygone flavolateralis, Petroica multicolor, Neolalage banksiana, Rhipidura spilodera, Rhipidura fuliginosa, Myiagra caledonica, Pachycephala pectoralis, Artamus leucorhynchus, Guadalcanaria notabilis, Zosterops flavifrons* (eye-ring only), *Zosterops lateralis* (eye-ring and lower abdomen).

SWALLOWS

***Pacific Swallow** (*Hirundo tahitica*): *See* Plate 3: 23. The subspecies *subfusca* Gould is widespread throughout the New Hebrides and Banks Isls. Can be confused only with the swiftlets (*Collocalia*). Differs from *C. esculenta uropygialis* and *C. spodiopygia leucopygia* by a blue-black rump and by the chestnut forehead and throat. Differs from *C. vanikorensis* by the glossy blue-black upperparts and the chestnut throat.

CUCKOO-SHRIKES

This family is represented in the New Hebrides by 3 species: 2 black and white trillers (*Lalage*), and the large, crow-like Melanesian Graybird (*Coracina*). The skinned specimens of the 2 trillers are very similar; it is as yet unknown whether they differ conspicuously in habits. In the Santa Cruz Isls. only *maculosa* is found, in the southern New Hebrides (Aneiteum to Erromanga), Banks and Torres Isls. only *leucopyga* is found. The 2 species overlap in the central and northern New Hebrides (from Efate northward). They can probably be differentiated in the field as follows:

Adult male. L. leucopyga is solid glossy black above except for a well-defined grayish white rump and sometimes a rather indistinct eye-stripe. Wings black except for a whitish patch on the shoulder. Underparts pure or buffy white. Lower mandible black. *L. maculosa.* Crown with white streaks; back faintly barred with white; lower back and rump grayish white; broad eye-stripe, continued to nape. Extensive white shoulder patch, wing-feathers edged with white. Sides of breast and flanks frequently barred with black. Lower mandible yellowish brown. Apparently a plumper bird.

Female and *immature*. *L. maculosa* is rather pale brownish above, *L. leucopyga* brownish black. The iris is brown in both species.

***Polynesian Triller** (*Lalage maculosa*): *Cf.* Plate 3: 24. Two races in the New Hebrides: *modesta* Mayr and Ripley 1941 (Espiritu Santo, Malo, Pauuma, and Epi) with more barring on the sides of the breast and sometimes with a buffy wash of underparts; *ultima* Mayr and Ripley 1941 (Efate) with more mottling of upperparts, more extensive light area on rump and almost pure white underparts.

***Long-tailed Triller** (*Lalage leucopyga*): Three races: *simillima* Sarasin 1913 (Loyalty Isls., Aneiteum, Tanna, Erromanga) with black lores and no eye-stripe, rump whitish gray; *albiloris* Mayr and Ripley 1941 (central and northern New Hebrides, from Efate northward) with white lores and sometimes an eye-stripe, rump more grayish; *deficiens* Mayr and Ripley 1941 (Banks and Torres Isls.) with little or no white on lores, no eye-stripe, rump gray.

Neolalage banksiana, the only other New Hebrides bird that somewhat resembles the trillers, can be distinguished at once by the black breast band and the orange buff abdomen.

***Melanesian Graybird** (*Coracina caledonica*): Two races in the New Hebrides: *seiuncta* Mayr and Ripley 1941 (Erromanga) somewhat paler and grayer than *thilenii* Neumann

1915 (Espiritu Santo, Malo and Malekula). The color of the iris is doubtful, either brown or yellow.

Recognizable by undulating direct flight with discontinuous wing beats and by a piercing single-noted call. In large trees of all types of landscape.

THRUSHES

***Island Thrush** (*Turdus poliocephalus*): At least 8 different subspecies in the New Hebrides. Young of all races olive brown, underparts with tawny, white, and black spots.

pritzbueri Layard (Tanna) sooty black; head and throat creamy white in adult males, gray brown in females; *albifrons* Ramsay (Erromanga) like *pritzbueri,* but head whiter, some white on lower belly. The other 6 races are of a single color: *vanikorensis* Quoy and Gaimard (Espiritu Santo, Malo), *efatensis* Mayr 1941 (Efate), and *whitneyi* Mayr 1941 (Gaua) are sooty black (at least the adult males), while *becki* Mayr 1941 (Mai, Epi, Lopevi, Pauuma), *malekulae* Mayr 1941 (Malekula, Ambrym, Pentecost), and *placens* Mayr 1941 (Vanua Lava, Bligh Isl.) are more grayish or brownish in varying degrees. Females and immature males are lighter and more brownish.

Differs from the shrikebill (*Clytorhynchus*) by yellow bill and feet and by the short, blackish tail (no white); differs from the Rusty-winged Starling (*Aplonis*) also by the yellow color of bill and feet and by lacking the rust-colored patch on the wings. There are additional differences of voice and habits.

WARBLERS

Thicket Warbler (*Cichlornis whitneyi* Mayr 1933): A slender, long-tailed bird of the size of a Reed Warbler or Catbird (6½). Upperparts brown; conspicuous eye-stripe; underparts ochraceous; wings and tail dark brown. Iris brown; bill and feet black. Secretive in the dense undergrowth of the primeval mountain forest, above 2400 feet. Occurs only in the mountains of Espiritu Santo where it was discovered by the Whitney Expedition in 1926.

Fantail Warbler (*Gerygone flavolateralis*): A typical small (4) warbler. Upperparts olive; head olive gray; feathers on eyelids white; throat whitish gray; flanks and abdomen lemon yellow. Wings and tail olive brown; lateral tail-feathers with subterminal white spots. The entire underparts are yellowish in immatures.

Differs from *Zosterops flavifrons* by smaller size, dark gray crown, and whitish throat, from *Lichmera incana* by much smaller size, short tail and bill, and by the yellow flanks. Iris dull crimson; bill and feet black. This species is the favorite foster parent of the parasitic cuckoo *Chalcites.*

The subspecies *correiae* Mayr 1931 has been recorded from the New Hebrides (Mai, Epi, Lopevi, Ambrym, Malekula, Aoba) and Banks Isls. (Gaua, Vanua Lava). Frequents the treetops of the forest, in second growth and native plantations. Has a characteristic pleasing song which has never been adequately described. The nest of all *Gerygone* is a neat structure of plant wool, spider webs, and lichens, with a lateral entrance. Usually 8–15 feet above the ground, it contains 3 or 4 eggs.

FLYCATCHERS

Spotted Fantail (*Rhipidura spilodera*): *See* Plate 3: 26. Small (6½–7) with a long tail. Upperparts dark, grayish on head and tail, brownish on back and wings; a broad eye-stripe and a short line behind the eye white. Underparts whitish; throat with partly concealed triangular blackish spots; flanks washed with buffy ochraceous. Lateral tail-feathers with white tips.

The subspecies *spilodera* Gray occurs throughout the central and northern New Hebrides, from Efate northward, and in the Banks Isls. (Gaua, Vanua Lava). Habits those of the genus.* Common in all habitats.

Collared Fantail (*Rhipidura fuliginosa*): Small (6). Upperparts slate gray, more blackish on tail; white eye-stripe and short white line behind the eye. The white throat is separated sharply by a black breast band from the ochraceous buff lower breast and abdomen. Lateral tail-feathers narrowly tipped with white. Two inconspicuous white wing-bars. Differs from *spilodera* by smaller size, the gray back, and the color of the underparts.

The subspecies *brenchleyi* Sharpe occurs throughout the New Hebrides and Banks Isls. Lowlands and mountains, second growth and true forest.

Broad-billed Flycatcher (*Myiagra caledonica*): Small (6). Male black with greenish gloss; abdomen white. Female with gray head, brownish wings and tail, and olive-brown back.

Throat and upper breast ochraceous orange; abdomen white. Iris brown; broad, flat bill bluish gray.

The subspecies *melanura* Gray (Aneiteum, Tanna, Erromanga) is slightly larger than *marina* Salomonsen 1934 (New Hebrides from Efate northward, Banks Isls., Torres Isls.). Habits those of the genus.* More common in the open country and near the coast than in the mountains.

Buff-bellied Flycatcher (*Neolalage banksiana* Gray): A small (5½), pied bird. Crown, back, part of wing, base of tail black. Upper throat, face, sides of head, rump, part of wing, and tip of tail white. A black band across the breast. Lower breast and abdomen orange buff. Iris brown; bill black; feet blue gray. Immature similar, but the black colors are replaced by brownish and grayish, and the white colors are less pure. The white face, black pectoral band, and orange-buff abdomen distinguish adults of this species from all other New Hebrides birds.

New Hebrides (from Efate northward) and Banks Isls. (Vanua Lava). Habits similar to those of *Monarcha*.* Friendly, with a melodious song. Near human habitations, in second growth, and along the edge of plantations.

Southern Shrikebill (*Clytorhynchus pachycephaloides*): Medium (7½). A rufous-brown to olive-brown bird with broad white tips on the lateral tail-feathers; lighter and more grayish underneath. A large, wedge-shaped bluish white bill; gape yellow. Iris brown; feet bluish gray. Bill of immatures brown. The subspecies *grisescens* Sharpe lives throughout the New Hebrides (from Erromanga northward), Banks Isls., and Torres Isls. (Hiu).

Hunts for insects in the substage of the true forest. "Frequents the most dense and gloomy forest, whence its melancholy long-drawn whistle sounds in mournful cadence" (Layard). Can be lured by imitating this call note. Nest unknown. Usually more frequent in the mountains or even restricted to them on some of the islands. A vigorous and pugnacious bird.

***Scarlet Robin** (*Petroica multicolor*): *See* Figure 14. These chunky little birds with scarlet breasts and short bill and tail cannot be mistaken for any other species. There are 5 races in the New Hebrides. Sexual dimorphism present in *similis* Gray (Tanna, Aneiteum) and in *ambrynensis* Sharpe (Tongoa, Lopevi, Pauuma, Ambrym, Aoba, and Santo, New Hebrides, and Meralav and Gaua, Banks Isls.). In the 3 other races the males are brown above, like the females, and differ only by a white spot on the forehead and by more scarlet on throat and lower abdomen: *cognata* Mayr 1938 (Erromanga), *feminina* Mayr 1934 (Efate, Mai), and *soror* Mayr 1934 (Vanua Lava, Banks Isls.).

WHISTLERS

***Golden Whistler** (*Pachycephala pectoralis*): *See* Plate 3: 29, 30. Medium (7). *Adult male*. Crown black; back, wings, and tail olive green. White throat separated from lemon-yellow abdomen by a black breast band. *Female*. Crown hair brown; back, wings, and tail dull brownish olive; throat white; abdomen yellowish, faint indication of a brownish or gray breast band. Immatures similar to females, but more rufous in plumage, particularly on wing.

Six subspecies in the New Hebrides. They differ (mainly

in the female plumage) by characters hardly apparent to the field student: *cucullata* Gray (Aneiteum), *chlorura* Gray (Erromanga), *efatensis* Mayr 1938 (Efate), *brunneipectus* Mayr 1932 (Mai, Tongariki, Epi, Lopevi, Pauuma, Ambrym), *intacta* Sharpe (Malekula, Malo, Santo, Aoba), and *banksiana* Mayr 1932 (Aurora, Pentecost, and Banks Isls.).

WOOD-SWALLOWS

***White-breasted Wood-Swallow** (*Artamus leucorhynchus*): *Cf.* Plate 3: 31. Habits and color pattern are diagnostic. Differs from the trillers by the black throat and the absence of white on the wing. The subspecies *tenuis* Mayr 1943 occurs throughout the New Hebrides and Banks Isls.

STARLINGS

Mountain Starling (*Aplonis santovestris* Harrisson and Marshall 1937): Size of a starling (7). Brown throughout. Crown blackish brown; lower back and rump rufous chestnut. Underside warm rufous brown. Wings and tail blackish brown. Iris gray green; bill and feet brownish black.

Restricted to the mountains of Espiritu Santo (above 3000 feet). Usually found singly or in pairs. Frequents the undergrowth of the cloud forest, where it searches for its food of fruits and seeds. The 2 white eggs are placed in a hole of a tree close to the ground. Sits silently on low boughs and stumps, flitting swiftly away through the dripping foliage when disturbed.

Rusty-winged Starling (*Aplonis zelandicus*): A small starling (7) with a heavy bill and short tail. Upperparts dark gray brown; rump rufous brown. Underparts dark gray with a buff tone. Wings and tail dark brown; a bright rufous chestnut patch on the wing. Iris brown; bill and feet dark.

The subspecies *rufipennis* Layard occurs in the central and northern New Hebrides (from Pauuma-Lopevi northward) and in the Banks Isls. (Bligh and Gaua). An arboreal bird of the lowland forest.

*__Indian Myna__ (*Acridotheres tristis* Linnaeus): Probably introduced on some of the islands of the New Hebrides.

HONEY-EATERS

White-bellied Honey-eater (*Guadalcanaria notabilis*): A medium-sized honey-eater (7–8) with a long, strongly curved black bill. Upperparts rufous or olive brown; crown black; a more or less distinct white eye-stripe. Underparts white; throat grayish white, lower breast and abdomen purer white, but with long, thin brownish streaks, particularly on sides of breast and flanks. Iris brown; feet blue gray. Young birds with light streaks above and without the dark streaks below.

Two subspecies, *notabilis* Sharpe (Banks Isls., also Aoba and Santo) and *superciliaris* Mayr 1932 (Aurora, Pentecost, Malekula, Ambrym, Pauuma, Epi). Habitat and life history unknown.

Silver-eared Honey-eater (*Lichmera incana*): *See* Figure 16. A small (6), slender bird with long tail and curved bill. Crown dark brownish gray; ear-coverts silver gray; back, wings, and tail olive. Throat scaly, grayish; abdomen dirty olive white. Females similar, but much smaller and rarer.

The subspecies *flavotincta* Gray occurs in the central New Hebrides (Erromanga, Efate, Makura, Mai, Tongoa, Epi, Lopevi, Pauuma, Ambrym, and Malekula).

A common bird in flowering trees, particularly in second growth, mangroves, native gardens, and near human habitations. Very partial to coconut trees. The reason why 90 per cent of the observed birds are males is unknown. Perhaps their feeding habits are slightly different (preference for coconut trees). Has a pleasing warbled song. Seems to be territorial on its nesting tree. Lays 2 eggs. Has protracted breeding season and probably several broods per year.

*__Cardinal Honey-eater__ (*Myzomela cardinalis*): *See* Plate 3: 36. Adult males in their scarlet and black plumage are unmistakable. Females and immatures with their more or less olive plumage might be mistaken for *Gerygone, Petroica,* or *Zosterops.* They can be distinguished by the thin, curved bill, by the scarlet wash of upper throat and crown, and by the absence of white on tail, forehead, and around the eye.

The subspecies *cardinalis* Gmelin (Aneiteum, Tanna, Erromanga) is larger than *tenuis* Mayr 1937 from the northern New Hebrides (from Efate northward) and the Banks Isls.

WHITE-EYES

There are 2 widespread species in the New Hebrides, which are easily told apart:

(1) *flavifrons*—entirely yellowish green, more greenish above, more yellowish underneath.

(2) *lateralis*—middle of back gray; throat and under tail-coverts

greenish yellow; breast and flanks brownish gray; middle of abdomen white.

Both species have broad white eye-rings. The color of the soft parts also seems identical. The iris is brown, the bill yellowish horn-color with a blackish tip, the legs are greenish, grayish, or brownish. Little is known about differences between the 2 species in habitat selection, habits, or song. *Z. lateralis* seems primarily a species of the open country, rare and absent in the true forest. *Z. flavifrons* occurs in all habitats and is perhaps the most numerous bird of the New Hebrides.

Yellow White-eye (*Zosterops flavifrons*): *See* Plate 3: 38. Size of a warbler (4½–5). Differs from other greenish yellow New Hebrides birds (*Gerygone, Erythrura, Lichmera, Pachycephala* ♀) by the rich yellow underparts, the yellowish olive upperparts with a yellowish forehead, the broad white eye-ring, and the short slender bill.

Three subspecies are bright and clear yellow below, yellowish olive above, and with a yellow forehead: *gauensis* Murphy and Mathews 1929 (Gaua, Banks Isls.), *efatensis* Mayr 1937 (Efate, Erromanga), and *flavifrons* Gmelin (Tanna, Aniwa). Four other subspecies are more greenish yellow below, darker above, and with little yellow on the forehead: *perplexa* Murphy and Mathews 1929 (Meralav and Vanua Lava, Banks Isls.; Pentecost, Ambrym, Aurora, Aoba, Pauuma, Lopevi, Epi, Tongoa), *brevicauda* Murphy and Mathews 1929 (Malo, Santo) *macgillivrayi* Sharpe (Malekula), and *majuscula* Murphy and Mathews 1929 (Aneiteum).

***Gray-backed White-eye** (*Zosterops lateralis*): Three subspecies: *macmillani* Mayr 1937 (Tanna, Aniwa) with much gray on the back and much black below the eye; *vatensis* Tristram (northern New Hebrides from Erromanga northward, Banks Isls. [except Valua], Torres group) intermediate; and *valuensis* Murphy and Mathews 1929 (Valua, Banks Isls.) with almost no gray on the warbler-green back.

WEAVER-FINCHES

Two parrot-finches or bamboo-finches of the genus *Erythrura* are the only 2 native weaver-finches in this area. The adults differ as follows:

(1) *trichroa*—long, pointed, rust red tail; forehead and sides of face blue; underparts bright green.

(2) *cyanovirens*—head and tail crimson red; throat and sometimes also abdomen and back bluish.

The immatures are more difficult. In *trichroa* the bill is small and dark, the underparts rather pale olive ochraceous, the legs yellowish. In *cyanovirens* the bill is swollen and thick, yellow at the base, the underparts are bluish green, hardly paler than the back; there always seems to be some red on the crown. There is considerable variation in the immature plumage.

***Blue-faced Parrot-Finch** (*Erythrura trichroa*): The subspecies *cyaneifrons* Layard is known from the Banks Isls. (Gaua), New Hebrides (Aoba, Ambrym, Lopevi, Efate, Erromanga, Tanna, Aneiteum) and Loyalty Isls. (Lifu, Maré). Prefers grasslands and other open areas, but occasionally found in glades in the forest. Feeds on grass seeds.

Red-headed Parrot-Finch (*Erythrura cyanovirens*): *See* Samoa. The blue or greenish plumage with crimson head and tail, and green wings are diagnostic. Females have less blue.

Three subspecies: *regia* Sclater (Mai, Tongoa, Epi, Lopevi, Pauuma and Gaua) with back and abdomen blue in adult males; *efatensis* Mayr 1931 (Efate); and *serena* Sclater (Aneiteum) with breast and nape blue, back and abdomen green.

VIII

The Land and Fresh-Water Birds of the Santa Cruz Islands

THE birds of the Santa Cruz Islands were almost unknown until about 20 years ago. A French expedition had collected some birds on Vanikoro Island in 1828, and a few odd specimens had been obtained since then, but the Whitney South Sea Expedition in 1926–27 made the first thorough survey of all the islands. Additional species and subspecies may still be discovered, particularly in the interior of Santa Cruz and Vanikoro. *Mayrornis schistaceus* and *Myiagra vanikorensis* are so far only known from Vanikoro, *Clytorhynchus nigrogularis, Zosterops sanctae-crucis,* and *Woodfordia lacertosa* only from Santa Cruz Island, and *Gallicolumba sanctaecrucis* from Tinakula and Utupua.

Mayrornis schistaceus, Zosterops sanctae-crucis, and *Woodfordia lacertosa* are the only 3 species that are endemic. Others extend to the New Hebrides, Fiji Islands, or Solomon Islands, and the bird fauna of the Santa Cruz Islands combines elements of these 3 neighboring island groups.

In this chapter, descriptions are given for birds of the entire Santa Cruz group, consisting of the Santa Cruz Islands proper (Vanikoro, Utupua, Santa Cruz), of the Swallow group (Tinakula, Nepani), the Reef Islands (Lomlom, Fenualoa), the Duff group (Treasurers Island, Disappointment Island), and of the isolated islands Tucopia, Anuda (Cherry), and Fataka (Mitre).

All species and genera marked with an asterisk are treated in more detail in the systematic section (Chapter 3, "The Land and Fresh-Water Birds of the Southwest Pacific") of Part I.

CORMORANTS

*__Little Pied Cormorant__ (*Phalacrocorax melanoleucus*): Recorded from Tucopia.

HERONS

*__Little Mangrove Heron__ (*Butorides striatus*): *See* Plate 1: 6. The subspecies *diminutus* Mayr 1940 has been reported from the Swallow group (Nepani), Reef group (Lomlom), Santa Cruz, and Utupua. It is a rather small and grayish race.

*__Reef Heron__ (*Demigretta sacra*): About 27 per cent of the birds of the Santa Cruz Islands are found in the white phase. Known from Tucopia and the entire Santa Cruz group.

DUCKS

*__Australian Gray Duck__ (*Anas superciliosa pelewensis* Hartlaub and Finsch): *See* Plate 1: 7. Recorded from Tucopia.

HAWKS

Pied Hawk (*Accipiter albogularis sharpei* Oustalet): A medium-sized Accipiter (13–16). Black above, white below. Sides of face blackish slate. An indication of a rufous breast band in males, and of rufous barring across the breast in females. An indistinct rufous band across the hind-neck. Eyes, feet, and cere yellow; bill black. Immature plumage unknown, but probably rufous brown above, buff with dark brown streaks below. Known from Vanikoro and Utupua.

RAILS

Only 2 rails are known from the Santa Cruz Isls., a tiny black rail, the Sooty Rail* (*Porzana t. tabuensis*), and the large Purple Swamphen* (*Porphyrio porphyrio* subsp. [*see* Plate 1: 10]). *See* New Hebrides. Locality records for *Porphyrio* are Utupua, Tinakula and Tucopia, for *Porzana* Tinakula only.

PIGEONS AND DOVES

There are only 5 species of pigeons known from the Santa Cruz Isls., all of which also occur in the New Hebrides (*see* key). Of 4 of these species even the subspecies are identical. Their range in the Santa Cruz group is as follows:

***Red-bellied Fruit Dove** (*Ptilinopus greyii* Bonaparte): Duff group, Reef Isls., Santa Cruz, Utupua, and Vanikoro.

***Pacific Pigeon** (*Ducula p. pacifica* Gmelin): *See* Plate 2: 13. Throughout the Santa Cruz Isls.

***Green-winged Ground Pigeon** (*Chalcophaps indica sandwichensis* Ramsay): On all the islands.

Santa Cruz Ground Pigeon (*Gallicolumba sanctaecrucis* Mayr): Known only from Tinakula and Utupua.

***Rufous-brown Pheasant Dove** (*Macropygia mackinlayi*): *Cf.* Plate 2: 14. The Santa Cruz Isls. subspecies *troughtoni* Kinghorn 1937 is like the New Hebrides race, but smaller and slightly deeper chestnut. The gray phase is unknown. Recorded from Vanikoro, Utupua, Santa Cruz, Tinakula, and Lomlom.

PARROTS

The same 2 species occur in the Santa Cruz Isls. that have been described from the New Hebrides (for which *see*):

***Coconut Lory** (*Trichoglossus haematodus massena* Bonaparte): *See* Plate 2: 16. Recorded from 4 islands: Lomlom, Santa Cruz, Utupua, and Tucopia.

Green Palm Lorikeet (*Vini palmarum* Gmelin): Recorded from 4 different islands: Duff group (Treasurers, Disappointment Isls.), Tinakula, and Vanikoro.

CUCKOOS

Both Santa Cruz species occur also in the New Hebrides (for which *see*):

***Shining Cuckoo** (*Chalcites lucidus layardi* Mathews 1912): Reported from Utupua, although its regular host, the warbler *Gerygone,* is unknown from this island. What is its host, or is it only a visitor?

***Long-tailed New Zealand Cuckoo** (*Eudynamis taitensis* Sparrman): *See* Figure 8. Reported from Tinakula, Nepani, Fenualoa, and Lomlom. Doubtless occurs on all islands.

BARN OWLS

***Barn Owl** (*Tyto alba*): *Cf.* Figure 9. The rusty subspecies *interposita* Mayr 1935 is the only owl in the Santa Cruz Isls. (Vanikoro only). *See* New Hebrides.

SWIFTS

Three swiftlets are found in the Santa Cruz Isls.* (*See also* New Hebrides):

***Vanikoro Swiftlet** (*Collocalia vanikorensis*): The subspecies *vanikorensis* Quoy and Gaimard has been recorded from Disappointment Isl., Lomlom, and Vanikoro.

***White-rumped Swiftlet** (*Collocalia spodiopygia*): *Cf.* Plate 2: 20. The subspecies *leucopygia* Wallace has been recorded from Treasurers Isl., Lomlom, Fenualoa, and Santa Cruz.

***Glossy Swiftlet** (*Collocalia esculenta*): The subspecies *uropygialis* Gray has been recorded from Vanikoro and Utupua.

KINGFISHERS

***White-collared Kingfisher** (*Halcyon chloris*): *Cf.* Plate 2: 22. The only species of kingfisher in the Santa Cruz Isls. At least 5 distinct subspecies: *melanodera* Mayr 1931 (Vanikoro); *utupuae* Mayr (Utupua); *ornata* Mayr (Santa Cruz, Tinakula); *brachyura* Mayr (Lomlom, Fenualoa); *vicina* Mayr (Disappointment Isl.); subsp. (Tucopia).

SONGBIRDS

Only 13 species of songbirds are known from the Santa Cruz Isls. Even though one or 2 additional species may yet be discovered in these insufficiently explored islands, the avifauna will still remain very poor. The 13 species can be distinguished by the following key. Identification should be checked against the descriptions given below.

Key to Santa Cruz Isls. Songbirds

(1) With scarlet red, yellow, or green in plumage 2
Without these colors 4

(2) Head and rump scarlet .... *Myzomela*
Head and rump not scarlet 3

(3) Abdomen yellow; throat white, grayish, or buff .... *Pachycephala*
Uniformly green, more yellowish below, darker above .... *Zosterops*

(4) Abdomen white 5
Abdomen black, gray, brownish, or rufous 6

(5) Entire underparts white; white wing-patch .... *Lalage*
Throat black; no white on wing .... *Rhipidura*

(6) Upperparts black 7
Upperparts brownish or grayish 9

(7) Upperparts glossy blue black or greenish black 8
Entire plumage sooty black; bill and feet yellow .... *Turdus*

(8) Throat blue black; abdomen pale rufous .... *Myiagra* (♂)
Forehead and throat chestnut; abdomen dark brownish gray .... *Hirundo*

(9) Small (5½). Pure, light slate gray; tail black .... *Mayrornis*
Not so 10

(10) Small (5). Underparts ochraceous orange; upperparts gray .... *Myiagra* (♀)
Not so 11

(11) Entire plumage more or less brownish or gray. *See Clytorhynchus* (male with black throat), *Turdus* imm., *Aplonis* (2 species), and *Woodfordia* (bill yellow).

Most families of songbirds are represented in the Santa Cruz Isls. by a single species only. Family headings have therefore been omitted in order to save space. All the species belong to widespread genera except *Mayrornis schistaceus* (Muscicapidae) and *Woodfordia lacertosa* (Zosteropidae).

***Pacific Swallow** (*Hirundo tahitica*): *See* Plate 3: 23. The subspecies *subfusca* Gould has been recorded from the Reef Isls. (Lomlom), Santa Cruz, and Utupua. For differences from the swiftlets, *see* New Hebrides.

***Polynesian Triller** (*Lalage maculosa*): *Cf*. Plate 3: 24. This white-bellied bird cannot be mistaken for any other Santa Cruz species. Two subspecies, *vanikorensis* Mayr and Ripley 1941 (Vanikoro) and *melanopygia* Mayr and Ripley 1941 (Utupua and Santa Cruz), the latter darker above.

***Island Thrush** (*Turdus poliocephalus*): The subspecies *vanikorensis* Quoy and Gaimard has been recorded from Vanikoro and Utupua. Adults are sooty black. Young birds are more brownish with underparts spotted like typical thrushes. Lower abdomen whitish.

Rufous-fronted Fantail (*Rhipidura rufifrons*): *See* Plate 3: 27. *See also* Solomon Islands. Two of the 3 subspecies in the Santa Cruz Isls. have a white forehead, contrary to the name of the species: *melanolaema* Sharpe (Vanikoro) upperparts earth brown; forehead, short eye-stripe, and spot on sides of throat white; rest of face and throat black; abdomen and tips of tail-feathers white; *utupuae* Mayr 1931 (Utupua) like *melanolaema* but forehead more white and back more rust colored; *agilis* Mayr 1931 (Santa Cruz) like *melanolaema* but forehead, eye-stripe, and rump tawny (rufous); chin and lower cheeks white; under tail-coverts ochraceous.

Slaty Flycatcher (*Mayrornis schistaceus* Mayr 1933): Small (6). Slate gray, lighter below; tail black; outer tail-feathers with white spots on tip. Iris brown; bill blue black; legs blue gray. Known from Vanikoro only. Habits unknown, possibly those of a *Monarcha*.*

Black-faced Shrikebill (*Clytorhynchus nigrogularis*): *See* Fiji. Smaller (7) than on Fiji. Upperparts brown; forehead, face, and throat glossy black; buff ear-spot; grayish eye-stripe. Underparts whitish, washed with ochraceous buff. A few blackish feathers on the upper wing-coverts and on the rump. The black-faced male is unmistakable. Female unknown, but probably brown throughout, lighter below; presumably differs from *Woodfordia lacertosa* by the absence of the eye-ring, by the dark feet and bill, and by the rather long tail. It differs from *Aplonis zelandicus* by being much paler underneath and by lacking the rufous wing-patch (*sanctaecrucis* Mayr 1933).

Vanikoro Broadbill (*Myiagra vanikorensis*): Small (5). *Adult male.* Head, throat, and wings blue black; back and tail dark gray with bluish gloss. Abdomen pale rufous or ocher. *Female.* Crown bluish gray, back (olive) gray. Wings and tail brownish; a whitish edge on outermost tail-feather. Underparts ochraceous orange, more whitish on chin. Iris brown; bill and feet blue gray. Known only from Vanikoro (*vanikorensis* Quoy and Gaimard).

***Golden Whistler** (*Pachycephala pectoralis*): *Cf.* Plate 3: 29. The 3 races occurring in the Santa Cruz Isls. are so distinct, that they require separate description:

Vanikoro Isl. (*vanikorensis* Oustalet). *Male.* Head, tail, and breast band black; throat white; abdomen golden yellow. Back and edge of black wing-feathers olive green. *Female.* Crown mouse gray; back, wings, and tail (brownish) olive. Throat white with narrow brownish streaks; abdomen bright yellow. An olive breast band. Iris brown; bill and legs black.

Utupua Isl. (*utupuae* Mayr 1932). *Male* like that of *vanikorensis. Female* more brownish above and with a cinnamon breast band.

Santa Cruz Isl., Swallow, Reef, and Duff Isls. (*ornata* Mayr 1932). *Male.* Underparts like those of *vanikorensis,* but entire upperparts glossy black. *Female.* Head brownish, back and wings brownish olive. Throat and breast suffused with cinnamon; only lower belly pure yellow.

Rusty-winged Starling (*Aplonis zelandicus*): *See* New Hebrides. Two subspecies in the Santa Cruz Isls., which differ from the New Hebrides race mainly by being darker gray underneath: *zelandicus* Quoy and Gaimard (Vanikoro), and the larger *maxwellii* Forbes (Santa Cruz).

Polynesian Starling (*Aplonis tabuensis*): *See* Samoa. A dull, earth-brown bird, with a short bill and tail; medium (7). Two subspecies: *pachyrhamphus* Mayr 1942 (Reef Isl., Swallow Isl., and Tinakula) with a greenish gloss on the crown, a whitish lower belly, and white streaks on the brownish breast; *tucopiae* Mayr 1942 (Tucopia Isl.) with a uniform brown plumage and a slight purple gloss on the crown. Iris yellow or brown; bill and legs dark brown.

***Cardinal Honey-eater** (*Myzomela cardinalis*): *Cf.* Plate 3: 36. The adult male of the Santa Cruz race *sanctaecrucis* Sarasin 1913 is all scarlet except for wings, tail, and lower abdomen, which are black. Females and immatures are sooty olive, paler below; rump, and in immature males also head and throat, dull scarlet. Recorded from Torres Isls. (Lo, Hiu), Vanikoro, Utupua, Santa Cruz, Reef Isls. (Nepani, Fenualoa, Lomlom), and Duff Isls. (Disappointment Isl., Treasurers Isl.)

In the subspecies *tucopiae* Mayr 1937 (Tucopia) the scarlet of the underside in adult males is restricted to the throat.

Santa Cruz White-eye (*Zosterops sanctae-crucis* Tristram): Small (5). Dull olive, lighter below; abdomen yellowish. A sooty colored eye-ring. Iris brown; bill black with a yellow base; legs and feet blue gray. Fairly common and restricted to Santa Cruz Isl. Habits unknown.

Sanford's White-eye (*Woodfordia lacertosa* Murphy and Mathews 1929): Medium (6), with a long (¾), slightly curved, straw-yellow bill. Upperparts umber brown, more rufous brown on wings and tail. Underparts clay color (buffy ocher), with an olive wash, particularly on the throat. A dirty white eye-ring and loral spot. Iris brown; bill and legs yellow. Occurs only on Santa Cruz Isl. The habits of this robust white-eye are unknown.

IX

The Land and Fresh-Water Birds of the Solomon Islands[1]

At least 148 species and subspecies of land and fresh-water birds, including migrants, occur in the area of the Solomon Islands, from Nissan to San Cristobal and Rennell Island. If all subspecies and geographically representative species are included, this number is swelled to a total of 300 forms (10 of them as yet undescribed), of which about 240 can be identified in the field. Such a rich fauna poses quite a problem to anyone who attempts to supply the field student with a key or with other means by which to identify all these forms. Furthermore, less has been recorded in the literature on the voices, habitat preferences, and habits of the birds of the Solomon Islands than of any other region in the Southwest Pacific. Those who use the subsequent descriptions should remember this scarcity of available information. The geographical key at the end of this section helps to reduce to 100 or less the number of forms that may be encountered on any one island.[2]

All species and genera marked with an asterisk are treated in more detail in the systematic section (Chapter 3,

[1] No comprehensive work on the birds of the Solomon Islands has ever been published. Two series of technical papers have appeared: (1) by Rothschild and Hartert, in the *Novitates Zoologicae,* on the collections made by Meek and Eichhorn; (2) by Mayr and others, in the *American Museum Novitates,* on the collections of the Whitney South Sea Expedition. The birds of Malaita are treated in *Novitates* no. 504; those of Rennell Island in *Novitates* nos. 486 and 488.

[2] The serial numbers used for each species in this chapter supply the key numbers for the geographical review of Solomon Islands birds on pp. 275–280.

"The Land and Fresh-Water Birds of the Southwest Pacific") of Part I.

GREBES

1) ***Red-throated Dabchick** (*Podiceps ruficollis*): The subspecies *tricolor* Gray has been found nesting on one inland lake on Bougainville.

CORMORANTS

2) ***Little Pied Cormorant** (*Phalacrocorax melanoleucus*): The subspecies *melanoleucus* Vieillot has been recorded from Guadalcanal and Santa Anna. A much smaller subspecies (*brevicauda* Mayr 1931) is endemic on Rennell Isl., where it is found on the inland Lake Tengano.

HERONS AND BITTERNS

Four species of this family occur in the Solomon Isls. The plumages and color phases can be keyed out about as follows (sizes approximate and averaged, since a hunched-up heron is much smaller than one with neck stretched out):

Key to Solomon Isls. Herons and Bitterns

(1) Back spotted or streaked; underparts with conspicuous dark streaks on a white or ocher background 2
Back uniform gray, rufous, or white; streaking (if any) of underparts restricted to the throat 3

(2) Small (13). Back grayish or fuscous; spots on wing elongated . . . . *Butorides* (juv.)

Large (18). Back rufous brown; spots on wing roundish .. .. *Nycticorax* (juv.)

(3) a. All white or pied (white and dark slate) ..... *Demigretta*
b. Back black or gray 4
c. Back rufous or brown 5

(4) a. Large (16–20). All blackish slate except for white line along middle of throat .... *Demigretta*
b. Medium (15). Black or dark gray; prominent pale ocher stripes on either side of throat, converging at base of throat .... *Dupetor* (♂)
c. Small (13–14). Top of head black; back gray. Underparts paler gray; middle of throat whitish, with or without a line of streaks along the middle .... *Butorides*

(5) Larger (18). Flight feathers and tail rufous like back. Upper throat and abdomen white; lower throat washed with rufous .... *Nycticorax*
Smaller (15). Flight feathers and tail black. Entire underparts rufous ocher .... *Dupetor* (♀)

3) ***Little Mangrove Heron** (*Butorides striatus*): *See* Plate 1: 6. The subspecies *solomonensis* Mayr 1940 occurs throughout the Solomon Isls. from Bougainville to San Cristobal.

4) ***Reef Heron** (*Demigretta s. sacra* Gmelin): Occurs throughout the Solomon Isls. About 25 per cent of the birds are in the white, and 6 per cent in the mottled phase, but more accurate counts are desirable.

5) ***Rufous Night Heron** (*Nycticorax caledonicus*): The subspecies *mandibularis* Ogilvie-Grant is found throughout the Solomon Isls. and western Bismarck Archipelago.

6) **Black Bittern** (*Dupetor flavicollis*): A small bittern with blackish males and brown females. *Adult male*. Upper parts,

wings, and tail black; underparts brownish black except for a yellowish white streak on either side of the throat. *Female.* Top of head black; back rich rufous chestnut; underparts deep ocher, paler on sides of throat; middle of throat with inconspicuous, small black spots. *Immature.* Pale rufous with dark bars and spots.

In the Solomon Isls. found in lowland marshes and mangroves, occasionally in the forest. Most active at night.

The subspecies *woodfordi* Ogilvie-Grant is apparently found throughout the Solomon Isls. It is either rare or retiring, and has been recorded so far only from Shortland, Choiseul, Vella Lavella, New Georgia, Rendova, Kicha, Guadalcanal, Beagle, and Ulawa. The subspecies *pallidior* Mayr 1931 (females paler) is restricted to Rennell Isl. (Lake Tengano).

DUCKS

7) ***Australian Gray Duck** (*Anas superciliosa*): *See* Plate 1: 7. The subspecies *pelewensis* Hartlaub and Finsch is found throughout the Solomon Isls. Except on Rennell, it is the only duck found in the area. The Pied Cormorant (*Phalacrocorax melanoleucus*) and the Red-throated Dabchick (*Podiceps ruficollis*) are the only other swimming fresh-water birds of the Solomon Isls.

HAWKS AND EAGLES

8) **Crested Hawk** (*Aviceda subcristata*): Medium (15-16). Head and throat gray, nape with a short blackish crest; mantle dark earth brown. Wings and tail dark gray with black

bars, tip of tail black. *Breast and abdomen white or buff with broad black bars.* Vent and under tail-coverts ocher or tawny without black bars. Iris yellow; bill black; feet whitish. The subspecies *gurneyi* Ramsay is common throughout the Solomon Isls., except on some of the small islands.

A conspicuous hawk in the forest, along the forest edge and in second growth, particularly abandoned native gardens. Feeds mainly on insects, lizards, but also on mammals and occasionally on birds. Has a thin, eery call note. Hovers occasionally.

9) **White and Red Eagle-Kite** (*Haliastur indus*): *See* Plate 1: 8. Large (16–18). Head, nape, throat, and breast white. Back, wings, tail, and belly chestnut red. Iris brown; bill and feet yellowish. Immatures have the same characteristic manner of flight, but are very differently colored: mantle and tail dark brown, wing-tips blackish; head and underparts very pale rufous brown with whitish streaks.

The subspecies *girrenera* Vieillot occurs throughout the Solomon Isls. Found mostly along the seashore, in harbors, along rivers, and in coastal clearings, but occasionally also inland. Feeds on fish, crabs, insects, lizards, carrion, and garbage. Has a long melancholy cry. Flight call: *ker-ree, ker-ree, ker-ree,* rapidly repeated. Resting call: a descending thin *yay-eeee.* Its graceful flight, capable of rapid turns, is diagnostic.

10) **Goshawk** (*Accipiter meyerianus* Sharpe): Very large (19–21). Adults black above; white below with a few faint gray bars on breast and flanks. Tail very long. Occasional specimens are all black (melanistic). Immatures are dark brown above with slight rusty barring on back and the indi-

cation of a rufous band across the hind-neck and a rust-colored eye-stripe. Underparts rufous with narrow black streaks. Iris reddish brown; bill blue black with yellow base; legs and feet yellow. Very rare. Reported only twice from the Solomon Isls. (Kulambangra, Guadalcanal). This close relative of the holarctic goshawk (*A. gentilis*) is apparently primarily an inhabitant of the mountain forest.

11) **Rufous-breasted Hawk** (*Accipiter novaehollandiae*): *See* Plate 1: 9. Medium (13–16). Adults uniformly pale ash gray above, including wings and tail. Upper throat and sides of head pale gray; rest of underparts rufous. Immatures are brown above, whitish below with large, roundish dark brown spots; thigh feathers pale rufous. Iris, cere, and legs orange yellow; bill black.

Five subspecies in the Solomon Isls.: *bougainvillei* Rothschild and Hartert (Bougainville, Shortland group), *rufoschistaceus* Rothschild and Hartert (Choiseul, Ysabel, Florida), and *rubianae* R. and H. (central Solomon Isls.) like above; *pulchellus* Ramsay (Guadalcanal) with very pale thighs, and *malaitae* Mayr 1931 (Malaita) with the upperparts dark gray and the underparts narrowly barred with white.

This is the common Accipiter of the Solomon Isls., although absent from San Cristobal and rare on Malaita. Found in the open country as well as in the deep forest, from the lowlands up to 3000 feet. Feeds on birds, insects, and lizards. Immatures are very similar to those of *A. albogularis*.

12) **Pied Hawk** (*Accipiter albogularis*): The manifold plumages and the geographical variation of this species are not yet fully understood. An observer who believes he has seen

an individual of this species should read the entire subsequent account. Medium (13–15½). *Adults* in 3 color phases: (1) slate black above with a rufous collar across the hind-neck, ending in a rufous patch either side of the throat; underparts white; (2) entire upperparts and sides of the throat slate black; underparts white; (3) all slaty black above and below.

Immature. Blackish brown above, more or less streaked and barred with rufous; whitish below with or without a strong rufous brown wash. Sides of throat, breast, abdomen, and flanks with brown streaks; flanks also with crossbars. Iris yellow; legs greenish yellow; bill blue black; cere yellowish green. Immatures differ from immature *novaehollandiae* by the greenish cere, by not having conspicuously rufous thighs, and by the more contrasting (black and rufous) upperparts. The tail is more conspicuously barred.

This is the common Accipiter on San Cristobal and Santa Anna. In the remainder of the Solomon Isls. it seems to be rarer than *novaehollandiae.* Recorded from Malaita, Guadalcanal, Florida, central Solomons, Ysabel, Choiseul, Mono, Shortlands, and Bougainville. On Choiseul and Ysabel it lives side by side with the extremely similar *eichhorni.*

13) **Imitator Hawk** (*Accipiter eichhorni imitator* Hartert 1926): Small (11–13). Adults all black above; underparts either all white, or throat and breast black; abdomen white. Immature like that of *albogularis.* Iris yellow; bill black; cere apparently orange or greenish yellow. Recorded from Choiseul and Ysabel. Always lacks the rufous collar; no all-black phase known. It is not yet determined how this short-legged species can be told in the field from *albogularis,* which occurs on the same islands.

14) **Sanford's Eagle** (*Haliaeetus sanfordi* Mayr 1935): Very large (2′–3′). All brown; darker above, more rufous below. Iris brown; bill blackish; feet dirty white. The only large eagle in the Solomon Isls. Immature eagles are similar in coloration to immature *Haliastur indus,* but much larger. The underparts are darker; no pronounced light patch on the underwing; tail black and more wedge-shaped. Recorded from Choiseul, Ysabel, Vella Lavella, New Georgia, Guadalcanal, Malaita, San Cristobal, and Ugi. Found along the seacoast as well as inland up to an altitude of 4000 feet. It feeds on pigeons, fish, and phalangers.

OSPREYS OR FISH HAWKS

15) ***Osprey** (*Pandion haliaetus*): Common throughout the Solomon Isls.

FALCONS

This family is very poorly represented in the Solomon Isls. The Peregrine Falcon is still unrecorded and of the Hobby only a single Solomon Isls. specimen is known.

16) **Oriental Hobby** (*Falco severus*): Small (10). Upperparts black; back blackish gray. Sides of face black. Upper throat buffy white; remainder of underparts rufous chestnut; breast slightly streaked with black. Iris brown; bill black; feet yellow. Feeds mostly on flying insects (dragonflies, beetles, etc.), rarely on birds. Once taken at Gizo Isl. (straggler from New Guinea?) (*papuanus* Meyer and Wiglesworth).

MEGAPODES

17) ***Incubator Bird** (*Megapodius freycinet eremita* Hartlaub): Found throughout the Solomon Isls. Most common along the seashore but occasionally also inland, rarely above 600 feet. Breeding habits seem different on each island, but detailed accurate data are not available.

BUTTON-QUAILS

18) **Spotted Button-Quail** (*Turnix maculosa*): *See* Figure 6. Very small (4½–5). Upperparts dark gray, mottled with black, chestnut, and buff. Eye-stripe, sides of head, throat, and breast orange rufous; abdomen pale ocher. Males more plainly colored; underparts whitish or buff; sides of breast and flanks barred with black. Iris whitish; bill and legs yellow.

The subspecies *salomonis* Mayr 1938 is known only from a single bird from the grasslands of Guadalcanal. The building of airfields in these grasslands may seriously have threatened the existence of this race. No true quail occurs in the Solomons.

RAILS AND GALLINULES

Up to now there are known from the Solomon Isls. 2 common rails (*Rallus, Amaurornis*), and 2 rare forest rails (*Nesoclopeus, Edithornis*), in addition to the ubiquitous Purple Swamphen (*Porphyrio*). The 2 small rails that are so widespread in Polynesia (*Porzana tabuensis* and *Poliolimnas*) have not yet been recorded from the Solomon Isls.

19) ***Banded Rail** (*Rallus philippensis*): The subspecies *christophori* Mayr 1938 has been recorded only from the eastern Solomon Isls. (Santa Anna, Ugi, San Cristobal, Guadalcanal, Florida). The pale gray eyebrow, the white spotting on the brownish back and wing, and the heavy black and white barring of breast and abdomen are diagnostic.

20) **Bushhen** (*Amaurornis olivaceus*): Medium (9). A plain rail, with a very short tail. Above dark olive brown, more walnut on wings and lower back. Below slate gray; middle of upper throat pale gray; flanks olive brown. Lower abdomen and under tail-coverts buff or pale chocolate color. Iris reddish brown; bill grass green; feet dirty yellow. Size, plain color, and greenish bill are diagnostic. Found in marshes, sago swamps, and in moist areas in secondary growth, sometimes even in the forest.

The race *nigrifrons* Hartert 1926 has been recorded from Bougainville, Gower, San Cristobal, and Santa Anna.

21) **Woodford's Rail** (*Nesoclopeus woodfordi* Ogilvie-Grant): Large (12). Heavy, short legs and a powerful, long bill. General coloration very dark; dark earth brown above, sooty gray below. Lower belly mottled with white and buff, underwing barred with white. Iris dark red; bill yellowish horn color; legs pale slaty blue. Known only from Bougainville, Ysabel, and Guadalcanal. Nothing is known about the habits of this secretive forest rail.

22) **San Cristobal Mountain Rail** (*Edithornis silvestris* Mayr 1933): A fairly large (10), apparently flightless forest rail with bright scarlet bill and legs. Head, neck, throat, and breast dark bluish slate color. Rest of body brownish black with an olive tinge on the wings. A bluish shield covers the

forehead as in gallinules. Tail practically absent. Iris brown. Bill, legs, and feet very powerful for size of the bird. Known from a single specimen from the mountains of San Cristobal, at 2000 feet. Native name: *Kee-a.*

23) ***Purple Swamphen** (*Porphyrio porphyrio*): *See* Plate 1: 10. Found throughout the Solomon Isls. from Bougainville to San Cristobal and Rennell.

PIGEONS AND DOVES

The Solomon Isls. are very rich in pigeons. Not only are they numerous in individuals, but they are represented by no fewer than 20 species. This includes 5 species of fruit doves (*Ptilinopus*), 7 species of large pigeons (*Ducula, Gymnophaps, Columba*), 4 species of small terrestrial doves (*Chalcophaps, Gallicolumba*), and various other kinds (*Macropygia, Reinwardtoena, Caloenas,* and *Microgoura*).

Key to the Solomon Isls. Green Fruit Doves (Ptilinopus)

Adult males of the 5 species can be distinguished as follows.

(1) Throat and breast deep red; no red on top of head .... *viridis*
Throat and breast grayish, yellowish, or greenish 2

(2) A broad yellow band (bib) across the breast ... *solomonensis*
Not so 3

(3) Top of head pale gray; tips of tail-feathers yellowish .... *richardsii*
Top of head purplish red; tips of tail-feathers pale gray 4

(4) Throat and breast green; a red spot in the middle of the abdomen .... *greyii*
Gray breast separated from white belly by a broad black band .... *superbus*

24) **Superb Fruit Dove** (*Ptilinopus s. superbus* Temminck): *See* Plate 2: 11. Small (8½). *Adult Male.* Top of head purplish violet. A broad orange-rufous collar from the sides of the throat across the hind-neck. Back and wings yellowish olive. A purplish black spot on the shoulder. Upper throat whitish; lower throat and breast pale gray. Flanks green; middle of abdomen and under tail-coverts white. A broad blue-black band across the lower breast. *Female.* Lacks the breast bar and all reddish color. Upperparts green with a blue-black spot on the crown. Upper throat grayish white; lower throat and breast greenish gray. Middle of abdomen and under tail-coverts yellowish white. Iris yellow; bill gray green; feet purplish red.

Widespread from the Moluccas to Australia and Melanesia. Throughout the Solomon Isls., in mangroves, lowland and hill forest. Usually in high fruit trees. Call: a loud guttural *whoot.*

25) **Yellow-bibbed Fruit Dove** (*Ptilinopus solomonensis*): Small (8½). All green above. Anterior part of crown or merely a spot in front of the eye dark violet. Throat, sides of breast, and flanks green. Under tail-coverts and broad band across the breast deep lemon yellow; abdomen pale purplish violet. Female green throughout except for yellowish on lower abdomen and under tail-coverts. Iris yellow; bill greenish slate; feet dark red.

Six races in the Solomon Isls. In 3 of them the entire fore part of the crown is dark lilac: *solomonensis* Gray (San Cristobal, Ugi), *vulcanorum* Mayr 1931 (Vella Lavella, Vangunu, Gatukai, Kulambangra, Rendova), subspecies (?) (Russell, Buena Vista, Ramos), *neumanni* Hartert 1926 (Nissan). In 3 other races, all of them restricted to mountains, the lilac red on top of the head is confined to a large or small spot in front of the eyes: *ocularis* Mayr 1931 (Guadalcanal), *ambiguus* Mayr 1931 (Malaita), and *bistictus* Mayr 1931 (Bougainville).

A mountain bird on most of the islands, but descending to the lowlands on San Cristobal, in the central Solomons, and on a few of the isolated islands.

26) **Red-throated Fruit Dove** (*Ptilinopus viridis*): *See* Plate 2: 12. Small (8½). Male and female alike. Back, wings, and tail olive green. Shoulder patch and a few spots on the tertials pale gray. Entire throat deep crimson red. Immatures without the red throat. Iris orange; bill and feet red.

Two very distinct races: *lewisi* Ramsay (entire western Solomons, east to Guadalcanal and Malaita) with lower breast and abdomen deep green, under tail-coverts yellowish, head and chin dark gray green and olive; *eugeniae* Gould (Ugi, San Cristobal) with head and chin snow white, breast and abdomen grayish green, tips of tail-feathers more conspicuously gray. A fairly common bird throughout the Solomon Isls. Calls *coo-coo,* with the emphasis on the second syllable. In flocks; lowland and mountain forest.

27) **Pink-spotted Fruit Dove** (*Ptilinopus richardsii*): A beautiful, small (8½) dove. Head, hind-neck, throat, and breast pale gray green; top of head pale gray; upper throat yellowish. Back olive green; wings blue green; shoulder feathers with partly concealed pink spots. Flanks pale yellow green; abdomen and under tail-coverts deep salmon orange; tip of tail yellow. Iris orange; bill light green; feet red. Two very similar races: *richardsii* Ramsay (*rhodostictus* Tristram of

some authors) on Ugi and Santa Anna; *cyanopterus* Mayr 1931 on Rennell Isl. In the lowland forest of small coral islands.

28) ***Red-bellied Fruit Dove** (*Ptilinopus greyii* Bonaparte): In the Solomon Isls. found only on Gower Isl.

Key to the Solomon Isls. Large Fruit Pigeons (Ducula)

This genus is represented in the Solomon Isls. by 4 species. *Ducula* species can possibly be confused with *Gymnophaps, Columba, Reinwardtoena,* and *Caloenas* (for which *see*).

(1) Abdomen gray or rufous gray; under tail-coverts chestnut 2
Abdomen and under tail-coverts rufous chestnut 3

(2) No knob on bill; upperparts pale gray; tail much darker, wings slightly darker and with faint greenish gloss .... *pistrinaria*
Large black knob on bill; head and uppermost back pale gray; mantle, back, wings, and tail glossy greenish blue ... . *pacifica*

(3) A large red knob on bill; top of head, uppermost back, and breast pale gray; mantle, back, and wings metallic green; tail metallic blue .... *rubricera*
No knob on bill; mantle, back, wings, and tail dark slate gray; top of head paler gray .... *brenchleyi*
Differences in the call notes of the 4 species, which undoubtedly exist, have not yet been described.

29) ***Pacific Pigeon** (*Ducula pacifica* Gmelin): *See* Plate 2: 13. An inhabitant of small, oceanic, coral islets. Recorded in the Solomon Isls. from Rennell, Sikaiana, Ongtong Java, Gower, Ramos, and Buena Vista.

30) **Red-knobbed Pigeon** (*Ducula rubricera*): Large (15). Highly colored. Upperparts as described in above key. Upper

throat pinkish buff; lower throat and upper breast pale gray; abdomen rufous chestnut. Iris red; bill gray; knob cherry red; feet purplish red. The subspecies *rufigula* Salvadori is widespread in the Solomon Isls. A common bird of the lowland forest, of mangroves, and of any habitat with fruiting trees up to an altitude of 3000 feet.

31) **Gray Pigeon** (*Ducula pistrinaria*): A large (15), pale pigeon. Has no knob. A line across the forehead and a ring around the eyes white. Underparts vinaceous gray, the purer and paler gray on the abdomen strongly contrasting with the chestnut under tail-coverts. Iris dark red; bill bluish slate; feet cherry red. Throughout the Solomon Isls. (*pistrinaria* Bonaparte); particularly common along the seacoast and on small offshore islets. Sometimes travels in flocks of several hundreds.

32) **Chestnut-bellied Pigeon** (*Ducula brenchleyi* Gray): A large (14), dark pigeon. Upperparts as described in key. Sides of head pale gray; upper throat buffy; throat and breast dark rufous gray; abdomen and underside of tail bright purplish chestnut. Iris red; bill slate; feet purplish red. This is a rather uncommon pigeon, partial to the true forest and particularly to the mountain forest. Found on Guadalcanal, Malaita, and San Cristobal.

33) **Mountain Pigeon** (*Gymnophaps solomonensis* Mayr 1931): A large (15), long-tailed, pale gray pigeon. Mantle and wings dark slate gray; feathers with black edges, producing a scale-like effect. Head, upper back, rump, tail, and entire underparts pale ash gray; breast and abdomen more or less washed with pinkish vinaceous. Iris orange; eyelid and bare

space around the eye red; bill straw yellow; feet purplish red.

Similar to the Crested Pigeon, but has no crest, has a pale gray tail and a pale gray abdomen. Lives in the mountain forest, rarely below 3000 feet. Often in small flocks of 5–8 birds. Bougainville, Kulambangra, Vangunu, Guadalcanal, and Malaita.

34) ***White-throated Pigeon** (*Columba vitiensis*): The subspecies *halmaheira* Bonaparte, which is widespread in the Papuan region, occurs on the larger islands of the Solomons. White throat and cheeks and strong purplish green iridescence of the dark gray plumage are diagnostic for this race. In the Solomons usually in the hill forest, recorded from Bougainville, Vella Lavella, Kulambangra, Vangunu, Gatukai, Florida, Guadalcanal, Malaita, San Cristobal.

35) **Yellow-legged Pigeon** (*Columba pallidiceps* Ramsay): A heavy-bodied, large (14–15) pigeon. Head and upper throat pale gray; wings and tail black. Body and mantle with a strong greenish or purplish gloss on a blackish feather basis. Iris orange; bill red with a yellow tip; feet yellow. Differs from the otherwise similar White-throated Pigeon by the gray head and the yellow legs and feet. A widespread but rather rare forest pigeon. Feeds often on the ground. Bismarck Archipelago, and Solomon Isls. (Bougainville, Choiseul, Vella Lavella, Gower, Florida, Ramos, Guadalcanal, San Cristobal.)

36) ***Rufous-brown Pheasant Dove** (*Macropygia mackinlayi*): *See* Plate 2: 14. The rufous-chestnut race *arossi* Tristram (*rufocastanea* Ramsay of some authors) is common and widespread in the Solomon Isls. It is particularly common along

the coast and on small offshore islands, but is also found in the mountains up to an altitude of 4000 feet.

37) **Crested Pigeon** (*Reinwardtoena crassirostris* Gould): A medium-sized pigeon with a very long graduated tail (total length 16). Mantle, wings, and tail blackish. Crest pale ochraceous gray; throat and sides of head pale gray. Upper back gray. Entire underparts gray, darkest on the lower abdomen. A bird of the true forest, particularly in valleys in the hill and mountain forest. Favors the substage of the forest. Has a mournful, far-carrying call note. Found on Bougainville, Choiseul, Kulambangra, New Georgia, Vangunu, Gatukai, Rendova, Guadalcanal, Malaita, San Cristobal.

38) **Brown-backed Ground Pigeon** (*Chalcophaps stephani*): A small (9), green-winged, brown bird. Entire plumage except head, wings, and rump rufous brown, more purplish on the back of the head and upper back. Two alternating blackish brown and ochraceous bars across lower back and rump. Entire forehead white in the male, gray in the female. A common bird of the lowland forest. Habits much like those of *Chalcophaps indica* (*see* New Hebrides). Similar also to *Gallicolumba*. Very evenly distributed throughout the Solomon Isls., on large and small islands, from Nissan and Bougainville to San Cristobal and Santa Anna (*mortoni* Ramsay).

**Ground-doves* (Gallicolumba)

Three species are known from the Solomon Isls., but only one (*beccarii*) is widespread. Another (*salamonis*) is known from 2 specimens, while the third species (*jobiensis*) is known from one adult and 3 juvenals. Adult males of the 3 species can be distinguished as follows:

(1) Throat and breast white; top and sides of head blackish gray with a white eye-stripe; shoulders and upper back glossy purplish; lower back, rump, and most of wing black with a dull green gloss; abdomen grayish black .... *jobiensis*

(2) Forehead, sides of head and neck, throat, and breast gray; upperparts, wings, and tail olive bronze; shoulders glossy purple; abdomen earth brown .... *beccarii*

(3) Head rufous brown; throat and breast cinnamon brown; back brown with a glossy purple tint; shoulders and mantel metallic violet purple; abdomen dark reddish chocolate brown (?male or female) .... *salamonis*

All 3 species are strictly terrestrial. They seem to prefer dense coastal woods and small islands to the primary forest of the large islands. Young of the 3 species lack the distinguishing characters of the adults and cannot be identified in the field. They are rufous chocolate brown with a slight bronzy or greenish gloss on the back. *G. beccarii* is smallest (7½), *jobiensis* medium (8½), and *salamonis* largest (9½) and with a heavy bill.

Chalcophaps differs from any of the 3 species of *Gallicolumba* by the red bill, chestnut back and tail, barring of rump, glossy green wing-patch and uniformly colored underparts.

39) **Gray-throated Ground Dove** (*Gallicolumba beccarii*): *See* Plate 2: 15. Females similar to males, but without the purple patch on the wing and with the breast dull brownish gray. Iris brown; bill black; feet purple red. Three races in the Solomons: *johannae* Sclater (Nissan), *intermedia* Rothschild and Hartert (Bougainville, Gizo, New Georgia), and *solomonensis* Ogilvie-Grant (Gower, Guadalcanal, San Cristobal, Santa Anna, and Rennell).

40) **White-throated Ground Dove** (*Gallicolumba jobiensis*): Breast of females often with a buff wash. Recorded from Vella Lavella (*chalconota* Mayr 1935) and from Guadalcanal.

41) **Thick-billed Ground Dove** (*Gallicolumba salamonis* Ramsay): Recorded from Ramos and San Cristobal.

42) ***Nicobar Pigeon** (*Caloenas n. nicobarica* Linnaeus): Found throughout the Solomon Isls., usually only along the coast.

43) **Crested Choiseul Pigeon** (*Microgoura meeki* Rothschild): Large (11½). Head (except face), back, and breast blue gray; lower back and rump grayish brown; tail glossy purple. A 2-inch crest of blue-gray hairy feathers on back of head. Feathers around base of bill black; upper throat partly bare. Abdomen bright rufous cinnamon; wings brown, washed with blue gray on mantle. Upper bill flattened at the base, chalk blue with a black tip, lower bill reddish; iris dark lemon, legs purplish red.

This splendid terrestrial pigeon, discovered by A. S. Meek on Choiseul Isl., has not been found again since 1904 and may have been exterminated by imported domestic cats.

PARROTS, COCKATOOS, AND LORIES

This family is represented in the Solomon Isls. by 11 species. They offer only few problems of field identification, since nearly all of the species are very distinct or restricted in range. Some of the social lories, like *Eos cardinalis* and *Trichoglossus haematodus,* belong to the most widespread and conspicuous of Solomon Isls. birds.

Rough Key to Solomon Isls. Parrots

(1) All (pinkish) white .... *Cacatua*
(2) Large; mostly red; no green in plumage ..... *Eos, Larius* ♀
(3) Large; mostly green; no red in plumage ....
.... *Geoffroyus, Larius* ♂
(4) Very small (size of a thumb); tail very short ... *Micropsitta*
(5) All green; small (6–6½ including tail); tail long ....
.... *Vini meeki, V. placentis* ♀
(6) Bill red orange; plumage mixed green and red ....
.... *Lorius, Trichoglossus, Vini margarethae, V. placentis* ♂

44) **Cardinal Lory** (*Eos cardinalis* Gray): Large (12) with a rather long tail. Head and body bright scarlet; wings and tail darker, more brownish blood red. Iris bright red; bill dark red; feet black. A bare (?dark reddish) ring around the eyes; chin also bare.

An exceedingly numerous and noisy parrot, large flocks of which are often seen flying from one island to the next. Feeds in coconut and other fruit trees. Found throughout the Solomon Isls. from Nissan to Ugi, but rare in the San Cristobal group.

45) ***Coconut Lory** (*Trichoglossus haematodus*): *See* Plate 2: 16. Common in the entire Solomon Isls. (probably *massena* Bonaparte).

46) **Yellow-bibbed Lory** (*Lorius chlorocercus* Gould): A large (10½), short-tailed lory. Plumage mostly red; wings and outer half of tail green. Top of head and spot on sides of throat black. A broad, lemon-yellow band across the throat.

Thighs royal blue; underwing red and blue. Iris orange; bill bright red; feet black.

Lowland forest up to an altitude of 3000 feet, rarely in coconut plantations. Feeds in small flocks. Eastern Solomon Isls. (Savo, Guadalcanal, Malaita, Ugi, San Cristobal, and Rennell).

47) **Meek's Lorikeet** (*Vini meeki* Rothschild and Hartert): Small (6½). Darker green above; paler green below. A dark bluish green spot in the middle of the crown. Upper back partly golden brown; underside of tail yellow. Iris pale red; bill dark red; feet orange.

In the mountains, usually above 3000 feet, rarely descending to the lowlands. Lives in the treetops, usually singly or in pairs; very active. Known only from Bougainville, Kulambangra, Guadalcanal, and Malaita.

48) **Blue-eared Lorikeet** (*Vini placentis*): Small (6), long-tailed. *Male.* Green; top of head and underparts pale green. Cheeks and chin, sides of breast, and flanks red. A (violet-) blue spot on the ear region. Tail feathers green and red with yellow tips. *Female.* All green; paler below. Yellow-striped ear-patch. Iris orange; bill bright red; feet dull red.

In coconut groves along the coast. The subspecies *pallidior* Rothschild and Hartert, which is widespread in the Bismarck Archipelago, reaches Fead Isl., Nissan, and Bougainville.

49) **Duchess Lorikeet** (*Vini margarethae* Tristram): *See* Plate 2: 17. Small (8). Underparts red; a broad yellow band across the breast, bordered with black. Forehead and hindneck red; occiput black. Back and wings dark green; middle

of lower back and rump golden olive. Tail red, lateral feathers with greenish yellow tips. Sides of rump red in males, yellow in females. Iris and feet orange; bill reddish orange.

Feeds in flowering trees. Usually in small, rather quiet flocks. More or less a mountain bird, but occasionally in lowland forest and coconut plantations along the seashore. Bougainville, Ysabel, Gizo, Kulambangra, Guadalcanal, Malaita, San Cristobal.

50) **Pigmy Parrot** (*Micropsitta* finschii*): *See* Plate 2: 18. Small (3–3½). Green. Iris orange; bill and feet gray. Cere and nostril pink in male, grayish in female. Four subspecies: *nanina* Tristram (Bougainville, Choiseul, Ysabel) with a blue spot on the crown and a bluish tail; chin bluish in male, pink in female. Similar are *tristrami* Rothschild and Hartert (central Solomons), and *aolae* Ogilvie-Grant (Russell, Florida, Guadalcanal, Malaita). The crown is pure green and the middle of the abdomen reddish in the male of *finschii* Ramsay (Ugi, San Cristobal, ?Rennell).

51) **Mountain Pigmy Parrot** (*Micropsitta bruijnii*): Small (3½). *Male.* Top of head, cheeks, and ear region pink. Hindneck and sides of throat bright blue. Back, wings, and flanks green. Middle of belly and under tail-coverts rose color. *Female.* All green, more yellowish below. Top of head blue. Iris brown; bill and feet gray.

Found in the mountain forest, occasionally down to 500 feet. Food fungi? Two races: *brevis* Mayr 1940 (Bougainville); *rosea* Mayr 1940 (Kulambangra, Guadalcanal).

52) **White Cockatoo** (*Cacatua ducorpsi* Bonaparte): Large (14). All white with a pink hue. Crested. Underside of wings

and tail partly yellow. Iris red (male) or brown (female); bill horn color; feet blackish.

Common, particularly in the lowlands. Likes to perch on high trees. Often in flocks. Very noisy, particularly in flight. Raises crest when excited. Does considerable damage in native gardens. From Bougainville to Malaita and Guadalcanal. Absent from the San Cristobal group.

53) **King Parrot** (*Larius roratus*): Large (11–13). Male and female strikingly different. *Male.* Green with outer wing- and tail-feathers blue. A red patch under the wing extending to the flanks. Iris orange; upper bill orange; lower bill and feet black. *Female.* Red and blue with a black bill. Head and throat bright red. Back, wings, and thighs dark (purplish) red. A band across upper back, abdomen, and underwing blue or purplish blue. Tail red with a pale tip. Outer wing-feathers blue.

Usually in pairs, occasionally in small parties. Very destructive to fruit crops in native gardens. Common in second-growth habitats and true forest. Mating call: a ringing whistle. Has also a cockatoo-like harsh call. The subspecies *solomonensis* Rothschild and Hartert is found throughout the Solomons, from Bougainville to San Cristobal.

54) **Song Parrot** (*Geoffroyus heteroclitus*): Medium (9–9½), mostly green; underwing blue. *Male.* Head dull yellow, a pale bluish gray collar encircling the neck. *Female.* Head blue gray. Iris pale yellow; upper bill yellow (male) or black (female), lower bill black; legs gray.

Lowland and mountain forest. Feeds in high trees, usually in pairs. Has a remarkable, eery song, occasionally performed in flight. Two subspecies: *heteroclitus* Hombron and Jacquinot (Bismarck Archipelago and all Solomon Isls. from Bougainville to Malaita and San Cristobal); *hyacinthinus* Mayr 1931 (Rennell) with the violet gray extended to upper back, breast, and flanks.

CUCKOOS AND COUCALS

Seven species of this family* have been reported from the Solomon Isls., but 3 of them are merely winter visitors, and only 2 species (*Cacomantis variolosus* and *Eudynamis scolopacea*) are widespread on the islands.

55) **Oriental Cuckoo** (*Cuculus saturatus* Blyth): Medium (11–12½). Gray above, wings more brownish, tail more blackish with a few inconspicuous white bars and spots. Throat pale gray; breast and abdomen white with narrow black transverse bars. Some females have a rufous phase, in which the upperparts are barred rufous and black; the underparts are buffy white with a few (on the abdomen) or many (on the throat) blackish brown crossbars. Iris and feet yellow; bill black with a yellowish base.

The ash gray upperparts and barred underparts of adults are diagnostic. The species is apparently silent in winter quarters. Most records are between October and April. Nests in eastern Asia; winters from India to Australia. A few records from the Solomon Isls. Rare.

56) **Brush Cuckoo** (*Cacomantis variolosus*): Small (9–9½). Upperparts dark slate gray with a slight greenish gloss, par-

ticularly on the wings; tail blackish with narrow white tip, outer feathers with white bars. Upper throat grayish; lower throat, breast, and abdomen brownish ocher. Immatures rufous, mottled with gray. Iris reddish brown; eyelid yellow; bill black with a horn-colored lower mandible; feet yellowish brown.

More often heard than seen, but rather common on most of the larger islands. Whistled call-note, heard during both night and day, insufficiently described. The subspecies *addendus* Rothschild and Hartert has been recorded from Bougainville, Ysabel, Kulambangra, New Georgia, Guadalcanal, Malaita, and San Cristobal.

57) ***Fan-tailed Cuckoo** (*Cacomantis pyrrhophanus*): *See* New Caledonia. Very similar to *variolosus,* but adults differ by the deep rufous underparts, immatures by being less rust colored. Breeds in New Caledonia (*pyrrhophanus* Vieillot). Rare winter visitor to the Solomon Isls. (Ysabel, Rennell).

58) ***Shining Cuckoo** (*Chalcites lucidus*). The New Zealand race (*lucidus* Gmelin) is a common winter visitor to the entire Solomon Isls., where it has been recorded from March to September. It likes Casuarina groves along the beach. An endemic race (*harterti* Mayr 1932) occurs on Rennell and Bellona. It is small (6) and heavily barred underneath.

59) **Koel** (*Eudynamis scolopacea*): Large (13–14), long-tailed. Male all black with a greenish blue gloss. Female mottled black and rufous chestnut; wings and tail barred black and rufous. Underparts paler, more ochraceous, finely barred. Iris red; bill greenish horn color; feet gray.

In the Solomon Isls. this parasitic cuckoo probably victimizes the myna (*Mino*) more than any other bird. Other hosts are possibly glossy starlings (*Aplonis*) and crows (*Corvus*). On San Cristobal, where *Mino* and *Corvus* are absent, it might lay its egg in the nests of *Dicrurus* or of *Meliarchus*. The 2-syllabled call note is often heard, even in the night, but the birds generally keep themselves well hidden in the foliage of tall trees. Lives in the lowland forest. The subspecies *alberti* Rothschild and Hartert has been recorded from Bougainville, Choiseul, Vella Lavella, Gizo, Rendova, Buena Vista, Guadalcanal, Malaita, and San Cristobal.

60) ***Long-tailed New Zealand Cuckoo** (*Eudynamis taitensis* Sparrman): *See* Figure 8. Recorded from the whole length of the Solomon Isls., particularly from the smaller, outlying islands.

61) **Buff-headed Coucal** (*Centropus* milo*): *See* Figure 7. A large (25–27), magpie-like, long-tailed bird. Bill big and strongly curved; feet powerful. Two subspecies: *milo* Gould (Guadalcanal, Florida). Head, upper back, throat, and breast buff; lower back, abdomen, wings, and tail black with a purplish blue gloss; *albidiventris* Rothschild (entire central Solomon Isls.) like preceding, but entire underparts buff or pale ochraceous. Immatures have head, upper back, and throat sooty; underparts dirty buff mottled with black. Wings and tail brown with black bars. Iris red; bill black; feet bluish gray.

Feeds on the forest floor, but spends much time in trees. Has a raucous call note: *na-ow*.

OWLS

62) *Barn Owl (*Tyto alba*): *Cf.* Figure 9. Rare. Recorded only 5 times from the Solomons (Nissan to Santa Anna). Birds may be referred to *crassirostris* Mayr 1935.

63) **Boobook Owl** (*Ninox jacquinoti*): *See* Plate 2: 19. Small (8–10). Different on each island of the Solomons but unmistakable since it is the only small owl of this area. Upperparts chocolate or rufous brown, with or without buffy white spots. Throat whitish; remainder of underparts either buffy white with a brown breast band, or chocolate or rufous brown with buff spots or bars. Underwing with a slight pink wash. Seven subspecies: *mono* Mayr 1935 (Mono); *eichhorni* Hartert 1929 (Bougainville, Choiseul); *jacquinoti* Bonaparte (Ysabel); *floridae* Mayr 1935 (Florida); *granti* Sharpe (Guadalcanal); *malaitae* Mayr 1931 (Malaita); *roseoaxillaris* Hartert 1929 (San Cristobal). Lowland and mountain forest. Voice not described.

64) **Fearful Owl** (*Nesasio solomonensis* Hartert): Large (15) with powerful bill and claws. Above densely mottled rufous and dark brown. Deep ocher below with narrow, blackish shaft streaks. Lowland and hill forest. Probably lives on opossums and birds. Restricted to Bougainville, Choiseul, and Ysabel. Rare. Call note unknown.

FROGMOUTHS

65) **Marbled Frogmouth** (*Podargus ocellatus*): Large (13), with a very broad (2) bill. Brown or rufous brown with an

inconspicuous pepper-and-salt pattern. Wings with conspicuous white spots (on upper wing-coverts). Underparts more or less spotted or barred with white. Wings and tail inconspicuously barred. Lowland forest. Voice not yet described. Known only from Bougainville, Choiseul, and Ysabel (*inexpectatus* Hartert).

NIGHTJARS

66) **White-throated Nightjar** (*Eurostopodus mystacalis*): Medium (11). Dark brown, with the disruptive camouflage pattern typical of nightjars. White or buffy white spot on wing (third to fifth primary). A white spot on either side of the throat. The Solomon Isls. are inhabited by an endemic race (*nigripennis* Ramsay), which has been recorded only from Bougainville, Shortland group, Ysabel, and central Solomon Isls. Usually found near or on the beach. Call note not yet described.

SWIFTS

Four species of cave swiftlets (*Collocalia*) are the only representatives of this family* in the Solomon Isls.

67) **Whitehead's Swiftlet** (*Collocalia whiteheadi*): The largest (5¼)) species of swiftlets in the Solomons. In the field probably indistinguishable from *vanikorensis*. Lower throat and breast are silvery gray in *whiteheadi;* upper throat and chin fuscous gray. Rump tends to be paler than back; tail only slightly forked. Is perhaps restricted to the mountains. The subspecies *orientalis* Mayr 1935 is known from a single specimen from Guadalcanal.

68) *__Vanikoro Swiftlet__ (*Collocalia vanikorensis*): The subspecies *vanikorensis* Quoy and Gaimard occurs throughout the Solomon Isls. from Bougainville to Santa Anna, but seems to be absent from some of the outlying islands (Nissan, Rennell).

69) *__White-rumped Swiftlet__ (*Collocalia spodiopygia*): *Cf.* Plate 2: 20. The subspecies *reichenowi* Stresemann 1912 has been recorded so far only from Guadalcanal and Kulambangra. It is possibly a mountain bird in the Solomon Isls.

70) *__Glossy Swiftlet__ (*Collocalia esculenta*): This is the most common swiftlet of the Solomon Isls. Three subspecies: *becki* Mayr 1931 (most of the Solomon Isls., from Nissan to Malaita and Guadalcanal) with a much-reduced white area on lower belly, gloss of upperparts bluish green; *makirensis* Mayr 1931 (San Cristobal) with the white of belly contrasting with gray breast, very small; *desiderata* Mayr 1931 (Rennell) with some white on rump, belly white.

CRESTED SWIFTS

71) **Whiskered Tree Swift** (*Hemiprocne** *mystacea*): *See* Figure 10. A large (9) swift with deeply forked tail and elongated outer tail-feathers. Back and underparts (blue) gray. Top of head, wings, and tail glossy blue black. Eyebrows (with a crest-like lengthening) and a pair of narrow whiskers from the base of the bill to the sides of the throat white. A small white patch on the inner wing-coverts. The subspecies *woodfordiana* Hartert occurs throughout the Solomon Isls. from Bougainville to Malaita and San Cristobal; Rennell Isl.

KINGFISHERS

The 8 kingfishers that occur in the Solomon Isls. belong basically to 2 groups.* One, consisting of 3 small-sized species of the genera *Alcedo* and *Ceyx,* comprises the fish-eating water kingfishers. (*Ceyx lepidus* is not quite typical, as it lives in the forest and feeds largely on insects.) The other group consists of 5 species of *Halcyon,* which have feeding habits similar to those of shrikes or flycatchers and which usually nest in hollow trees.

Key to Solomon Isls. Kingfishers

(1) Underparts washed with buff, ocher, or rufous 2
Underparts white without a yellow or rufous wash 6

(2) Bill yellow or orange red 3
Bill black with or without a whitish horn-colored base 4

(3) Small (5); top of head blue black .... Some subspecies of *Ceyx lepidus*
Large (10½); top of head rufous brown .... *Halcyon bougainvillei*

(4) Medium (8–9); a distinct buffy, or rufous collar across the hind-neck .... *H. chloris* and *H. sancta*
Smaller; no collar; middle of back blue 5

(5) Small (5); underparts bright yellow or orange; wings blackish with blue spots; lives in the forest .... Some subspecies of *Ceyx lepidus*
Larger (6); underparts deep ocher; wings blue; lives along streams or the beach .... *Alcedo atthis*

(6) Top of head blue or greenish blue 7
Top of head white .... *Halcyon saurophaga*

(7) Small (4½–5½); no white collar across hind-neck 8
Larger (7–9); white collar across hind-neck 9

(8) Small (4½); upperparts uniform ultramarine blue; complete or interrupted blue breast band; feet blackish .. *Ceyx pusillus*
Small (5½); upperparts blackish blue with light blue spots and streaks; no breast band; feet orange . *C. lepidus gentianus*

(9) Medium (7); upperparts deep purplish blue .... *Halcyon leucopygia*
Larger (8–9); upperparts greenish blue .... *H. chloris*

72) **River Kingfisher** (*Alcedo atthis*): Entire upperparts, sides of head, wing, and tail dark blue, lighter blue on the middle of the back. An indistinct buff spot on either side of the neck. Throat buff white; remainder of underparts deep rufous ocher. Iris brown; bill black with reddish base; feet reddish brown.

Habits as in the European subspecies. Voice: a shrill *teet-teet*. Found not only on rivers, but also along the sea-coast, wherever the action of the waves has produced steep banks. The subspecies *salomonensis* Rothschild and Hartert is found throughout the Solomon Isls. from Bougainville and Mono to Malaita and San Cristobal.

73) **Mangrove Kingfisher** (*Ceyx pusillus*): *See* Plate 2: 21. Three subspecies in Solomon Isls.: *richardsi* Tristram (central Solomon Isls.; ?Ysabel) with the blue breast band complete or nearly so; *bougainvillei* Ogilvie-Grant 1914 (Bougainville, Choiseul) with the breast band broadly interrupted; *aolae* Ogilvie-Grant (Guadalcanal, ?Florida) breast band interrupted; larger. Iris brown; bill black; feet dark brown.

This diminutive blue and white kingfisher is partial to

mangroves. It is rarely found away from the estuaries of lowland rivers and from the seacoast. Voice a high-pitched whistle: *teet*. Flight rapid.

74) **Dwarf Forest Kingfisher** (*Ceyx lepidus*): Most of the 6 races of this species in the Solomon Isls. are so divergent that no single description would fit them all. On the whole the upperparts are some shade of blue (from greenish to purplish) with head and wings spotted blue on a blackish background; the feathers on the middle of the back, rump, and upper tail-coverts are lighter and brighter blue. There is a light spot on the lores and 2 similar ones on the sides of the neck, corresponding to the color of the underparts. The underparts are either deep orange ocher, yellowish buff, or white; the throat is usually much paler than breast and belly. Iris brown; feet fleshy white to orange red.

The 6 subspecies are: *pallidus* Mayr 1935 (Buka, Bougainville) and *meeki* Rothschild (Choiseul, Ysabel) with black bill; blackish upperparts with pale greenish blue markings; underparts yellowish to orange buff; *collectoris* Rothschild and Hartert (central Solomon Isls.) with orange-red bill; upperparts deep purplish blue, lower back light blue; underparts deep rufous ocher; *nigromaxilla* Rothschild and Hartert (Guadalcanal) similar to *collectoris* but upper bill black; *malaitae* Mayr 1935 (Malaita) similar, but lighter above and below; *gentianus* Tristram (San Cristobal) with black bill; white below; middle of back light blue.

This confiding forest kingfisher usually nests in the banks of small creeks and steep slopes, but is often found far from water and up to 4000 feet altitude. Its high-pitched slightly sibilant whistle is frequently heard, but the bird sits so quietly and well concealed in some low tree of the primeval forest that it is seldom seen. Feeds on insects, mostly water insects.

75) ***White-collared Kingfisher** (*Halcyon chloris*): *See* Plate 2: 22. Five subspecies in the Solomon Isls.: *alberti* Rothschild and Hartert (Bougainville to Ysabel, Florida, Savo, Guadalcanal, and central Solomon Isls.) males deeper ochraceous underneath, throat and middle of belly of females whitish; *mala* Mayr 1935 (Malaita) paler ochraceous underneath, more greenish blue above; *pavuvu* Mayr 1935 (Pavuvu) with very large, buff loral spots; *solomonis* Ramsay (San Cristobal, Ugi, Santa Anna) medium (8½), males with the rust color reduced (conspicuous rusty breast band), females all white underneath, immatures with the breast barred with black; *amoena* Mayr 1931 (Rennell) much smaller (7½), males very blue above, rufous restricted to eye-stripe, lores, nuchal collar, and sides of throat; females without rufous.

76) **Beach Kingfisher** (*Halycyon saurophaga*): Large (10½). Head and entire underparts white. Back, wings, and tail brilliant azure blue; back more greenish blue in the female. Iris brown; bill black with a horn-colored base; feet blackish.

Everywhere along the beaches and the estuaries of rivers. Perches on coral rocks or on branches overhanging the shore. Has a loud rattling call. Feeds on crab, fish, lizards, and insects. The subspecies *saurophaga* Gould is widespread from northern New Guinea to the Bismarck Archipelago and the Solomon Isls. (from Nissan to San Cristobal and Santa Anna).

77) ***Sacred Kingfisher** (*Halcyon sancta*): Common throughout the Solomon Isls., particularly between April and September. A visitor from Australia.

78) **Ultramarine Kingfisher** (*Halcyon leucopygia* Verreaux): Small (7). Entire underparts white except vent which is chestnut purple. Upperparts mostly a beautiful, deep ultramarine blue with a broad white collar; middle of back of males white, of females ultramarine. A violet patch on either side of the rump. A bird of the true forest, usually perched on rather high trees. Northern chain of islands: Bougainville, Shortland, Choiseul, Ysabel, Florida, and Guadalcanal.

79) **Moustached Kingfisher** (*Halcyon bougainvillei*): Large (10½). Underparts a rich rust color; throat paler. Top of head and upper back deep rufous. Wings and tail dark ultramarine blue. Feathers on middle of lower back and rump light greenish blue. A narrow blue line circles around the hind-neck from eye to eye; it is separated by a rufous tuft of feathers from a blue moustache which begins at the base of the bill. The scapulars, which in the male are blue like the wing, are light olive brown in the female. Iris brown; bill and feet red.

Nothing is known of the habits of this rarest and most handsome of the kingfishers of the Solomon Isls. Two subspecies: *bougainvillei* Rothschild (lowlands of South Bougainville); *excelsa* Mayr 1941 (mountains of Guadalcanal) pale ocher underneath; scapulars of the female blackish olive.

BEE-EATERS

80) **Rainbow Bird** (*Merops* ornatus* Latham): Medium (7½). A greenish appearing bird with a rather long and somewhat curved bill. In full breeding plumage with a black patch on the middle of the throat and a broad black line from

the bill through the eye. Back and abdomen green with a bluish or golden wash. Rump and under tail-coverts light blue. Hind-neck and a patch on the wings brown. Central tail-feathers elongated to a streamer. Immatures with all the colors duller and without a black patch on the throat. Very variable. Breeds in Australia; a rare winter visitor to the Solomon Isls., between March and October.

ROLLERS

81) **Dollar Bird** (*Eurystomus orientalis*): *See* Figure 11. A large (12), more or less bluish bird with a bright red bill. Top and sides of head sooty black; back dull greenish blue, wings brighter. Throat purplish blue with lighter streaks; breast and abdomen blue. Tail and outer wing-feathers black with an ultramarine tinge. A very light blue roundish patch (the size of a silver dollar) visible on the spread wing. Iris dark red; bill orange red; feet brownish red.

A conspicuous bird. Perches on treetops or prominent branches from where it sallies out, like a flycatcher, for flying insects. During the mating season it indulges in spectacular display flights ("roller"). Voice rather loud and disagreeable. Nests in hollow trees. Open country, edge of forest; restricted to lowlands. The subspecies *solomonensis* Sharpe is found throughout the Solomons, from Bougainville to San Cristobal and Santa Anna.

HORNBILLS

82) ***Papuan Hornbill** (*Rhyticeros plicatus*): *See* Figure 12. Two subspecies in the Solomon Isls.: *harterti* Mayr 1934

(Buka, Bougainville, Shortland group); *mendanae* Hartert 1924 (Choiseul, Ysabel, Malaita, and Guadalcanal) smaller and with a more slender bill. Absent from San Cristobal and the central Solomon Isls. A single record from Vangunu may be erroneous.

SONGBIRDS

JEWEL-THRUSHES

83) **Black-faced Jewel-Thrush** (*Pitta anerythra*): *See* Figure 13. A robust, short-tailed, ground bird (6). Face and sides of head black; back dark moss green. A concealed patch of glittering turquoise (blue green) on the lesser upper wing-coverts. Chin black; rest of underparts clay color or pale brown. Iris brown; bill black; feet pale gray. In the subspecies *anerythra* Rothschild (Ysabel) the crown is rich chestnut brown, paler on the nape, and the underparts are deep ocher; in *pallida* Rothschild (Bougainville) the crown is mostly black, the underparts pale clay color; *nigrifrons* Mayr 1935 (Choiseul) is intermediate.

A shy forest bird with habits typical of the genus.* Usually in mountain valleys or alluvial plains. Calls mostly in the early morning, late evening, and during rain.

SWALLOWS

Only 2 species of swallows occur in the Solomon Isls., a common resident one and a rare migrant visitor from Australia.

84) ***Pacific Swallow** (*Hirundo tahitica subfusca* Gould): *See* Plate 3: 23. Throughout the Solomon Isls.

85) **Australian Tree Martin** (*Hirundo nigricans*): Small (5–5½). Upperparts bluish black or sooty brown with a conspicuous light (pale rufous or buff) rump. Tail slightly forked. Forehead rufous. Underparts dirty white with or without a pale rufous wash; throat with inconspicuous narrow streaks. The pale belly and rump separate this species from *tahitica*. Its manner of flight and pale underparts distinguish it from the White-rumped Swiftlet. Breeds in Australia (*nigricans* Vieillot). Winters occasionally in the Solomon Isls. Recorded from Guadalcanal.

CUCKOO-SHRIKES

This family is represented in the Solomon Isls. by at least 7 species.

Key to Solomon Isls. Cuckoo-Shrikes

(1) Underparts brown (cinnamon or rufous) .... *Edolisoma tenuirostre* ♀
Underparts white, gray, or black 2

(2) Underparts all black .... *E. holopolium* ♂
Underparts with white or gray 3

(3) Abdomen or entire underparts white 4
Abdomen gray or barred black and white 6

(4) Small (6½). Entire underparts white or buffy white; rump white; a white patch on wing .... *Lalage leucopyga*
Larger; upperparts gray 5

(5) Medium (9–10). Underparts all white (except breast which is more or less grayish). A broad black bar from eye to bill and forehead. Tail dark gray or black ...... *Coracina papuensis*

Large (12). Tail-feathers, except middle pair, with white tips .... *C. novaehollandiae*

(6) Eye yellow .... *C. lineata*

Eye brown 7

(7) Very large (12–13) with a big bill .... *C. caledonica*

Medium (8–10) *Edolisoma tenuirostre* ♂, *E. holopolium* ♀

86) ***Long-tailed Triller** (*Lalage leucopyga*): The subspecies *affinis* Tristram is found only on Ugi and San Cristobal where it is more common in the mountains than in the lowlands.

87) **Black-bellied Graybird** (*Edolisoma holopolium*): Medium (8–9). *Adult male.* Forehead, sides of head, entire underparts, and tail glossy black. Rest of upperparts clear gray, wings slightly lighter. *Female.* All gray, including lores. Tail and wing-tips black. Iris brown; bill and legs black.

The subspecies *holopolium* Sharpe, as described, occurs on Buka, Bougainville, Choiseul, Ysabel, and Guadalcanal. The smaller race *pygmaeum* Mayr 1931 has been recorded only from Kulambangra and Vangunu. The subspecies *tricolor* Mayr 1931 (Malaita) has a whitish gray patch on the black wings and (in the male) a narrow black collar across the hind-neck. A bird of the true forest, particularly between an altitude of 1500 and 3000 feet. Voice not yet described. Rather rare.

88) ***Cicada Bird** (*Edolisoma tenuirostre*): Three subspecies in the Solomons: *erythropygium* Sharpe (Russell, Florida, Savo, Guadalcanal, Malaita) with the gray male differing from the female *holopolium* by darker color, by a black band between eye and bill, and by a blackish ear region,; adult females have the back dark brown, wings and tail rufous, and

a grayish cap; the cap is brownish in immature females; *saturatius* Rothschild and Hartert (northern Solomons from Bougainville to Ysabel and central Solomons) darker; *salomonis* Tristram (San Cristobal) entire upperparts, wings, and tail of females gray; underparts deep rufous. Lowland forest and second growth.

89) **Yellow-eyed Graybird** (*Coracina lineata*): Medium (8½–9½). *Male.* Blue gray with a black mask extending from eye to eye across the forehead. Wings and tail black. In *females* only the throat is blue gray; breast and abdomen barred black and white. Iris yellow; bill and feet black. The male differs from the male *Edolisoma tenuirostre* and from the female *E. holopolium* by the yellow eye, the short blunt bill, and the strong bluish tone in the gray plumage.

Six subspecies: *nigrifrons* Tristram (Bougainville, Choiseul, Ysabel), *ombriosa* Rothschild and Hartert (central Solomons), *solomonensis* Ramsay [formerly called *pusilla*] (Guadalcanal), and *malaitae* Mayr 1931 (Malaita) as described above; *makirae* Mayr, 1935 (San Cristobal) with inconspicuous white and gray (males) or white and black (females) barring of breast and abdomen; *gracilis* Mayr 1931 (Rennell Isl.) with the males barred black and white, exactly as the females. Lowland and mountain forest. Rarer along the edge of forest and in clearings.

90) **White-bellied Graybird** (*Coracina papuensis*): *See* Plate 3: 25. Medium (9–10). Underparts white; breast more or less shaded with pale gray. Upperparts pearl gray; wings and tail dark gray. A black mask extends from eye to eye across the forehead. Iris brown; bill and feet black.

Three subspecies not distinguishable in the field. The

palest (*perpallida* Rothschild and Hartert 1916) from Bougainville to Choiseul, Ysabel and Florida Isl.; an intermediate race (*elegans* Ramsay) from Vella Lavella through the central Solomon Isls. to Russell and Guadalcanal; and a large, dark race (*eyerdami* Mayr 1931) on Malaita. Not found on San Cristobal. Extremely common along the coast, in coconut plantations, second growth, and along the edge of the forest. Conspicuous and noisy. Call: *oo-REE-ah*.

91) ***Melanesian Graybird** (*Coracina caledonica*): Large (12–13). The males of the 3 Solomon Isls. subspecies are very dark with the sides of the head, throat, and part of breast glossy black. Females grayer. They are: *bougainvillei* Mathews 1928 (Bougainville), *welchmani* Tristram (Ysabel), and *kulambangrae* Rothschild and Hartert 1916 (Kulambangra, New Georgia, Vangunu). Iris brown. Forest, apparently often at higher altitudes.

92) **Black-faced Graybird** (*Coracina novaehollandiae melanops* Latham): Large (12). Upperparts pearl gray. *Adult.* Face and throat black; breast gray; abdomen white. Wings and tail blackish, lateral tail-feathers with broad white tips. *Immature.* Similar but with less black. Line through the eye to the ear black. Forehead gray; throat whitish; breast gray with indistinct white crossbars.

Breeds in Australia; migrates to the tropics, but reaches the Bismarck Archipelago and the Solomon Isls. only sparingly. On the coast, particularly in Casuarina groves. Usually in flocks, noisily chattering.

THRUSHES

93) ***Island Thrush** (*Turdus poliocephalus*): All 3 subspecies from the Solomon Isls. are black with yellow bill and tail. The subspecies *bougainvillei* Mayr 1941 (Bougainville) and *kulambangrae* Mayr 1941 (Kulambangra) are mountain birds. The Rennell Isl. race (*rennellianus* Mayr 1931) occurs in the lowland forest. The species remains to be discovered in the mountains of Guadalcanal and possibly those of San Cristobal.

94) **Ground Thrush** (*Zoothera dauma*): Medium (8½). Brown above, lighter and more rufous on the rump; crown and back with blackish crescents. Underparts buff, more ocher on breast, also with scattered blackish crescents. Wings dark brown with pale rufous spots. Iris and bill dark brown; feet pale flesh color. The subspecies *choiseuli* Hartert 1924 (Choiseul) is known from a single specimen.

95) **San Cristobal Ground Thrush** (*Zoothera margaretae* Mayr 1935): Medium (8). Brown above with 2 wing-bars formed by white spots. Face and underparts mottled brown and white; feathers of breast and flanks with brown margins; middle of throat and lower abdomen almost pure white or with a tawny wash. Iris brown; bill black; feet pinkish white. Mountain forest of San Cristobal above 1800 feet. A secretive ground bird whose habits are still unknown.

WARBLERS

96) **Shade Warbler** (*Vitia parens* Mayr 1935): Small (4½). Dark brown above; underparts much lighter. Throat ochra-

ceous; breast and abdomen olive gray with a brownish wash. An indistinct pale brown eye-stripe. Iris red brown; bill brown; legs brownish flesh color. Mountains of San Cristobal above 1800 feet. This nondescript-looking, dark little warbler seems to live in the undergrowth of the mountain forest. Habits and song unknown.

97) **Reed Warbler** (*Acrocephalus arundinaceus*): Small (5½–6). Plain brown above; buffy white below; breast and flanks washed with ocher. An indistinct white eyebrow. Iris brown; bill blackish, horn-colored below; legs and feet grayish brown. The subspecies *meyeri* Stresemann 1925 has been recorded in the Solomon Isls. from Guadalcanal and from Gijunabena Isl. (near Ysabel).

Lives in the reed beds of swamps and along lowland rivers, occasionally in grassy fields. Sings frequently (probably: *carr-carr-keet-keet*), even at night, but is rarely seen since it likes to remain well hidden. The nest is a deep cup woven between reed stems, about 2–3 feet above the water or ground. Breeding season and voice of Solomon Isls. subspecies insufficiently known.

98) **Kulambangra Warbler** (*Phylloscopus amoenus* Hartert 1929): Small (4). Dark olive brown above, almost blackish. Face blackish, mottled with olive. Underparts dull yellowish olive, washed with brownish on sides of breast and flanks; throat and breast streaky. Iris brown; bill brown (yellowish below); legs and feet grayish. Known only from the mountain forest of Kulambangra. Habits unknown. Differs from *Phylloscopus tr. pallescens* by the brownish olive underparts and by the blackish top of the head. *Zosterops murphyi* differs by its white eye-ring and its olive green upperparts.

99) **Island Leaf Warbler** (*Phylloscopus trivirgatus*): Small (4–4½). Dull olive green above; throat whitish; breast and abdomen yellow. Top of head darker than back, a whitish eye-stripe present. Eye-stripe, whitish throat, and yellow belly distinguish it from *Zosterops ugiensis* and *Z. murphyi*. Iris brown; bill black (horn color below); legs and feet gray.

A lively bird of the forest canopy. Flits actively through the treetops gleaning insects from twigs and leaves. Found also in smaller trees on the edge of the forest and in second growth. Song strophe high pitched, thin, and often repeated: *sisse-birredje.*

The 4 subspecies in the Solomon Isls. are restricted to the mountain forest, above 1500 feet, most common above 3000 feet: *becki* Hartert 1929 (Guadalcanal, Malaita, Ysabel); *bougainvillei* Mayr 1935 (Bougainville); *pallescens* Mayr 1935 (Kulambangra) with the yellow of the abdomen very pale, almost whitish; and *makirensis* Mayr 1935 (San Cristobal) with the abdomen rich lemon yellow.

FLYCATCHERS

100) **Rufous-fronted Fantail** (*Rhipidura rufifrons*): *See* Plate 3: 27. Small (5–6). Forehead bright tawny. Hind-neck, upper back, and wings brown. Lower back, rump, and base of tail tawny (light fox red); rest of tail black with white tips. Upper throat white; black band across the lower throat with a "scaly" border against the white belly.

Seven subspecies in the Solomon Isls., which differ mainly in the amount of rufous on tail and back: *commoda* Hartert 1918 (Bougainville, Shortland, Choiseul, Ysabel, and neighboring islands); *granti* Hartert 1918 (central Solomon Isls.); *rufofronta* Ramsay (Guadalcanal) and *brunnea* Mayr 1931 (Malaita) with very little rufous on tail; *russata* Tristram (San Cristobal) and *kuperi* Mayr 1931 (Santa Anna) with a very rufous back and a narrow black collar across the throat; *ugiensis* Mayr 1931 (Ugi) with the entire throat black.

A common bird of forest, edge of forest, second growth, occasionally even mangroves. On some islands, Malaita for example, only in the mountain forest. Habits those of the genus.*

101) **Mountain Fantail** (*Rhipidura drownei*): Small (5½). Head mouse gray with a white eye-stripe. Back, wings, and tail dusky gray brown; wings and tail with a rufous wash. Throat white; breast and abdomen gray with white streaks and an ochraceous wash. Iris brown; bill and feet black. Two subspecies: *drownei* Mayr 1931 (Bougainville), and *ocularis* Mayr 1931 (Guadalcanal) with a white stripe behind the eye and less of a rufous-ocher wash on abdomen, wings, and tail. Mountain forest. Voice and habits not yet described.

102) **Dusky Fantail** (*Rhipidura tenebrosa* Ramsay): Medium (6½). Smoky brown, head blackish. Tail-feathers with broad white tips. Upper throat mottled with white. Two rufous bars across the wings (formed by tips of wing-coverts). Endemic on San Cristobal. More common in the mountains than in the lowlands. The dark abdomen and the white tip of the tail are diagnostic.

103) **Collared Fantail** (*Rhipidura fuliginosa*): *See* New Hebrides. Found in the mountains of San Cristobal (*?brenchleyi*

Sharpe). Differs from *tenebrosa* by buff abdomen, white throat and eyebrow.

104) **Malaita Fantail** (*Rhipidura malaitae* Mayr 1931): Small (6). Pale rust color, below paler, more ochraceous. Top of head brown. Wing-tip blackish. Iris red brown; bill and feet blackish. Found only in the mountains of Malaita between 2000 and 4000 feet.

105) **Cockerell's Fantail** (*Rhipidura cockerelli*): Medium (6–7). Head black except for a concealed white spot above the eye. Upperparts grayish or black; abdomen white. Seven races, some very distinct. The subspecies *septentrionalis* Rothschild and Hartert 1916 (Buka, Bougainville, Shortland Isl.), *interposita* Rothschild and Hartert 1916 (Choiseul, Ysabel), *floridana* Mayr 1931 (Florida, Tulagi), *cockerelli* Ramsay (Guadalcanal), and *lavellae* Rothschild and Hartert 1916 (Vella Lavella, Ganonga) have chin and throat all black and the breast black with drop-shaped white spots. The back is grayish black and there is a white line on the wing (edges of secondaries). *Rh. c. albina* Rothschild and Hartert (Kulambangra, New Georgia, Vangunu, Rendova, and Tetipari) has the breast almost uniformly black; *coultasi* Mayr 1931 has the chin black, but the throat white and very large white spots on the breast; the back is gray, the white line on the wing inconspicuous.

A common fantail in the forest from sea level at least up to an altitude of 4000 feet. With the habits of this genus.* Differs from *leucophrys* by smaller size, spotted breast (except *albina*), white on wing, different habitat and actions.

106) **Willie Wagtail** (*Rhipidura leucophrys*): A large (7½), black and white fantail. Wings, tail, entire upperparts, throat, and sides of breast black. Abdomen and middle of breast white. A partly concealed eye-stripe and a few inconspicuous spots on the side of the throat also white. Iris reddish brown; bill and feet black. The subspecies *melaleuca* Quoy and Gaimard is found in the New Guinea region, in the Bismarck Archipelago, and throughout the Solomon Isls.

The familiar and tame Willie Wagtail is one of the most abundant and conspicuous birds of the Solomon Isls. Most common along the beach and on lowland streams, it is rarely found far from the water. Occasionally it follows streams up to an altitude of 500 or 800 feet. The little bird is continuously in motion, wagging the tail from left to right and back. The nest, a neat little cup with 2–3 eggs is usually placed over water. The metallic, twittering song is heard far into the night, particularly if the moon shines.

107) **Islet Monarch** (*Monarcha* cinerascens*): Medium (6½). Upperparts, throat, and breast pearl gray, abdomen rufous (pale chestnut). Iris brown; bill and feet blue gray. Occurs in a number of very similar subspecies on small coral islets, but is almost never found on the adjacent shores of the larger islands, even though the light coastal forest may appear very similar.

Nissan, Bougainville, Shortland Isls., Choiseul, Ysabel, Murray, Ramos, Gower, and Ongtong Java.

108) **Chestnut-bellied Monarch** (*Monarcha castaneiventris*): Variable (6–7½). Four strikingly different subspecies (or species?) and 2 minor races. *M. c. castaneiventris* Verreaux (Choiseul, Ysabel, Florida, Guadalcanal, and Malaita),

obscurior Mayr 1935 (Russell Isls.), and *megarhyncha* Rothschild and Hartert (San Cristobal) have upperparts, throat, and breast glossy blue black, and a chestnut abdomen. The Ugi Isl. subspecies *ugiensis* Ramsay is entirely blue black; *erythrosticta* Sharpe (Shortland Isls., Bougainville) is like *castaneiventris,* but males have a white, females a rufous, spot before the eye. The race of the central Solomon Isls. (*richardsii* Ramsay) is so distinct that it might be considered a separate species; it is like *castaneiventris* but has occiput and hind-neck snow white, while the immature is gray and chestnut like *M. cinerascens.* Iris brown; bill light blue gray; feet blue gray.

This is a fairly common bird of the lowland and mountain forest. Song a slow, descending whistle, consisting of 3 or 4 notes: *ree-ee-ee-ee.* Call note: *chet-chet-chet.*

109) **Pied Monarch** (*Monarcha barbata*): *See* Plate 3: 28. Small (5½–6½). (Blue-) black and white; both sexes alike. Immatures are very different: gray brown or dark brown above; tail blackish with white tips; underparts pale rufous or ochraceous; throat darker or blackish. The following subspecies occur in the Solomon Isls.:

barbata Ramsay has throat and upperparts blue black; a patch on the wing, tips of lateral tail-feathers, sides of throat, and breast and abdomen white (Bougainville, Choiseul, Ysabel, Florida, and Guadalcanal); *malaitae* Mayr 1931 (Malaita) similar but lateral tail-feathers entirely white.

browni Ramsay is similar, but throat *and* breast black; a white spot on sides of throat (Kulambangra, New Georgia Vangunu and Gatukai); *meeki* Rothschild and Hartert (Rendova, Tetipari); *ganongae* Mayr 1935 (Ganonga) with a white breast as in *barbata,* but with more white on tail and less on the wing; *nigrotecta* Hartert (Vella Lavella, Bagga) like *ganongae* but with the wing entirely black.

vidua Tristram (San Cristobal) is mostly black; white areas include a collar across the hind-neck, the rump, underparts except throat, a big patch on the wing (with a scaly pattern), and tips of lateral tail-feathers; *squamulata* Tristram (Ugi) is similar to *vidua,* but breast black with white drop-shaped spots.

Some of these subspecies are so different that they might actually be regarded as species. They are easily identified in the field because they all agree in basic color pattern, habits, and calls.* The Pied Monarch is a common bird of the forest up to about 4000 feet, less frequent at sealevel.

110) **Broad-billed Flycatcher** (*Myiagra* ferrocyanea*): Small (4½–5¼). Male and female very different. Adult male black with a white abdomen. Female has a gray head and brownish back; underparts white with or without a gray or rufous wash. Iris brown; bill and feet blue gray.

ferrocyanea Ramsay (Choiseul, Ysabel, Guadalcanal) and *cinerea* Mathews 1928 (Bougainville). *Male.* Black with a purplish gloss. *Females.* Underparts whitish. Back and wings rufous brown, tail tawny.

feminina Rothschild and Hartert (central Solomons); *malaitae* Mayr 1931 (Malaita). Males similar. Back of females dark gray, wings and tail fuscous; underparts pure white.

cervinicauda Tristram (San Cristobal). *Male.* Black with a greenish blue gloss; back bluish gray. *Female.* Throat and breast orange rufous; abdomen pale ocher. Top of head blue gray; back olive brown. Wings and tail fuscous; rump and lateral tail-feathers fawn color.

Common in the lowland and hill forest up to an altitude of 4000 feet; also in second growth and along edge of forest. Call: *zhay-zhay-zhay, chit-chit.* Song: *teree-tree-tree-tree-tree.*

111) ***Scarlet Robin** (*Petroica multicolor*): *See* Figure 14. Three subspecies in the mountains of the Solomon Isls.: *polymorpha* Mayr 1934 (San Cristobal) with typical black-headed and nontypical rusty-headed males. Female rather similar to male, with the back sooty black or brownish, underparts pale scarlet; top of head dull rufous brown; *septentrionalis* Mayr 1934 (Bougainville) and *kulambangrae* Mayr 1934 (Kulambangra) with typical black-headed males; females with the upperparts rufous brown, underparts pale salmon color with a brownish hue on throat and flanks. There is no other bird in the mountain forest (above 1800 feet) of the 3 islands with which the Scarlet Robin could be confused, even in its inconspicuous rusty-brown immature plumage.

WHISTLERS

112) ***Golden Whistler** (*Pachycephala pectoralis*): *Cf.* Plate 3: 29, 30. This species reaches its greatest diversity in the Solomon Isls. It is the only whistler in the lowlands and lower mountains of these islands. Some of the 12 subspecies are so distinct that they might actually be considered as species.

P. p. bougainvillei Mayr 1932 (Buka, Bougainville, Shortland); *orioloides* Pucheran (Choiseul, Ysabel, Florida); *cinnamomea* Ramsay (Guadalcanal); and *pavuvu* Mayr 1932

(Russell Isls.). *Adult male.* Rich golden yellow underneath, with a black collar across the lower throat. Head black, separated from the olive-green back by a yellow collar. Wings olive, tail black. *Female.* Different on nearly every island: *bougainvillei* dull olive above, underparts grayish with a greenish yellow wash; *orioloides* rufous olive above, rufous brown on crown and wing, yellow underneath more or less washed with russet; *cinnamomea* dull grayish olive above, pale grayish below, washed with cinnamon; *pavuvu* olive above, yellowish below, bill yellow not brown; wing rather rufous.

Central Solomon Isls.: *centralis* Mayr 1932 (Kulambangra, New Georgia, Vangunu, Gatukai) male like *orioloides,* but yellow collar across hind-neck interrupted; female olive green above with rufous wings, underneath pale olive yellow, throat whitish; *melanoptera* Mayr 1932 (Rendova, Tetipari) males similar, but with black wings; females rufous above with an olive wash, rufous below with yellow on the abdomen; *melanonota* Hartert (Vella Lavella, Ganonga) males with the entire upperparts, wings, and a broad breast band jet black; throat and abdomen deep golden yellow; females very variable, usually dull brownish olive on back and tail, rufous on head, rump and wings, and lemon yellow underneath with an indistinct breast band; upperparts and breast band sometimes mixed with blackish.

sanfordi Mayr 1931 (Malaita). Males with black head and tail, olive back and wings, and golden-yellow underparts (no breast band!); females with greenish olive upperparts, and dirty white underparts with a yellow wash and dark gray mottling, particularly on breast and flanks. Wing rust color.

christophori Tristram (San Cristobal, Santa Anna). Upperparts olive; head olive or blackish; underparts golden yellow with a broad black breast band, yellow of lower breast sometimes stained with rust color; female has upperparts olive, underparts yellow with a more or less distinct breast band.

feminina Mayr 1931 (Rennell). Male and female alike, similar to females of *centralis* (*see* above).

whitneyi Hartert 1929 (Momalufu, Akiki, and Whitney Isls.). A hybrid population between *bougainvillei* and *dahli;* combines the characters of these 2 forms in various combinations.

dahli Reichenow (Nissan and many islands of the Bismarck Archipelago). *Adult male.* Throat white; head and breast band black; breast, abdomen, and collar across hindneck yellow; back olive, tail black, wing edged with gray. *Female.* Head ash gray; back drab yellowish olive; throat white mottled with gray or brownish; belly pale yellow.

In habits and voice there is little difference between these 12 races. However, some of them live in open, coastal growth (*dahli, whitneyi*), others in the lowland forest (*orioloides*), while some of the races are absent in the alluvial flats and reach their peak of abundance in the lower mountain forest (*bougainvillei, sanfordi*). The exact altitudinal distribution has not yet been determined for any of these races.

113) **Mountain Whistler** (*Pachycephala implicata*): Small (6½). Male and female very different. Two strikingly distinct subspecies in the Solomon Isls. Iris brown; bill black; feet dark.

implicata Hartert 1929 (Guadalcanal). *Adult male.*

Black head and an ash-gray throat. Tail blackish; back and wings olive; breast and abdomen yellowish olive. *Female.* Gray crown; brownish olive back; dirty white throat; dirty yellow breast; abdomen tinged with olive.

richardsi Mayr 1932 (Bougainville). *Adult male.* Black head, throat, upper breast, and tail; golden olive back; dull yellow abdomen tinged with olive. *Female.* Like that of *implicata,* but back greenish olive, throat and breast white with a grayish wash, and abdomen bright greenish yellow. Females and immatures differ from immature *pectoralis* by the gray crown, by the olive, *not* rufous wing, and by the blackish bill and tail.

The Mountain Whistler is found only on 2 islands—Guadalcanal and Bougainville. Its altitudinal range is probably from 3000 to 8000 feet. Voice and habits unknown.

STARLINGS

In addition to the Papuan Myna (*Mino*) and the introduced Indian Myna (*Acridotheres*) there are 5 species of glossy starlings (*Aplonis*) known from the Solomon Isls.

Key to Solomon Isls. Aplonis

(1) Underparts white, densely covered with black streaks 2
Underparts more or less uniform dark 3

(2) Usually in rather large flocks; tail long ...... *metallicus* juv.
Usually solitary or in small family parties; tail short (*see also brunneocapillus* below) .... *cantoroides* juv.

(3) Found on Nissan, Rennell, Ongtong Java, or other outlying islands, adults with a uniformly bluish green gloss . *feadensis*

Found on the main islands of the Solomons 4

(4) Iris white .... *brunneocapillus*

Iris red 5

(5) Large (10) except on San Cristobal. Wing-feathers brown .... *grandis*

Smaller (7–8). Wing-feathers glossy black 6

(6) Small (7–7½). Solitary or in small parties, usually near coconut trees; tail short; with a uniform weak greenish gloss; nests in hollow trees .... *cantoroides* ad.

Larger (8), with a strong greenish gloss and some purple on throat and upper back; usually in large colonies; constructs globular hanging nests in large trees, often in solitary trees in clearings; tail long .... *metallicus* ad.

114) **Little Starling** (*Aplonis cantoroides* Gray): *See* Plate 3: 32. Iris of adults bright red, of immatures yellowish red. Usually lives in pairs; likes to nest in rotten coconut tree stumps. Most common near the shore in coconut plantations and near houses. Rare or absent in the true forest. Song insignificant. Immatures striped underneath. Common throughout the New Guinea area, Bismarck Archipelago, and all of the Solomons except the outlying islands. A single record (accidental?) from Rennell Isl.

115) **Atoll Starling** (*Aplonis feadensis*): Black. Very similar to *cantoroides,* but heavier, with a rounder wing and thicker bill. Gloss bluish green, not bottle green. Two subspecies in the Solomon Isls.: *feadensis* Ramsay (Nissan, Fead Isl., Ongtong Java) large (8); immatures glossy greenish black with pale edges to feathers of the underparts (scaly effect); in coconut trees and forest. *insularis* Mayr 1931 (Rennell Isl.) small (7); immatures uniformly dark slate color with slight green-

ish gloss. The species is found only on outlying coral islands and atolls.

116) **Brown-winged Starling** (*Aplonis grandis*): Head, hind-neck, breast, and throat covered with long, dark purplish hackles; rest of body glossy greenish black. Outer wing-feathers pale brown. Iris dark red; bill and feet black. Four subspecies: *grandis* Salvadori (Bougainville, Choiseul, Ysabel, Florida, and central Solomon Isls.); *macrurus* Mayr 1931 (Guadalcanal); *malaitae* Mayr 1931 (Malaita) smaller and with a greener breast; *dichrous* Tristram (San Cristobal). The last subspecies is much smaller (7½) and rather differently colored. Wings and tail are brown, head and body plumage black with a slight gloss; pointed feathers of head and throat short.

Principally a bird of the forest, up to about 3000 feet. Feeds in the substage and in higher trees. Lives in pairs and seems to nest in hollow trees. Voice not described.

117) **Colonial Starling** (*Aplonis metallicus*): Tail very long. The subspecies *nitidus* Gray is evenly distributed throughout the Solomon Isls. from Bougainville to Santa Anna. Nests colonially, about 50 or more weaver-bird-like nests hanging down from a high tree usually situated in a clearing, occasionally in the forest. The twittering chatter of a nesting colony can be heard for a long distance.

118) **White-eyed Starling** (*Aplonis brunneocapillus* Danis 1938): Small (8). Glossy green; upper throat purplish black; top of head brownish with a slight crest. Tail slightly elongated, bill highly arched. *Iris white;* bill and feet black. Differs from *metallicus* by the white eye, heavy bill, and short

tail. Very rare and probably not colonial. Lowland forest. Known only from Bougainville and Rendova.

119) ***Indian Myna** (*Acridotheres tristis* Linnaeus): Introduced on Russell Isls. and other islands of the Solomons. Rarely found away from the coastal coconut plantations.

120) **Papuan Myna** (*Mino dumontii*): *See* Plate 3: 33. A large (9½) starling. All black with a bluish gloss. Rump, under tail-coverts, and a short wing bar white. Middle of lower abdomen lemon yellow. The white patches on wing and rump are diagnostic in flight. Bill and bare sides of head orange; iris and legs yellow. Two subspecies: *kreffti* Sclater (New Ireland, New Hanover, Bougainville, Choiseul, Ysabel, Florida, central Solomons, Russell Isls.); *sanfordi* Hartert 1929 (Guadalcanal, Malaita) smaller.

This is one of the most conspicuous birds of the lowland forest. Its loud melodious whistles and calls are quite diagnostic: *ree-o-leet! oo-oo-oork! ree-ee-arr!* Usually in the tops of large fruit trees. Not social.

DRONGOS

121) **Spangled Drongo** (*Dicrurus bracteatus*): *See* Figure 15. Large (11). Entirely black with some bluish green gloss. Wings and top of head glossy. Upper back and throat with glossy spots (spangles). Tail long (5), distinctly forked. Strong, curved bill. Iris dark red; bill and legs black. Two very distinct races of this widespread species occur in the eastern Solomon Isls.: *longirostris* Ramsay (San Cristobal) and *meeki* Rothschild and Hartert (Guadalcanal) with a smaller bill and pronounced hackles on the sides of the throat.

Singly or in pairs, usually in the interior of the forest. Habits those of the family.*

CROWS

There is only one crow on any one island of the Solomon Isls. However, the black-billed crow of Bougainville (*meeki*) is so different from the pale-billed crow (*woodfordi*) of the Choiseul to Guadalcanal chain of islands that it is generally regarded as a separate species.

122) **Bougainville Crow** (*Corvus meeki* Rothschild): Large (16). All black with a bluish green gloss on head and throat and a purplish gloss on the rest of the body. Iris brown; bill and feet black. Lowland forest. Bougainville and Shortland group.

123) **White-billed Crow** (*Corvus woodfordi*): Like *meeki,* but plumage somewhat duller. Bill white with a blackish tip. Iris brown or whitish. Two subspecies: *vegetus* Tristram (Choiseul, Ysabel) and *woodfordi* Ogilvie-Grant (Guadalcanal). A bird of the true forest, rarely in the open. Usually flies in small flocks (?family parties). Can be attracted by imitating its high-pitched *caw*ing call note.

SUNBIRDS

124) **Yellow-bellied Sunbird** (*Nectarinia jugularis*): *See* Plate 3: 34, 35. Small (4), with a slender, strongly curved bill. Male yellowish olive above; throat and breast black with a purplish blue gloss; belly bright yellow. Tail black, lateral feathers with white tips. In the female the entire underparts are yellow. Iris brown; bill and feet black. The metallic breast

shield of the male and the bright yellow underparts of the female are diagnostic. Otherwise similar to small honey-eaters (*Myzomela*).

In open formations only, never inside the true forest. Visits flowers, feeding on nectar and insects. Call note a metallic twitter followed by a trill: *teep-teep-teep-teep-kee-ree*. The subspecies *flavigaster* Gould has been recorded from nearly every island of the Solomons.

HONEY-EATERS

This family is represented in the Solomon Isls. by 6 species or species groups. Each of the 3 larger species (nos. 128, 129, 130) is restricted to a single island, and 2 of them to the mountains. Only the small honey-eaters of the genus *Myzomela* are widespread. Their identification in the field is very simple, however, since only a single species occurs on any given island, except on San Cristobal (?and Ugi) where a black and a red species coexist. This makes the identification of the Solomon Isls. honey-eaters a relatively simple matter and the subsequent plumage descriptions are, therefore, kept short. The habits of most species of this family are very similar.* The voice is diagnostic for each species, but it is not yet well described for the forms in the Solomon Isls.

125) ***Cardinal Honey-eater** (*Myzomela cardinalis*): *See* Plate 3: 36. The 2 subspecies in the eastern Solomon Isls. are very distinct.

sanfordi Mayr 1931 (Rennell). Adult male all scarlet except lores, wings, tail, and vent, which are black. Female with head, throat, and rump scarlet; remainder of plumage brownish olive, darker on back, more buffy below. Immatures similar, but with the scarlet faded out.

pulcherrima Ramsay (San Cristobal, Ugi). Adult male like *sanfordi,* but with more black on the flanks. Female with head, throat, breast, middle of back, and rump scarlet; wings and tail blackish; wing edged with olive; abdomen grayish olive.

126) **Small Solomon Islands Honey-eaters** (*Myzomela lafargei* group): *See* Figure 16. The Solomon Isls. (except San Cristobal) are inhabited by a group of small honey-eaters, which complement each other geographically, but are too different to be included in a single species. They are best classified as 4 species, belonging to one superspecies.

The plumage is partly sooty black, partly olive. The adult male of *melanocephala* has no red, in *lafargei* a big patch on the back of the head is scarlet, in *eichhorni* rump and throat are scarlet, and in *malaitae* rump and most of the underparts are scarlet. Immatures of all 4 species are dull grayish cinnamon with more or less scarlet on the throat, top of head, and rump. Females are intermediate between adult males and immatures. Iris brown; bill long, curved, black; feet blue gray. The inconspicuously colored immatures and females can possibly be confused with *Zosterops, Dicaeum, Nectarinia, Phylloscopus,* and *Acrocephalus.*

The distribution is as follows: *lafargei* Pucheran (Buka, Bougainville, Shortland Isls., Choiseul, and Ysabel); *eichhorni* Rothschild and Hartert (Gizo, Kulambangra, New Georgia, Vangunu, Rendova, and Tetipari), *e. ganongae* Mayr 1932 (Ganonga) and *e. atrata* Hartert (Vella Lavella, Bagga); *melanocephala* Ramsay (Florida, Savo, Guadalcanal); *malaitae* Mayr 1931 (Malaita). Common in the lowlands and at higher altitudes.

127) **Black Honey-eater** (*Myzomela nigrita*): A small (4½–5), black honey-eater. Adult males and females are all sooty black. Iris brown; bill and feet black. Immatures have a yellowish bill with a black tip; upperparts are dull black, the underparts gray, mottled with black. The subspecies *tristrami* Ramsay is restricted to the easternmost Solomon Isls. (San Cristobal, Ugi, Santa Anna). A bird of the lowlands and mountains, second growth and forest treetops.

128) **Bougainville Honey-eater** (*Meliphaga bougainvillei* Mayr 1931): Large (7). Upperparts olive brown; underparts ash gray with a slight brownish olive wash. Tail rather short; bill long and curved. Iris brown; bill black; legs bluish gray. The species is characterized by its lack of distinguishing features. Females much smaller than males. Found only in the mountains of Bougainville.

129) **Guadalcanal Honey-eater** (*Guadalcanaria inexpectata* Hartert 1929): Large (8). Upperparts slate gray; wings and tail olive. Throat whitish; remainder of underparts light gray; throat and breast with numerous dark gray streaks. Ear-coverts silver gray. A conspicuous golden yellow tuft of feathers on either side of the throat. Iris brown; bill black; legs bluish gray. Found only in the mountains of Guadalcanal.

130) **San Cristobal Honey-eater** (*Meliarchus sclateri* Gray): Large (10–11). Upperparts mostly greenish brown; rump and tail more rufous brown. Top of head greenish black with narrow greenish white streaks. Underparts dirty white, slightly washed with greenish on breast and abdomen; breast and ab-

domen streaked with black. Throat bordered on both sides by a black band, beginning at the bill. A greenish white ring around the eye, bordered in front by black. Iris dirty white; eyelids pale blue; upper bill pale green, lower bill straw yellow or horn color; legs silvery blue. San Cristobal, lowlands and mountains. A noisy bird of the forest and edge of forest. Common.

WHITE-EYES

Eight species and 17 subspecies of this family are known from the Solomons. Most of the species are extremely similar to one another and their identification would be nearly impossible if all of them occurred together. Fortunately never more than 2 species are found on any one island. A geographical key is, therefore, the best method of facilitating the correct identification of the species observed at a given locality.

Geographical Key to the Species of White-eyes in the Solomon Isls.

[Islands are listed in a northwest to southeast sequence]

NISSAN .... *griseotincta eichhorni*

BOUGAINVILLE (1) Lowlands; throat yellow; upperparts yellowish olive; no distinct eye-ring . *metcalfei exigua*

(2) Mountains; throat dusky green; breast dark gray; upperparts dark olive; narrow white eye-ring .... *ugiensis hamlini*

SHORTLAND GROUP, CHOISEUL, YSABEL, FLORIDA .... *metcalfei*

CENTRAL SOLOMON ISLS., EXCEPT KULAMBANGRA .... *rendovae*

KULAMBANGRA (1) Lowlands and hills; bright olive throughout; lower belly yellowish olive; white eye-ring narrow; bill black; forehead and lores black; legs yellow .... *rendovae kulambangrae*

(2) Mountains; greenish olive; very broad white eye-ring; base of lower mandible yellow; legs gray; forehead and lores green ..... *murphyi*

GUADALCANAL .... *ugiensis oblita*

MALAITA .... *stresemanni*

SAN CRISTOBAL .... *ugiensis*

RENNELL ISL. (1) Small (4½). All olive green; no eye-ring; bill and feet yellow ....
.... *rennelliana* (*see* Rennell Isl., p. 282)

(2) Large (5½). Brownish above; dirty white below; forehead and eye-stripe white; bill brown; feet blue gray ....
.... *Woodfordia* (*see* Rennell Isl., p. 282)

No species of white-eye is known from Mono, Murray, Russel, Ramos, Savo, Gower, Santa Anna, or Ongtong Java.

Females of *Nectarinia* differ by their bright yellow underparts, the long curved bill, and the white tips on the lateral tail-feathers. Females of *Dicaeum aeneum* differ by their slate-gray upperparts with a greenish gloss, by the grayish sides of head and breast, and by the light-colored zone along the middle of the underside, from bill to tail.

131) **Yellow-throated White-eye** (*Zosterops metcalfei*): Small (4½). Upperparts and wings yellowish olive. Throat bright yellow; under tail-coverts pale yellow; breast and abdomen white. White eye-ring inconspicuous or absent. Iris light brown; bill black above and horn-colored below; feet gray. Three very similar races: *exigua* Murphy 1929 (Buka,

Bougainville, Shortland Isls., and Choiseul); *metcalfei* Tristram (Ysabel); and *floridana* Rothschild and Hartert (Florida, Tulagi). A common white-eye of forest and second growth. From the sea coast to the hills.

132) **Gray-throated White-eye** (*Zosterops ugiensis*): Medium (5). Upperparts dark olive or brownish olive. Underparts without any yellow (except sometimes on the under tail-coverts). Iris brown; bill black; legs and feet slate gray.

Three subspecies: *ugiensis* Ramsay (San Cristobal), throat and breast dirty white, more grayish on the sides; abdomen and under tail-coverts white; face and forehead washed with dark brown; no white eye-ring. *oblita* Hartert 1929 (Guadalcanal) throat and breast more grayish; under tail-coverts pale yellow; face and forehead olive green as the back; no eye-ring. *hamlini* Murphy 1929 (Bougainville) upper throat greenish olive; lower throat, breast, and flanks dark gray; middle of belly white; under tail-coverts yellow; forehead and face sooty brown; a narrow white eye-ring.

Strictly a mountain bird on Guadalcanal and Bougainville. On San Cristobal it is most common in the mountains, but also reaches the lowlands. There is no well-substantiated record from Ugi.

133) Superspecies **Zosterops lutea:** This group is represented in the Solomons on 2 of the outlying islands (*griseotincta* on Nissan, *rennelliana* on Rennell) and on the central Solomon Isls. (*rendovae*).

Nissan White-eye (*Zosterops griseotincta*): Small (4). Yellowish olive above; olive yellow below; throat and middle of abdomen purer yellow. A narrow white eye-ring: Bill yellow; legs and feet grayish yellow. The subspecies *eichhorni* Hartert 1926 is found on Nissan only.

Central Solomons' White-eye (*Zosterops rendovae*): *See* Plate 3: 39. Each of the 6 races of this species is so different from the other 5 that not a single description fits them all. A yellowish olive upper side, a reddish brown iris, and yellow legs and feet are the only features they have in common. Small (4½). These 6 subspecies are:

vellalavellae Hartert (Vella Lavella, Bagga) bill yellow; yellow upper throat separated from white belly by an olive breast band; no black in face; white eye-ring.

splendida Hartert 1929 (Ganonga) forehead and lores blackish; underparts golden yellow; sides of breast olive; bill black; broad white eye-ring.

luteirostris Hartert (Gizo) forehead and eye region black; bill yellow; entire underparts yellow; sides of breast olivaceous; white eye-ring.

kulambangrae Rothschild and Hartert (Kulambangra, New Georgia, Vangunu, Gatukai) forehead and eye region blackish; entire underparts olive yellow, more yellowish on lower belly; bill black; narrow white eye-ring.

rendovae Tristram (Rendova) forehead, throat, and breast olive; abdomen and under tail-coverts canary yellow; bill black; no white eye-ring.

tetiparia Murphy 1929 (Tetipari) like *rendovae,* but abdomen white.

134) **Kulambangra Mountain White-eye** (*Zosterops murphyi* Hartert 1929): Medium (4½–5). All olive green, more yellowish on the middle of the throat and abdomen. Very broad white eye-ring. Iris brown; bill black with a yellow

base; legs and feet gray. Endemic in the mountains of Kulambangra.

135) **Malaita White-eye** (*Zosterops stresemanni* Mayr 1931): Medium (5½). All olive green, more yellowish underneath. No trace of a white eye-ring. Iris light brown; upper bill grayish, lower bill yellow with a gray tip; feet greenish gray. Endemic on Malaita. A common bird from the seacoast to the mountains.

FLOWER-PECKERS

136) **Midget** (*Dicaeum aeneum*): *See* Plate 3: 37. A very small (3–3½), short-billed, short-tailed bird. Upperparts and wings slate gray with a metallic green gloss; sides of head gray; tail black. *Male.* Underparts: a bright scarlet red patch on the breast; middle of upper throat whitish; sides of throat and breast gray; flanks citrine olive; middle of upper abdomen dark gray, middle of lower abdomen and under tail-coverts buffy white. *Female.* Without red underneath. Sides of throat and breast gray; flanks olive. Middle of throat, breast, and abdomen (buffy) white. Iris brown; bill and feet black. Two subspecies, which differ slightly in size: *aeneum* Pucheran (Bougainville, Choiseul, Ysabel, Malaita) and *becki* Hartert 1929 (Florida, Guadalcanal). A common bird at all altitudes and habitats.

137) **San Cristobal Midget** (*Dicaeum tristrami* Sharpe): A small (3½–4), brown and white bird. Upperparts brown, mottled with white on forehead and on the upper back; wings brown; tail blackish. Upper and lower throat pale brown; lower breast and abdomen whitish. Eyebrow and ear region

whitish; cheeks dark brown. Iris brown; bill and feet black. Small size and absence of green and reddish from plumage distinguish this midget at once from all other San Cristobal birds. Found on San Cristobal only. Particularly abundant in the mountains.

WEAVER-FINCHES

138) ***Blue-faced Parrot-Finch** (*Erythrura trichroa*): The subspecies *woodfordi* Hartert is known from Guadalcanal only. It probably lives in the grasslands of the northwestern part of that island.

GEOGRAPHICAL REVIEW OF THE BIRDS OF THE SOLOMON ISLANDS

Only a few of the approximately 140 species of land and fresh-water birds of the Solomon Islands are distributed so evenly that they can be expected on every island. The majority of species are either endemic on a single island or at least restricted to part of the Solomons. Sometimes a number of islands are inhabited by a rather similar birdlife. On the basis of their distribution of birds, the Solomon Islands can be subdivided into the following faunal districts.

A. The main chain
   a. Northern isls. (Buka, Bougainville, Shortland group, Choiseul, Ysabel)
   b. Guadalcanal group (Florida group, Savo, Guadalcanal)
   c. Russel Isls. (formerly called Pavuvu)
   d. Malaita (? and Ulawa)

B. Central Solomon Isls.
  a. Western section (Vella Lavella and Bagga, Ganonga, and Narovo)
  b. Main section (Gizo, Kulambangra, New Georgia, Vangunu, Gatukai, Kicha)
  c. Rendova section (Rendova, Tetipari)

C. San Cristobal group (San Cristobal, Ugi, Santa Anna)

D. Small and outlying isls. with reduced faunas (Nissan, Fead, Mono [also called Treasury Isl.], Murray Isl., Gower Isl., Ongtong Java, Sikaiana).

E. Rennell and Bellona Islands.

Guadalcanal and Bougainville have a considerable number of species that are restricted to the mountains. Kulambangra, Malaita, and San Cristobal have about 6 mountain species each. One or two mountain species also occur on Vangunu and Ysabel.

There is not a single island on which one can expect to find more than 100 species. Most of the smaller islands, and in particular the outlying ones have much smaller lists. To be sure, not one of the islands is explored ornithologically to such an extent that additional records can no longer be expected, but they are known sufficiently well to enable me to prepare fairly complete lists. Such lists will be of considerable help to the field observer, not only by narrowing down the number of probable species for each island, but also by indicating what species might still be added as new locality records.

To conserve space, the species are not listed by their vernacular or scientific names, but by the serial numbers of the preceding systematic list of Solomon Islands birds. A number in parenthesis indicates that the species might be expected from that island but has not yet actually been recorded. To avoid duplication, migrants and other species that are widespread in the Solomons and can be expected on all but a few outlying islands, are summarized separately. These species will have to be added in each case to the list of each island. An (m) added after the serial number indicates that the species in question is likely to be found in the mountains only.

Migrant Visitors: 55, 57, 58, 60, 77, 80, 85, 92.

Introduced Species: 119.

Widespread Species: Probably found on all islands from Bougainville to San Cristobal, but absent on some of the outlying islands (*see* below). 3, 4, 5, 7, 9, 17, 23, 31, 36, 38, 42, 44, 45, 70, 75, 76, 81, 84, 106, 114, 117.

Bougainville: 1, 8, 11, 12, (14), (15), 20, 21, 24, 25 (m), 26, 30, 33 (m), 34, 35, 37, 39, 47 (m), 48, 49, 50, 51 (m), 52, 53, 54, 56, 59, 63, 64, 65, 66, 68, 71, 72, 73, 74, 78, 79, 82, 83, 87, 88, 89, 90, 91, 93 (m), 99 (m), 100, 101 (m), 105, 107, 108, 109, 110, 111 (m), 112, 113 (m), 116, 118, 120, 122, 124, 126, 128 (m), 131, 132 (m), 136.

Shortland Group: 6, 8, 11, 12, 15, 24, 26, 30, 52, 53, 54, 66, 71, 78, 82, 88, 89, 90, 100, 105, 107, 108, 109, 110, 112, 116, 120, 122, 124, 126, 131, 136.

Mono (= Treasury Island): Complete list excluding migrants—5, 12, 24, 31, 38, 44, 52, 53, 63, 72, 84, 88, 110, 117, 120, 124.

Choiseul and Ysabel: (C) = Choiseul only; (Y) = Ysabel only—6 (C), 8, 11, 12, 13, 14, 15, 21 (Y), 24, 26, 30, 35 (C), 37 (C), 43 (C), 49 (Y), 50, 52, 53, 54, 56 (Y), 59 (C), 63, 64,

65, 66 (Y), 68 (C), 71, 72, 73, 74, 78, 82, 83, 87, 88, 89, 90. 91 (Y), 94 (C), 97 (Y), 99 (Y), 100, 105, 107, 108, 109, 110, 112, 116, 120, 123, 124, 126, 131, 136.

Vella Lavella: 6, 8, 11, 12, 14, (15), 24, 25, 26, 30, 34, 35, 40, 50, 52, 53, 54, 59, 61, 62, 68, 71, 72, 73, 74, 88, 89, 90, 100, 105, 108, 109, 110, 112, 116, 120, 124, 126, 133.

Gizo: 8, 11, 16, 26, 30, 39, 49, 50, 52, 53, 54, 59, 61, 66, 71, 72, 73, 88, 89, 90, 100, 108, 110, 116, 120, 124, 126, 133.

Kulambangra: (6), (8), 10, (11), 12, (14), (15), 24, 25, 26, 30, 33 (m), 34, 37, (39), 47 (m), 49, 50, 51 (m), 52, 53, 54, 56, (59), 61, 66, (68), 69, 71, 72, 73, 74, 87, 88, 89, 90, 91, 93 (m), 98 (m), 99 (m), 100, 105, 108, 109, 110, 111 (m), 112, 116, 120, 124, 126, 133, 134 (m).

New Georgia, Vangunu, Gatukai: About the same fauna as Kulambangra, but without 47, 51, 69, 93, 98, 99, 111, 134.

Rendova: 6, 8, 11, 12, (14), 15, 24, 25, 26, 30, 37, 50, 52, 53, 54, 59, 61, 66, 71, 72, 73, 74, 88, 89, 90, 100, 105, 108, 109, 110, 112, 116, 118, 120, 124, 126, 133.

Murray: Complete list excluding migrants—5, 31, 53, 107, 124.

Ramos: Complete list excluding migrants—17, 25, 29, 31, 35, 38, 41, 42, 107, 114, 117.

Russel Islands (Pavuvu): Complete list excluding migrants—5, 8, 9, 17, 25, 26, 31, 36, 38, 42, 44, 45, 50, 52, 70, 75, 76, 81, 88, 90, 108, 112, 117, 119, 120, 124.

Florida Group: 11, 12, 15, 19, 24, 25, 26, 29, 30, 34, 35, 50, 52, 53, 54, 59, 61, 63, 73, 78, 88, 90, 105, 108, 109, 110, 112, 116, 120, 124, 126, 131, 136.

Guadalcanal: 2 6, 8, 10, 11, 12, 14, 15, 18, 19, 21, 24, 25 (m), 26, 30, 32, 33 (m), 34, 35, 37, 39, 40, 46, 47 (m), 49, 50, 51 (m), 52, 53, 54, 56, 59, 61, 63, 67, 68, 69, 71, 72, 73, 74, 78, 79 (m), 82, 87, 88, 89, 90, 97, 99 (m), 100, 101 (m), 105, 108, 109, 110, 112, 113 (m), 116, 120, 121, 123, 124, 126, 129 (m), 132 (m), 136, 138.—The species 22, 93, 94, 96, 98, and 111 may yet be discovered in the mountains of Guadalcanal.

Malaita: 8, 11, 12, 14, 15, 20, 24, 25 (m), 26, 29, 30, 32, 33 (m), 34, 37, 46, 47 (m), 49, 50, 52, 53, 54, 56, 59, 62, 63, 71, 72, 74, 82, 87, 88, 89, 90, 99 (m), 100, 104 (m), 105, 108, 109, 110, 112, 116, 120, 124, 126, 135, 136.

San Cristobal: 8, 12, 14, (15), 19, 20, 22 (m), 25, 26, 30, 32, 34, 35, 37, 39, 41, 46, 49, 50, 53, 54, 56, 59, 63, (68), 71, 72, 74, 86, 88, 89, 95 (m), 96 (m), 99 (m), 100, 102, 103 (m), 108, 109, 110, 111 (m), 112, 116, 121, 125, 127, 130, 132, 137.

Ugi: Complete list excluding migrants. Well-substantiated records: 9, 25, 26, 27, 31, 38, 44, 46, 50, 53, 68, 75, 81, 86, 100, 108, 109, 110, 125.

Records requiring confirmation: 5, 7, 8, 12, 14, 17, 19, 24, 30, 32, 35, 36, 37, 42, 45, 54, 56, 63, 70, 71, 76, 90, 106, 112, 114, 117, 124, 127, 130, 132.

Santa Anna: Complete list excluding migrants—2, 4, 7, 9, 12, 17, 19, 20, 27, 30, 31, 36, 38, 39, 42, 62, 68, 75, 76, 81, 84, 100, 106, 108, 109, 110, 112, 114, 117, 127.

Gower: Complete list excluding migrants—3, 4, 5, 9, 15, 17, 20, 23, 26, 28, 29, 35, 36, 38, 39, 42, 45, 52, 70, 75, 76, 81, 107, 114, 124.

Outlying Islands: Complete list excluding migrants.

Nissan: 5, 9, 17, 25, 31, 36, 38, 39, 42, 44, 45, 48, 62, 70, 76, 84, 107, 112, 115, 117, 133.

Ongtong Java: 4, 17, (23?), 29, 42, 107, 115.

Rennell: 2, 4, 6, 7, 15, 23, 27, 29, 39, 42, 46, 50, 54, 58, 70, 71, 75, 89, 93, 112, 114, 115, 125, 133. The following additional species occur on Rennell Isl., which are not found elsewhere in the Solomon Isls.

LIST OF RENNELL ISLAND SPECIES NOT FOUND ELSEWHERE IN THE SOLOMON ISLANDS

*__Australian Dabchick__ (*Podiceps novaehollandiae*): The subspecies *rennellianus* Mayr 1943, endemic on Rennell, has the same field characters as the other races of the species. Common on Lake Tengano.

White Ibis (*Threskiornis aethiopicus*): A large (about 2′), black and white wading bird with a long (5), strongly curved black bill. Entire plumage white except tips of primaries, which are black, and some of the secondaries, which are mottled purple black and white. Head, neck, and throat more or less bare and black, in immature birds sparsely covered with blackish feathers. Nests in trees in colonies of dozens to 100 birds. The subspecies *pygmaeus* Mayr 1931 is endemic on Rennell Isl. and Bellona.

White Spoonbill (*Platalea leucorodia regia* Gould): An all-white wading bird (about 2′) with black legs, a broadened black bill, and black tips on a few of the wing-feathers. A rare inhabitant of Lake Tengano on Rennell Isl.

Gray Teal (*Anas gibberifrons*): *See* New Caledonia. The endemic Rennell subspecies (*remissa* Ripley 1942) has the same identification marks as the other races of the species. It is found on the inland lake.

Australian Goshawk (*Accipiter fasciatus*): *See* New Caledonia. The Rennell Isl. population seems to be indistinguishable from the New Caledonian subspecies (*vigilax* Wetmore 1926).

The Barn Owl (*Tyto alba*) occurs on Rennell according to native reports, but it has not yet been collected on the island.

Fantail Warbler (*Gerygone flavolateralis*): *See* New Hebrides. Throat whitish; rest of underparts bright yellow in the Rennell subspecies (*citrina* Mayr 1931). Back green; rather little white in the tail. This tame warbler is common in the lower trees of forest and gardens.

Rennell Shrikebill (*Clytorhynchus hamlini* Mayr 1931): A medium-sized (7½) monarch-like flycatcher. Cinnamon to rufous brown with a black mask. Underparts paler, more rusty ocher. Forehead, face, ear region, and chin black. Axillaries and under wing-coverts whitish. Bill extremely long (almost one inch). Iris brown; bill bluish slate gray with a whitish tip; feet dark blue gray. Common in the underbrush of the forest, often feeding in small flocks.

Broad-billed Flycatcher (*Myiagra caledonica*): *See* New Hebrides. The endemic Rennell Isl. subspecies (*occidentalis* Mayr 1931) has the same field characters as the other races of the species.

Rennell Fantail (*Rhipidura rennelliana* Mayr 1931): A small (5½–6), long-tailed flycatcher. Upperparts drab gray brown. Tail blackish, outer feathers with white edges or tips. Underparts smoky gray with a dirty white mottling on the middle of throat, breast, and abdomen. A partly concealed whitish spot in front of the eye. Iris brown; bill and feet dark. Endemic on Rennell Isl. Habits like those of other fantails.* Very common and tame.

Rennell White-eye (*Zosterops rennelliana* Murphy 1929): Small (4½). Olive green, more yellowish green underneath, particularly on the throat. No eye-ring. Iris brown; bill and feet yellow. Endemic on Rennell Isl.

Woodford's White-eye (*Woodfordia superciliosa* North): Medium (5½). Upperparts dull brownish olive, more brownish on top of head; wings more olive. Underparts dirty white with a yellowish brown wash on the abdomen; lower throat brownish; upper throat, forehead, eye-stripe, and a stripe below and behind the eye whitish. Iris light brown; bill long, brownish horn color; legs bluish gray. The lores and a ring around the eye are naked. Endemic on Rennell Isl.

X

The Land and Fresh-Water Birds of Micronesia[1]

The zoogeographer includes under Micronesia the islands from Palau and the Marianas in the west to the Carolines, Marshalls, and Gilbert Islands in the east. In this enormous area with an east-west extension of almost 3000 miles, there are only few islands large enough to be the home of land birds. The number of species of native birds recorded from these islands is as follows: Palau 32, Marianas 21, Ponape 18, Kusaie 10, Marshall Islands 3. The total number of species of land birds is 48, to which would have to be added 5 species that were introduced on Guam and other islands.

A special problem is posed by migrant visitors from Asia. Every autumn numerous Japanese and Asiatic birds are carried out to the Marianas and even more of them reach Palau. Thirty such species have so far been recorded for Micronesia, many of them only a single time. At least twice that many species will be added to this list if a resident observer keeps a sharp lookout for migrants. The present handbook is not the place to give the identification marks and descriptions of all

[1] Finsch, O. 1875. "Die Vögel der Palau Gruppe." *Jour. Mus. Godeffroy,* 3:133–83. Hartert, E. 1900. "The Birds of Ruk in the Central Carolines." *Novitates Zoologicae,* 7:1–11. Kuroda, N., et al. 1932. "List of the Birds of Micronesia." In *A Hand List of Japanese Birds,* p.169–98. Tokyo: Orn. Soc. Japan. Oustalet, E. 1895–96. "Les Mammifères et les Oiseaux des Iles Mariannes." *Nouv. Arch. Mus. d'Hist. Nat.,* 7:141–228; 8:25–74.

these species. Lack of space prevents me from giving more than a list. (*See* end of this chapter).

The bird fauna of Micronesia is a mixture of various elements. The genera *Ixobrychus, Gallinula, Asio, Otus, Caprimulgus,* and *Acrocephalus* were derived from Asia. The Micronesian forms of the genera *Pandion, Megapodius, Rallus, Rallina, Caloenas, Halcyon chloris, Edolisoma, Colluricincla,* and *Artamus* came from the Papuan region, either directly or via the Philippine Islands. The Polynesian element is conspicuous in the genera *Ptilinopus, Ducula, Aplonis,* and *Myzomela.* Remarkable is the almost complete absence of parrots and honey-eaters, the small number of pigeons and the absence of such widespread genera as *Lalage, Turdus,* and *Pachycephala.* Five genera are endemic: *Aphanolimnas* (Kusaie), *Psamathia* (Palau), *Metabolus* (Truk), *Cleptornis* (Marianas), and *Rukia* (Micronesia).

All species and genera marked with an asterisk are treated in more detail in the systematic section (Chapter 3, "The Land and Fresh-Water Birds of the Southwest Pacific") of Part I.

CORMORANTS

***Little Pied Cormorant** (*Phalacrocorax m. melanoleucus* Vieillot): Palau Isls. and (? as straggler) Marianas.

HERONS

***Reef Heron** (*Demigretta s. sacra* Gmelin): Found throughout the area, including Marshall and Gilbert Isls. The mottled phase is rare; about two-thirds of the birds are gray.

***Rufous Night Heron** (*Nycticorax caledonicus*): The subspecies *pelewensis* Mathews 1926 is dull maroon above; the occipital plumes may be entirely white. Palau Isls. and Truk group (Carolines).

Chinese Least Bittern (*Ixobrychus sinensis* Gmelin): A very small (12) heron. *Adult male.* Buff (sand color) below. Top of head black; hind-neck rufous. Back brown; tail black. Wing-tip (i.e. outer half of wing) black, inner half of wing pale clay color. *Immature* and *female.* Streaked with pale brown below; mottled brown and sandy above. Tail and wing-tips black. Iris yellow; bill yellowish green, black above; feet greenish yellow.

Japan, eastern China, Marianas, Palau, Carolines (Yap, Truk), and island belt from the Indian Ocean to New Guinea and the Bismarck Archipelago (New Britain). Nests in parts of Micronesia, but apparently only a winter visitor to the Papuan region. No well-defined subspecies. In marshes, rice paddies, occasionally in the mangroves. Mostly nocturnal. Food principally insects. Call *kaka-kakak.*

DUCKS

Marianas Mallard (*Anas oustaleti* Salvadori): Large (20). Dark brown above; lighter and more rufous below. Top of head black with an indistinct buff eye-stripe. Cheeks and throat buff, finely streaked with black. Wing plain gray brown; speculum bluish green, bordered with black and white. Iris brown; bill olive gray; feet reddish. Differs from *superciliosa* by larger size, lack of a clearly defined eye-stripe, and the color of the wing, particularly the broad white bands along the black borders of the speculum.

Endemic on the Marianas. Now nearly exterminated. Habits probably similar to those of the common Mallard of the Northern Hemisphere. Nests among reedy swamps and along streams.

*__Australian Gray Duck__ (*Anas superciliosa pelewensis* Hartlaub and Finsch): *See* Plate 1: 7. Medium (17). Occurs in the Palau Isls. and Carolines (Truk).

OSPREYS

*__Osprey__ (*Pandion haliaetus melvillensis* Mathews): Recorded (apparently breeding) from Palau. The only other hawks that have been recorded from Micronesia are winter visitors from Asia.

MEGAPODES

Incubator Bird (*Megapodius lapérouse*): Large (12). Uniformly dark slaty brown. Face and upper throat scantily feathered, bare skin red. Iris brown; bill yellow with a blue-black base; legs and feet dirty yellow; toes partly black. Two subspecies, *lapérouse* Gaimard (Marianas) with crest and top of head dark ash gray, *senex* Hartlaub (Palau) with crest and top of head light pearl gray, strongly contrasting with the back. Partial to the smaller offshore coral islets. Species possibly near extermination. Habits typical of the genus.*

QUAILS AND PHEASANTS

*__Domestic Fowl__ (*Gallus gallus*): Feral fowl are found in the Marianas, Palau Isls., and Carolines.

Pigmy Quail (*Excalfactoria chinensis*): *Cf.* Figure 5. Very small (5). Brown above, with buffy white streaks and a mottling of black. Males blue gray below; middle of chest and abdomen chestnut. Face and throat with a pretty pattern of black and white. Females buffy below, barred with blackish. The subspecies *lineata* Scopoli has been introduced on Guam from the Philippines. It lives in the grass and has typical quail habits.

RAILS

The rails, with 7 native species, are particularly well represented in Micronesia. This includes one endemic genus (*Aphanolimnas*) and one endemic species (*Rallus owstoni*). Most of the other species have been recorded only from Palau or the Marianas.

***Banded Rail** (*Rallus philippensis*): The subspecies *pelewensis* Mayr 1933 is restricted to Palau. It is a rather dark race, with the rufous breast band usually present.

Guam Rail (*Rallus owstoni* Rothschild): Large (11). Upperparts brown. A gray superciliary stripe from the bill to the hind-neck. A brown stripe through the eye. Throat ash gray. Breast, abdomen, and part of wings barred black and white. Iris red; bill dark brown; legs gray. Restricted to Guam (Marianas). In grasslands and second growth. Call note not yet described.

Malay Banded Crake (*Rallina fasciata* Raffles): Small (8). Rufous brown above. Head, throat, and breast rufous. Abdomen white, coarsely barred with black. Wings brown, barred with buff. Iris red; bill brown; legs red. This seems to be a true swamp rail. Malay Archipelago and Palau Isls. Native name: *Olaratta.*

Kusaie Rail (*Aphanolimnas monasa* Kittlitz): Small (7). All sooty black; middle of throat lighter, more slate gray. Underwing and undertail with a few inconspicuous white bars. Iris and feet red; bill black(?). Endemic on Kusaie Isl. In shady places of the humid forest. Calls frequently. Not taken for more than 50 years and probably extinct.

***White-browed Rail** (*Poliolimnas cinereus*): Reported from Palau, Marianas (Guam), Carolines (Yap, Truk), and Marshall Isls. (Bikini). Micronesian birds seem to belong to *collingwoodi* Mathews 1926.

Moorhen or **Gallinule** (*Gallinula chloropus*): Large (12–13). Sooty slate color. Under tail-coverts, lower belly, and a line along the flanks white. Iris red; bill red with a yellow tip; legs and feet olive green. Forehead covered by a horny red shield, a continuation of the bill. Found throughout the Marianas (*guami* Hartert 1917). In swamps and taro fields.

***Purple Swamphen** (*Porphyrio porphyrio*): *See* Plate 1: 10. The subspecies *pelewensis* Hartlaub and Finsch is restricted to the Palau group.

PIGEONS AND DOVES

Marianas Fruit Dove (*Ptilinopus roseicapillus* Lesson): Small (8½). Upperparts green; top of head dark red. Underparts many-colored. Middle of upper throat whitish; sides of neck gray; breast grayish green. Flanks and under tail-coverts peach color; lower belly yellow. A purple spot in middle of lower breast. Tip of tail grayish. Iris yellow; bill dark green; legs dark red.

Marianas. The only fruit dove on this island group. With the habits of the genus.* Call: *toot, toot, toot-toot-toot, toot, toot,* increasing and then decreasing in volume and rapidity.

***Crimson-crowned Fruit Dove** (*Ptilinopus porphyraceus*): Three subspecies in Micronesia, similar to the Samoan race: *hernsheimi* Finsch (Kusaie) with broad tail-tip yellow; *ponapensis* Finsch (Truk, Ponape) with the whole plumage washed with greenish yellow, under tail-coverts orange; *pelewensis* Hartlaub and Finsch (Palau) with a purple patch in the middle of the gray throat. Upper abdomen orange, lower abdomen yellow; under tail-coverts purplish red. Unmistakable. The only fruit dove of the islands mentioned.

Micronesian Pigeon (*Ducula oceanica*): Large (16). Similar to *D. pacifica* (*see* Plate 2: 13), but gray throat and breast contrasting with chestnut belly. Top of head and upper back light or dark gray. Back, wings, and tail dark glossy green. Bill and knob black; feet dark purplish red.

Five races: *monacha* Momiyama 1922 (Palau, Yap) and *teraokai* Momyiama 1922 (Truk) with crown and upper back pale gray; *townsendi* Wetmore 1919 (Ponape) and *oceanica* Lesson and Garnot (Kusaie, Carolines; Jaluit and Elmore Isls., Marshalls; ?Gilbert Isls.) with crown and upper back blackish gray; *ratakensis* Takatsukasa and Yamashina 1932 (Arno and Wotje, Marshall Isls.) smaller.

Habits like those of all big *Ducula*. Persecution has driven the species to the remote interior on most islands.

Philippine Turtle Dove (*Streptopelia bitorquata dusumieri* Temminck): Medium (11). Head vinaceous gray. Back light brown; wings and tail more grayish. A slate-gray nuchal collar. Throat and breast vinaceous (ashy pink); lower belly white. Tip and edge of outermost tail-feathers white. Iris orange; bill dark slate; feet cherry red.

This pale, long-tailed turtle dove was introduced on the Marianas. Is now abundant. Feeds on the ground; partial to grasslands, rice fields, or other open country. Lives in pairs or small flocks.

White-throated Ground Dove (*Gallicolumba xanthonura*): Small (10). Forehead, throat, and breast white; belly black. Mantle glossy purple. Two very distinct subspecies: *xanthonura* Temminck (Marianas, Yap) with the female brown; back with a slight greenish gloss; tail rufous with a black subterminal bar; male with the entire head and upper back white, top of head and nape washed with pale cinnamon; *kubaryi* Finsch (Truk, Ponape) with male and female nearly alike; forehead and eyebrow white; nape and ear region blackish; female paler than male, lower back and rump with an olive-green gloss.

With the habits of the genus.* Lives in the deep forest. Call a deep, low moan.

Palau Ground Dove (*Gallicolumba canifrons* Hartlaub and Finsch): Small (8½). Forehead, face, and sides of neck ash gray, changing to pinkish buff on lower throat and breast. Abdomen dark chocolate brown. Occiput and upper back cinnamon. Remainder of upperparts glossy bronze olive. Shoulders (lesser upper wing-coverts) glossy purple. A rufous patch on the wings. Iris dark brown; bill black; feet bright red. Restricted to Palau. Rare. Favors uninhabited coral islets.

***Nicobar Pigeon** (*Caloenas nicobarica*): Restricted to the uninhabited coral islets of southern Palau (*pelewensis* Finsch). Nearly extinct.

PARROTS

Red Lory (*Trichoglossus rubiginosus* Bonaparte): Medium (9). Dark purplish red with indistinct blackish bars, particularly on the underparts. Wing-feathers dull olive; tail olive with yellowish tip. Iris grayish; bill orange; feet blackish. Endemic on Ponape. Habits apparently similar to *T. haematodus*.* Coast and inland. Very noisy.

OWLS

Palau Scops Owl (*Otus podarginus* Hartlaub and Finsch): Small (9). Cinnamon or rufous brown; lighter below and with irregular white spots or bars. No conspicuous "ears." Endemic on Palau. Its note is probably the usual *too-whoo-too-whit* of scops owls. Tends to change its perch after calling for 3 minutes. Forest. Nests in hollow trees, February–March. Not uncommon near villages.

Short-eared Owl (*Asio flammeus*): Large (14). Dark brown above with buff streaks. Buff below with broad, dark brown streaks on the breast, with narrow streaks on the abdomen. Wing and tail dark brown, barred with buff. Iris yellow; bill dark slate.

The subspecies *ponapensis* Mayr 1933 is endemic on Ponape. Hunts over grasslands. It nests in the grass on the ground. The Asiatic *flammeus* Pontoppidan seems to reach the Marianas occasionally on migration.

NIGHTJARS

Jungle Nightjar (*Caprimulgus indicus*): Small (9½). Long-tailed, with the usual concealing coloration of night birds—brown with black streaks and spots, and with a mottling of rufous and buff. A white spot on either side of throat. Male with a white wing-bar and with a subterminal white bar across the tail. Iris, bill, and feet dark. Restricted to Palau Isl. (*phalaena* Hartlaub and Finsch). Call note probably an accelerating *chuck-chuck* - - - - - ("hammer-beat-like call") when perched. In flight a *karump karump*-like call. Mangroves and edge of lowland forest.

SWIFTS

Carolines Swiftlet (*Collocalia inquieta*): Small (4½). Black above; smoky gray below. Three similar subspecies: *rukensis* Kuroda 1915 (Yap, Truk); *ponapensis* Mayr 1935 (Ponape); *inquieta* Kittlitz (Kusaie). With the habits of *C. vanikorensis*.*

Edible Nest Swiftlet (*Collocalia inexpectata*): Small (4). Sooty black above; rump slightly paler. Smoky gray below. Two subspecies in Micronesia: *pelewensis* Mayr 1935 (Palau), *bartschi* Mearns (Marianas). Nests in caves; most active at dawn and dusk.

KINGFISHERS

Two species of kingfishers overlap on Palau. On all other islands the locality assures correct identification. On Palau *H. chloris* has the top of the head blackish olive and lives more on the beach, in coconut groves, and in villages; *H. cinnamomina* has the top of the head cinnamon and lives in the forest.

Micronesian Kingfisher (*Halcyon cinnamomina*): Underparts white or orange cinnamon. Top of head cinnamon; back, wings, and tail dark greenish blue.

Three very distinct subspecies: *cinnamomina* Swainson (Guam), large (9½), throat of female and entire underparts of male orange cinnamon; *pelewensis* Wiglesworth (Palau) small (8), underparts white; *reichenbachii* Hartlaub (Ponape) large (9), white underneath, immature males cinnamon. Substage of the forest, also near villages. Habits those of *H. chloris*. Voice and food similar.

***White-collared Kingfisher** (*Halcyon chloris*): *Cf.* Plate 2: 22. Four subspecies, all white below, with back, wings, and tail bluish: *teraokai* Kuroda 1915 (Palau) and *orii* Takatsukasa and Yamashina 1931 (Rota) with the top of head greenish blue; *albicilla* Dumont (Saipan, Tinian) with the entire head white; *owstoni* Rothschild (Almagan, Pagan, Agrigan, Assuncion) intermediate, forehead white.

CUCKOO-SHRIKES

***Cicada Bird** (*Edolisoma tenuirostre*): Three subspecies, strongly marked in the female plumage. Male of all 3 dark blue gray. *Female: monacha* Hartlaub and Finsch (Palau) pale ocher below, loosely barred with black; crown dark blue gray; back dull fuscous brown; *nesiotis* Hartlaub and Finsch (Yap) similar, barred only on sides of breast, wings and upperparts deeper rufous; a rufous eye-stripe; *insperata* Finsch (Ponape) crown and sides of head gray, remainder of plumage deep rufous, darker above; no barring. Iris brown. Call: *too-too-wee, too-too-wee*. Lives in Micronesia in the dark forest.

WARBLERS

Palau Warbler (*Psamathia annae* Hartlaub and Finsch): Medium (6). Rather long bill and tail. Brownish olive above; dull yellowish olive below. Iris brown; legs and base of bill yellow. Very similar to *Rukia palauensis,* but legs long and yellow. Bill slender.

Palau. Common in secondary scrub and grasslands. Lives in low bushes, often feeding on the ground. Tame; frequently near human habitations. Call: "a shrill whistle, usually breaks off into a rather beautiful song."

Nightingale Reed Warbler (*Acrocephalus luscinia*): A group of very distinct, but closely related forms. Pale buffy yellow below; rufous brown or grayish olive brown above. *A. l. luscinia* Quoy and Gaimard (Guam, Agrigan, Saipan, Almagan) large (8), bill over an inch long, curved; *yamashinae* Takatsukasa 1931 (Pagan) with a shorter bill and warmer brown above; *syrinx* Kittlitz (throughout the Carolines) small (7), bill shorter than head, back cinnamon; *rehsei* Finsch (Nawodo or Pleasant Isl.) smaller (6).

A beautiful singer. Mostly in reed beds, on some islands

also in second-growth vegetation and in gardens. Nearly extinct in the southern Marianas.

FLYCATCHERS

Rufous-fronted Fantail (*Rhipidura rufifrons* group): *See* Plate 3: 27. *See also* Solomon Isls. The 5 Micronesian forms of this group may all be considered subspecies of *rufifrons,* or *lepida* and *kubaryi* may be called distinct species.

lepida Hartlaub and Finsch (Palau). Upperparts bright rufous, wings brown, tail brown tipped with rufous. Upper throat and middle of breast white. Sides of face and a broad band across lower throat black; flanks and abdomen rufous.

uraniae Oustalet (Guam) and *saipanensis* Hartert (Saipan, Tinian, Rota). Upperparts and wings brown. Forehead and rump rufous. Upper throat black; flanks rufous; *versicolor* Hartlaub and Finsch (Yap), rump browner.

kubaryi Finsch (Ponape). Dark brown gray above. Forehead, cheeks, abdomen, and tips of tail-feathers white. Throat black.

Truk Monarch (*Metabolus rugensis* Hombron and Jacquinot): Large (7½–8½). Extremely variable. With or without a black face and throat. Either all white, or whitish with rufous-cinnamon upperparts, wings, and tail, or all a sooty slate-color. Long blue-gray bill.

Endemic on Truk (Caroline Isls.). Habits probably those of all monarchs.*

Yap Island Monarch (*Monarcha godeffroyi* Hartlaub): Medium (6½). Either white with head, upper throat, wings, and tail black, or black with a broad white ring (collar) around the neck, or grayish ocher above, pale ocher below. Endemic on Yap Isl.

Tinian Island Monarch (*Monarcha takatsukasae* Yamashina 1931): Small (6). Male and female alike. Tawny ocher below; vent white. Face and sides of head ocher. Back olive brown; wings and tail black. Two white or buff wing-bars. Rump and tips of tail-feathers white. Iris dark brown. Endemic on Tinian Isl. (Marianas).

Micronesian Broadbill (*Myiagra oceanica*): The 4 races of this species are so distinct that they might also be considered 4 different species. All 4 have the typical habits of broad-billed flycatchers.*

erythrops Hartlaub and Finsch (Palau). Small (5). Gray brown above, with a rufous face. Tawny below, with a white vent.

freycineti Oustalet (Guam). Female similar to *erythrops*, male blue gray above, white below; breast may be slightly buff.

oceanica Pucheran (Truk). Similar to *erythrops*, but face blue gray, like top of head. Upper throat and abdomen whitish; breast ochraceous. Medium (5½).

pluto Finsch (Ponape). All blackish slate; head with blue gloss. Medium (6).

On each of the 4 islands there is no similar bird that could be mistaken for a broadbill. The call is a thrice-repeated whistle like *peter-peter-peter*, or *here-here-here*. Birds lift feathers of head to a crest when excited.

WHISTLERS

Morning Bird (*Colluricincla tenebrosa* Hartlaub and Finsch): Medium (7½). Plain brown throughout; upperparts darker, cap almost blackish. Iris yellow; bill and feet dark. No light marks on wing or tail.

Palau only. Lives in the rain forest, either on the ground or in low bushes. The best songster of the Palau Isls., most active before sunrise. More common on the outlying islands. Native name *Tu tau.*

WOOD-SWALLOWS

***White-breasted Wood-Swallow** (*Artamus leucorhynchus*): *Cf.* Plate 3: 31. The subspecies *pelewensis* Finsch is endemic on Palau.

STARLINGS

Micronesian Starling (*Aplonis opacus*): Large (8½–9). Bill heavy, well curved. Adults black with a slight greenish or blue-green gloss. Immatures duller and somewhat streaky underneath; on Guam whitish with numerous black streaks. Iris yellow, dull in immatures.

Seven poorly defined races: *aeneus* Takatsukasa and Yamashina 1931 (Agrigan, Pagan, Almagan, northern Marianas); *guami* Momyiama 1922 (Guam, Rota, Tinian, Saipan, southern Marianas); *orii* T. and Y. 1931 (Palau); *kurodai* Momyiama 1921 (Yap); *angus* Momyiama 1922 (Truk and western Carolines); *ponapensis* T. and Y. 1931 (Ponape);

and *opacus* Kittlitz (Kusaie). Habits those of *A. tabuensis* (*see* Samoa).

Ponape Mountain Starling (*Aplonis pelzelni* Finsch): Small (7½). Dark brownish slate color; immatures lighter and more brownish, not streaky. Differs from *opacus* by small size, brown, not yellow, iris, plain color (no gloss), more slender bill, and by living in the mountains (above 1400 feet). A bird of the forest. Rather quiet. Endemic on Ponape.

Kusaie Mountain Starling (*Aplonis corvinus* Kittlitz): Very large (?10). All glossy black with a long tail and a long, curved bill. Iris red. Formerly on Kusaie. Apparently extinct.

CROWS

Guam Crow (*Corvus kubaryi* Reichenow): Small (15). All glossy black. Iris brown. Bill rather slender. Restricted to Guam and Rota (Marianas).

HONEY-EATERS

Golden Honey-eater (*Cleptornis marchei* Oustalet): Small (6). Head, rump, and underparts deep yellow with a golden-bronze tone. Back, wings, and tail golden olive. Bill and feet orange. Endemic on Saipan.

***Cardinal Honey-eater** (*Myzomela cardinalis*): *Cf.* Plate 3: 36. The 6 Micronesian races (the *rubratra* group) are very similar to each other. Small (5½). Adult male all scarlet, but wings, tail, and stripe from eye to bill black. Female similar, but with less scarlet: top of head partly (Palau) or entirely black (Ponape), tail sometimes olivaceous (Guam, Palau). *M. c. saffordi* Wetmore 1917 (all Marianas), *kobayashii* Momyiama 1922 (Palau), *kurodai* Momyiama 1922 (Yap), *major* Bonaparte (Truk), *dichromata* Wetmore 1919 (Ponape), and *rubratra* Lesson (Kusaie). Small size and partly scarlet coloration are diagnostic.

WHITE-EYES

The number of white-eyes in Micronesia seems to be bewildering. The latest list enumerates no less than 10 species with 14 subspecies. Actually the family is represented by only 3 groups of geographically representative species, all 3 of them occurring together on Ponape and Palau. None of the other islands has more than 2 species of white-eyes. The 3 groups are a small green white-eye (*conspicillata*), a small gray or brownish white-eye (*cinerea*), and a large white-eye (*Rukia*).

Bridled White-eye (*Zosterops conspicillata*): Small (4). Yellowish below; greenish above. Forehead yellow or whitish. White eye-ring usually narrow. Iris yellow or whitish; upper mandible brown, lower yellow; legs blue gray.

Seven subspecies: *conspicillata* Kittlitz (Guam) and *saipani* Dubois (Saipan, Tinian) with broad white eye-ring, forehead white, underparts whitish yellow, back and sides of neck grayish green; *rotensis* Takatsukasa and Yamashina 1931 (Rota), *semperi* Hartlaub and Finsch (Palau), *hypolais* Hartlaub and Finsch (Yap), *owstoni* Hartert (Truk), and *takatsukasai* Momyiama 1922 (Ponape) more yellow, white eye-ring narrow.

Common in gardens and along edge of forest. Call note:

chip-chip. Also a melodious short song. Often in flocks. Feeds on small berries; also found on flowering bushes and trees.

Gray-brown White-eye (*Zosterops cinerea*): Small to medium (4–4½). No green in plumage. No white eye-ring. Iris bright brown. Bill and legs dark.

Three subspecies: *cinerea* Kittlitz (Kusaie) ash gray above, pale gray below; *ponapensis* Finsch (Ponape) umber brown above, forehead and underparts pale ash gray, flanks brownish; *finschi* Hartlaub (Palau) similar but face also brownish.

The large Micronesian white-eyes (Genus *Rukia*): Each of the islands of Palau, Yap, Truk, and Ponape has an endemic species of large white-eye. They are so distinct that each has been put in a separate monotypic genus: *Megazosterops* (Palau), *Kubaryum* (Yap), *Rukia* (Truk), *Rhamphozosterops* (Ponape), but it seems more convenient to combine these related species in a single genus (*Rukia*). The habits, so far as known, seem similar in all 4 species.

Large Palau White-eye (*Rukia palauensis* Reichenow 1915): Large (5½). Fulvous olive; dark above, pale below. Indistinct eye-ring, ear-coverts dark with irregular pale yellow mottling. Iris grayish; bill yellow (light brown above); legs and feet tan. Restricted to Peliliul Isl. (Palau). Might be confused with *Psamathia* (*see* above). Differs from *Colluricincla* by the olive color and from the 2 species of *Zosterops* by much larger size.

Large Yap White-eye (*Rukia oleaginea* Hartlaub and Finsch): Large (5). Similar to *palauensis,* eye-ring satin white, ears blackish. Iris reddish white. Yap Isl. Differs from *Zoste-*

rops conspicillata by being larger, darker, and more brownish olive.

Large Truk White-eye (*Rukia ruki* Hartert): Large (5¾). Dark brownish olive above and below. Eye-ring invisible. Iris reddish; bill black; legs orange. Endemic on Truk. Differs from *Acrocephalus* by the dark underparts and from *Z. conspicillata* by the brownish olive color, orange legs, and lack of eye-ring.

Large Ponape White-eye (*Rukia sanfordi* Mayr 1931): Large (5¼). Back buffy olive, brighter on rump. Underparts much lighter, buffy. Upper throat pale yellowish. No visible eye-ring. Iris and bill brown; feet yellowish. Bill long, thin, and curved, like that of a honey-eater.

Differs from *Acrocephalus* by the grayish green throat, greenish upperparts, and pale legs, from *Zosterops* by the long curved bill, large size, and yellowish legs. Endemic in the mountains of Ponape (above 1800 feet). Feeds among flowers of a gum tree. Voice: "a musical, deep-throated sibilation" (Coultas). Rare.

WEAVER-FINCHES

Black-breasted Weaver-Finch (*Lonchura nigerrima*): Small (3½). All black, top of head and nape whitish, rump and tail golden chestnut. A subspecies (*minor* Yamashina 1931) has been described from the grasslands of Ponape. (?Also Truk.)

***Blue-faced Parrot-Finch** (*Erythrura trichroa*): Three similar subspecies in Micronesia: *pelewensis* Kuroda 1922 (Palau);

clara Takatsukasa and Yamashina 1931 (Truk, Ponape); and *trichroa* Kittlitz (Kusaie). Feeds in the grasslands, but spends much time in the adjoining forest.

MIGRANT VISITORS TO MICRONESIA

Egretta i. intermedia, Bubulcus ibis coromandus, Butorides striatus amurensis (Palau); *Nycticorax n. nycticorax* (Marianas, Yap); *Gorsakius goisagi, Gorsakius m. melanolophus* (Palau); *Dupetor f. flavicollis* (Guam); *Ixobrychus eurythmus* (Palau); *Anas crecca, Anas penelope, Anas acuta, Anas clypeata, Nyroca fuligula* (throughout); *Falco peregrinus* subsp. (Palau, Yap); *Accipiter soloensis* (Yap); *Accipiter virgatus gularis* (Marianas); *Rallina eurizonoides* subsp. (Palau); *Fulica a. atra* (Marianas); *Cuculus canorus telephonus, Cuculus saturatus horsfieldi* (Palau); *Eudynamis taitensis* (throughout); *Caprimulgus indicus jotaka, Eurystomus orientalis pacificus, Hirundo rustica gutturalis, Turdus o. obscurus, Monticola ph. philippensis, Luscinia c. calliope, Muscicapa n. narcissina, Muscicapa griseisticta,* and *Sturnus philippensis* Forster (Palau).

Glossary

arboreal—living in trees

asterisk—an * indicates a cross reference from the geographical section to the same species or genus in the systematic section (chapter 3)

axillaries—a fan-shaped usually elongated group of feathers, under the wing, growing from the axilla or "armpit," and closing the space between the last flight-feathers and the body when in flight

casque—horny outgrowth on top of hornbill's beak (see fig. 12)

Casuarina—tropical tree usually growing on beaches. Looks like a conifer, but is a flowering plant.

cere—a fleshy or soft skin-like covering of the base of the upper bill, in which the nostrils open. Found in most hawks and parrots

crown—top of head (see fig. 1)

eclipse plumage—inconspicuous plumage worn outside the breeding season

endemic—restricted to a certain locality and not found elsewhere

Erythrina—tropical tree with bright red flowers

flight feathers—primaries and secondaries (see fig. 1)

gular pouch—bag-like enlargement of the throat

hackles—long, narrow feathers, usually in the neck region, as in the domestic fowl

knob—fleshy skin fold at base of bill in certain pigeons

lores—region between eye and base of bill (see fig. 1)

mandible—lower half of bill. Upper half is sometimes referred to as upper mandible
mantle—upper side of body, including back, scapulars and upper surface of wings (upper wing-coverts)
maxilla—upper jaw or upper bill
nape—region on hindneck (see fig. 1)
nuchal collar—a band or ring across the hindneck
occipital plumes—long feathers rooted at the back of the head
pectoral band—band across the breast
primaries—flight feathers inserted on the hand bones (see fig. 1)
rump—region on lower back above the base of the tail (see fig 1)
scapulars—shoulder feathers (see fig. 1)
secondaries—flight feathers inserted on the arm bone (see fig. 1)
shoulder—scapulars or wing bend (see fig. 1)
spangles—bright, glossy spots in plumage
speculum—a brightly colored band across the wing, usually consisting of the secondaries or tips of the upper wing-coverts
streamers—lengthened tail feathers
subterminal—not quite at the tip
superciliary—a stripe above the eye, an eyebrow
S.W.P.—Southwest Pacific
terrestrial—living on the ground
thighs—feathering of the legs (see fig. 1)
vent—region on lower abdomen (see fig. 1)
wattle—skin fold, usually in the face or on the throat

Index